DISCOVERING MODERN ALGEBRA

DISCOVERING MODERN ALGEBRA

by

K. L. GARDNER
(St Luke's College, Exeter)

OXFORD UNIVERSITY PRESS

1966

Oxford University Press, Ely House, London W.1

GLASGOW NEW YORK TORONTO MELBOURNE WELLINGTON
BOMBAY CALCUTTA MADRAS KARACHI LAHORE DACCA
CAPE TOWN SALISBURY NAIROBI IBADAN
KUALA LUMPUR HONG KONG

PRINTED IN GREAT BRITAIN BY JOHN WRIGHT & SONS LTD.
AT THE STONEBRIDGE PRESS, BRISTOL

PREFACE

As an undergraduate I always treated with suspicion a mathematics book containing the word 'elementary' in its title. To one of my addled wits this invariably meant pain, anguish and considerable hard labour. By that level this is a sub-elementary text. It deals with certain aspects of 'modern mathematics' in a lighthearted and tolerably earthy fashion and is meant as a lead-in to more formal texts. As such it is hoped that it will be found helpful as a first text for training college students, undergraduates and practising teachers who wish to keep up-to-date.

Chapters 1–5 give what I consider to be a reasonably simple-minded approach to group axioms. Chapters 6–7 deal with matrices both for their own sake and to show the usefulness of group axioms in developing new mathematical toys. Chapters 8–11 show groups and matrices in action on the subjects of permutations, isomorphisms and geometry. In Chapter 12 we tentatively wet our toes in the seas of more complex mathematical structures with a view to getting our efforts into some sort of perspective.

As with most books, I was not the only one to suffer in the construction of this. My thanks are due to my head of department, D. Paling, who aimed and fired me in this direction, and to a multitude of colleagues, St. Luke's students and other lecturees who had on occasion to field a very hot catch. My thanks are also more than due to my wife who, during all this, has had to bear the full brunt of Gardner rampant.

Finally I should like to thank Messrs. Collins Ltd. and the Royal Scottish Country Dance Society for permission to quote so liberally from Milligan's 101 *Scottish Country Dances* and also the Cambridge University Press for their beautiful fish and the transformation ceremony on *Argyropeleas Olfersi* of Chapter 11 which are taken from D'Arcy Thompson's classic *Growth and Form*.

Saint Luke's College　　　　　　　　　　　　　　　K. L. GARDNER.
Exeter.
June 1965.

CONTENTS

1. A CURIOUS ARITHMETIC

1.1 A Mathematical Assignment

The mathematician in industry and research finds himself faced with many problems which refuse to succumb to the attack of normal numerical methods. Similarly most of us will have suffered the frustrations of problems which seem to have a mathematical or mathematico-logical basis, but which we cannot quite see our way through. Many of these problems can certainly be solved mathematically, although the form of the mathematics is unfamiliar.

Let us assume, for example, that we have been commissioned by the Royal Scottish Country Dance Society to analyse the movements involved in Scottish country dancing. We must break down a problem of this size into small sections. We will therefore first of all concentrate on the series of movements, which require two couples thus:

FIG. 1 Initial position.

To simplify matters still further we will only consider movements where pairs of dancers change places. This leaves us with the following processes.

From the initial position (Fig. 1):

Process *A*. *Change places crossways.*

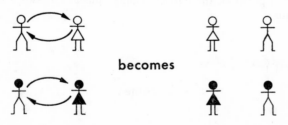

becomes

FIG. 2

Process *B.* Again from the initial position, *change places up and down.*

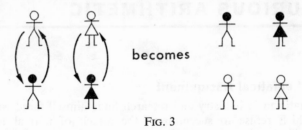

FIG. 3

Process *C.* Again from the initial position, *change places diagonally.*

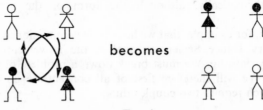

FIG. 4

Finally, for the sake of completeness, we define **process** *I* where *everybody more or less stands still* so that

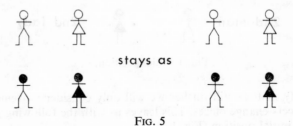

FIG. 5

Now let us assume that, at a given point in the dance, the dancers are in the initial position and perform process *A* followed by process *B*. This means that, from the initial position, the dancers change places crossways and then up and down thus:

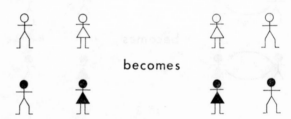

which becomes

This is mathematically equivalent to saying

becomes

which is process *C*. Thus *A* followed by *B* gives the same result as *C*. For ease of writing we shall abbreviate this to

$$A \text{ f } B = C,$$

where *A*, *B* and *C* are the processes involved, f stands for 'followed by', and = stands for 'gives the same result as'.

I has been neglected so far, but appears frequently enough. Suppose that the dancers do process *A* twice in succession. In other words, the dancers change crossways and then change crossways once again.

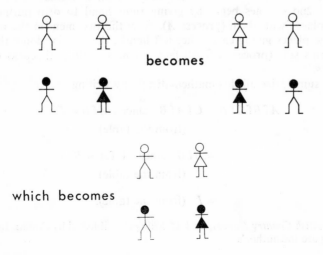

becomes

which becomes

The final position is the same as the initial one and mathematically speaking they might just as well have stayed where they were. Symbolically this is written

$$A f A = I.$$

Examples 1a

Compute the results of the following pairs of processes using diagrams, coins, or chessmen as preferred:

$$A f C, \quad A f I, \quad B f A, \quad B f B, \quad B f C, \quad B f I, \quad C f A,$$

$$C f B, \quad C f C, \quad C f I, \quad I f A, \quad I f B, \quad I f C, \quad I f I.$$

These results may be tabulated in the same way as a multiplication table at school or the results of an all-play-all tennis tournament.

second process

	f	I	A	B	C
	I	I	A	B	C
first	A	A	I	C	B
process	B	B	C	I	A
	C	C	B	A	I

TABLE 1

Let us now use the table to find out the position of our four dancers after following the procedure which is technically known as 'rights and lefts'.

'1st and 2nd couples begin by giving right hand to own partners and changing places with them (process A). Now the two men on the women's side change places giving each other left hands, the women doing the same on the men's side (process B). All face partners again and repeat the two movements.'†

We can summarize all this mathematically by writing

$$A f B f A f B = C f A f B \quad \text{since} \quad A f B = C$$
$$\text{(from the table)}$$

$$= B f B \quad \text{since} \quad C f A = B$$
$$\text{(from the table)}$$

$$= I \quad \text{(from the table).}$$

† *101 Scottish Country Dances*, by J. C. Milligan, published by Collins. Insertions in brackets are the author's.

Thus the four processes described result in the dancers being back in their original positions. If suspicious use diagrams or other aids as before.

To clarify our thoughts let us compare this problem with one in normal arithmetic. 'I have four apples and my sister has three. My mother gives us two more each. How many have we got altogether?' The answer is $4+3+2+2 = 11$. Here we are lucky in that we already know the system of arithmetic that we are going to use and we do not have to prepare a '+' table corresponding to the 'f' table in the dancing example. Otherwise the two solutions have much in common. In each case we have a practical situation that we convert into mathematical symbols. Technically speaking we form a mathematical model of the original problem. Once this is done we forget all about the original problem and work out our solution entirely from the '+' system or the 'f' system as the case may be. We then convert from symbols back to the terms of the original problem which, barring accidents, gives us the correct answer.

The two problems tackled above are trivial, but the line of attack is not. We may represent it by a flow diagram as follows.

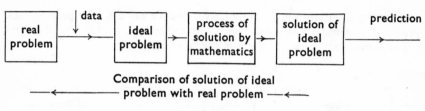

Comparison of solution of ideal
problem with real problem

FIG. 6

The above is taken from J. Crank's *Mathematics and Industry.* He in turn borrowed it from O. G. Sutton's *Mathematics in Action.* They have used the term 'ideal problem' where we have used 'mathematical model', but the approach is the same, so that we are mirroring exactly the technique of the industrial mathematician. One last point. If a problem produced any new ideas, the industrial mathematician would examine it carefully and file the results for future use. We learn little from the apples problem, but the dancers problem resulted in the construction of an entirely new arithmetic, which must be at least mentally filed away for future reference.

1.2 Fishes

Let us practise constructing mathematical models as we have shown that this is a vital part of problem solving.

A rectangular tile with a picture of a fish on it is prised off the bathroom wall by 'Junior', who is just about old enough to know better. Mama's voice brings pangs of remorse and fears of chastisement, so that the tile is rapidly rammed back into position. Junior has one chance in four of putting it back correctly.

in its correct position

will again look like

Process *I*
FIG. 7

Since the situation is apparently unchanged we will call this 'putting back' process *I*, because it has similar properties to the *I* we used in the 'f' system. But Junior may have got the fish upside down so that

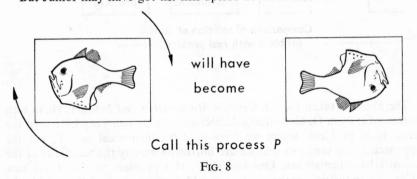

will have

become

Call this process *P*
FIG. 8

On the other hand, he may have put the picture side to the wall. This he could have done in one of two ways. Either he could have twisted the tile horizontally so that

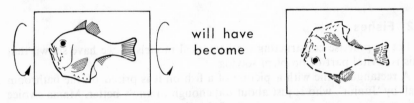

will have

become

Call this process *Q*
FIG. 9

Or he could have twisted it vertically so that

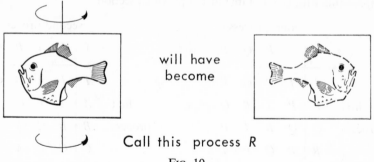

will have
become

Call this process R

FIG. 10

These are the only four ways in which the tile could be fitted into its accustomed place.

We can virtually guarantee however that Junior will have waved the tile about in mid-air quite vigorously once he had loosened it and that its gyrations would therefore be a most complex combination of the processes I, P, Q and R. Let 'c' mean 'combined with'. Then, as before, PcQ means process P (turning the tile upside down) combined with process Q (twisting the tile about the horizontal axis). Thus:

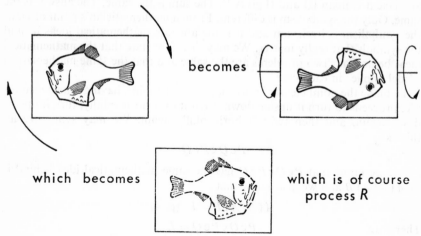

becomes

which becomes

which is of course
process R

Therefore as before we may write:

$$PcQ = R.$$

Examples 1b

Compute the following:

$$IcI, \quad IcP, \quad IcQ, \quad IcR, \quad PcI, \quad PcP, \quad PcR, \quad QcI,$$
$$QcP, \quad QcQ, \quad QcR, \quad RcI, \quad RcP, \quad RcQ, \quad RcR,$$

using a cardboard tile if necessary.

2

We may now write the results as a 'c' table, and it is very interesting to compare this with the 'f' table of the previous section.

<table>
<tr><td colspan="5" align="center">second process</td></tr>
<tr><td>c</td><td>I</td><td>P</td><td>Q</td><td>R</td></tr>
<tr><td>I</td><td>I</td><td>P</td><td>Q</td><td>R</td></tr>
<tr><td>first   P</td><td>P</td><td>I</td><td>R</td><td>Q</td></tr>
<tr><td>process   Q</td><td>Q</td><td>R</td><td>I</td><td>P</td></tr>
<tr><td>R</td><td>R</td><td>Q</td><td>P</td><td>I</td></tr>
</table>

'c' table

TABLE 2

<table>
<tr><td colspan="5" align="center">second process</td></tr>
<tr><td>f</td><td>I</td><td>A</td><td>B</td><td>C</td></tr>
<tr><td>I</td><td>I</td><td>A</td><td>B</td><td>C</td></tr>
<tr><td>first   A</td><td>A</td><td>I</td><td>C</td><td>B</td></tr>
<tr><td>process   B</td><td>B</td><td>C</td><td>I</td><td>A</td></tr>
<tr><td>C</td><td>C</td><td>B</td><td>A</td><td>I</td></tr>
</table>

'f' table

TABLE 1 (repeated)

If we replace f by c, A by P, B by Q and C by R the two tables become exactly the same. This means that if we do any calculation in the 'f' system and then do the corresponding one in the 'c' system we get corresponding answers. Thus if we get an answer C in the 'f' system the corresponding calculation is bound to give us R in the 'c' system.

We have a parallel case in ordinary arithmetic. To us 3 and 2 gives 5. To an ancient Roman III and II gives V. The sum is the same. The answer is the same. Only the symbolism is different. From a mathematician's point of view, the symbolism is irrelevant and it is the abstract mathematical ideas behind the symbols that really matter. We may therefore state that the mathematical ideas behind our two problems are the same and that the same mathematical model applies in each case.

To make the point clearer let us suppose that Junior, having unfastened his tile, proceeds to turn it upside down, twist it over horizontally, turn it upside down again, and then twist it horizontally again. We may symbolize all this as

$$P\,c\,Q\,c\,P\,c\,Q.$$

But we know that $P\,c\,Q\,c\,P\,c\,Q$ has the same mathematical idea behind it as $A\,f\,B\,f\,A\,f\,B$ and we also know that

$$A\,f\,B\,f\,A\,f\,B = I \quad \text{(p. 4)}$$

Therefore $P\,c\,Q\,c\,P\,c\,Q = I.$

Check the argument from the 'c' table if you are suspicious.

1.3   Substitutions

Lest the reader should despair of seeing any orthodox algebra anywhere in this book let us consider the four expressions $x, -x, \dfrac{1}{x}, -\dfrac{1}{x}$ where x is a plain, old-fashioned number. We could combine them by $+$ or $\times$ in the usual manner, but it is more pertinent to our present study to link them by the combining operation 'r' where $M\,r\,N$ means 'replace x in M by N', M and N

being x, $-x$, $\dfrac{1}{x}$, or $-\dfrac{1}{x}$. Several examples are necessary to explain this unlikely procedure.

Let us evaluate $\dfrac{1}{x}\mathrm{r}(-x)$. This means replace x in $\dfrac{1}{x}$ by $(-x)$. Thus

$$\frac{1}{x}\mathrm{r}(-x)=\frac{1}{(-x)}=-\frac{1}{x}.$$

Again let us evaluate $-\dfrac{1}{x}\mathrm{r}\dfrac{1}{x}$. This means replace x in $-\dfrac{1}{x}$ by $\dfrac{1}{x}$. Thus

$$-\frac{1}{x}\mathrm{r}\frac{1}{x}=-\frac{1}{\left(\dfrac{1}{x}\right)}=-x.$$

$x\mathrm{r}x$ may cause trouble. This means replace x by x in x. Therefore $x\mathrm{r}x=x$. Anything $\mathrm{r}x$ means that we replace x by x which leaves the expression exactly the same as it was before. Therefore x tends to behave in the same way as the I of the first two examples.

Examples 1c

Compute the following and put them into the usual table:

$$x\mathrm{r}(-x),\quad x\mathrm{r}\frac{1}{x},\quad x\mathrm{r}\left(-\frac{1}{x}\right),\quad (-x)\mathrm{r}x,\quad (-x)\mathrm{r}(-x),\quad (-x)\mathrm{r}\frac{1}{x},$$

$$(-x)\mathrm{r}\left(-\frac{1}{x}\right),\quad \frac{1}{x}\mathrm{r}x,\quad \frac{1}{x}\mathrm{r}\frac{1}{x},\quad \frac{1}{x}\mathrm{r}\left(-\frac{1}{x}\right),\quad \left(-\frac{1}{x}\right)\mathrm{r}x,\quad \left(-\frac{1}{x}\right)\mathrm{r}(-x),$$

$$\left(-\frac{1}{x}\right)\mathrm{r}\left(-\frac{1}{x}\right).$$

The table is

	r	x	$-x$	$\dfrac{1}{x}$	$-\dfrac{1}{x}$
	x	x	$-x$	$\dfrac{1}{x}$	$-\dfrac{1}{x}$
first expression	$-x$	$-x$	x	$-\dfrac{1}{x}$	$\dfrac{1}{x}$
	$\dfrac{1}{x}$	$\dfrac{1}{x}$	$-\dfrac{1}{x}$	x	$-x$
	$-\dfrac{1}{x}$	$-\dfrac{1}{x}$	$\dfrac{1}{x}$	$-x$	x

second expression

TABLE 3

and, as the reader will doubtless have anticipated by now, if we replace r by f, x by I, $-x$ by A, $\frac{1}{x}$ by B and $-\frac{1}{x}$ by C we get the 'f' system. If, on the other hand, we replace r by c, x by I, $-x$ by P, $\frac{1}{x}$ by Q, $-\frac{1}{x}$ by R we get the 'c' system. In other words by extending the arguments of the end of section 1.2 (p. 8) we see that the 'f' system, the 'c' system and the 'r' system all have the same abstract mathematical structure behind them. It is therefore too limiting to think in terms of dancing procedures I, A, B and C or ways of moving fishy tiles I, P, Q and R or even algebraic expressions x, $-x$, $\frac{1}{x}$, $-\frac{1}{x}$, and we must produce an entirely new symbolism to show that our mathematical structure is independent of any of the three examples that we have given or of any others that we might have given if we had had the space.

We therefore take a set of 'elements' e, a, b and c. 'Elements' is merely the technical term for 'things' or 'members of a set'. We must no longer talk in terms of 'processes' or 'expressions' as we do not wish to bias ourselves towards any of the three systems. We also take a combining operation '∗' which again means nothing in particular and is merely a way of linking the four undefined things e, a, b and c.

We now give e, a, b and c specific rules of behaviour under '∗' and produce the familiar table

second element

∗	e	a	b	c
e	e	a	b	c
a	a	e	c	b
b	b	c	e	a
c	c	b	a	e

first element

TABLE 4

This is a purely abstract system and the symbols ∗, e, a, b, and c are completely undefined. All we know about them is that their behaviour is determined by the above table. If the system were of sufficient importance to teach children we could make them recite 'a star b equals c'. If our educational high-mindedness makes us demonstrate that 3×2 really is 6 with oranges it will also make us demonstrate that $a ∗ b$ really is c with fishy tiles.

Figure 11 indicates more clearly the nature of the abstraction and is self-explanatory.

We may well ponder over the fact that a development, such as we have outlined above, must have taken place at some time with ordinary numbers. Both children and primitive races have to reach a fair degree of mathematical sophistication before they can realize that the 'seven' in the statements 'seven elephants' and 'seven apples' is in fact the same 'seven'.

Smeltzer in his book *Man and Number* makes the point that although 'couple', 'brace' and 'pair' all mean 'two'—we speak of a couple, but not a brace or pair of eggs and a pair, but not a brace or couple of horses. Furthermore Dantzig in *Number, the Language of Science*, mentions a tribe in British Columbia who have different sets of number words for flat objects and animals, round objects and time, men, long objects and trees, canoes, measures, and, finally, a special set for counting when no definite object is being counted.

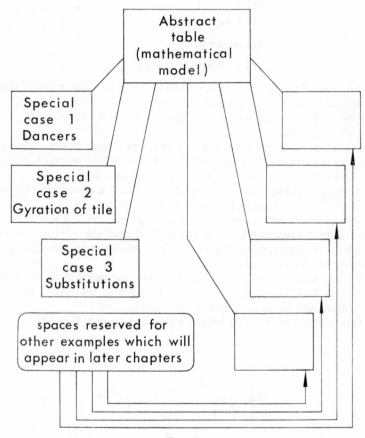

Fig. 11

Finally, now that we have the technique of abstraction, let us present the ideas of this chapter in a slightly different form. General movements by the dancers after the style of section 1.1 may be represented by the mathematical model of Table 1. Specific problems concerning dancers such as the result of 'rights and lefts' may be represented by a mathematical model such as *A f B f A f B*. Once a new type of problem has been solved we may extract and generalize the new techniques involved. This gives rise to the abstract form of Table 4. The new techniques are then readily available for problems giving rise to identical models, such as the tile problem and the substitutions problem.

Examples 1d

   1. Find the result of (a) $a*b*c$,

   (b) $b*a*c$,

   (c) $c*a*b$,

   (d) $c*a*c$,

   (e) $b*a*b$,

   (f) $a*b*c*b*a*c$.

Make a list of all the short cuts you have taken and either justify them or start again. In particular discard those short cuts which you attempt to justify by saying, 'Well, it's obvious', because it usually is not. Keep your list for future reference.

   2. From the initial position of Fig. 1 partners change places, men change places and ladies change places, and then first man and second lady change places and second man and first lady change places. Follow this through as best you may with diagrams, coins or other aids and then translate the movements into I's, A's, B's and C's and check your result.

Construct a new mathematical model using the 'standing still' movement and the three movements listed at the beginning of the question. Compare this with the original version. Is your result surprising or are we wasting time? Keep your results and decide later.

   3. Junior twists his tile three times horizontally, twice vertically and five times round itself in its plane before replacing it in the wall. Calculate its final position and check by repeating his actions.

   4. Junior drops his tile and breaks it down the middle!

FIG. 12

He realizes that he must put it back with the fish showing, and with the head on the left, but he so moves the separate pieces that he is most unlikely to get the two halves of the fish together again. Analyse all possible versions after the style of section 1.2 and construct a mathematical model as usual.

5. We must learn to recognize the pattern of Table 4 as it will occur frequently in later chapters. To avoid confusion with symbols, represent each element by a different-coloured shape and produce the table as a pretty pattern thus:

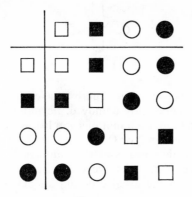

TABLE 5

List as many properties of the pattern as you can and interpret them where possible by referring back to Table 4 and the various examples. A typical property is that the pattern is symmetrical about the leading (N.W.–S.E.) diagonal. Construct other tables having some of the more obvious properties that you have listed. Finally, list sufficient properties to enable you to recognize the original pattern when it occurs again. Keep your results as a piece of personal research. The answers will appear in the next three or four chapters.

6. Rewrite Table 4 in the form

*	e	b	a	c
e	.	.	.	.
b	.	.	.	.
a	.	.	.	.
c	.	.	.	.

filling in the blank spaces from Table 4. Since e, a, b, and c are arbitrary symbols, we could easily call 'a' 'b' and 'b' 'a'. Rewrite the table you have just completed using 'a' for 'b' and 'b' for 'a'. The table should now look the same as it did before we started. If you have been wasting your time explain why. If you have made a great discovery explain what. The last two sentences of Question 5 again apply.

7. Three coloured pegs, red, blue and yellow, sit in three holes in a line. We play a game where we are allowed to swap over any two pegs at each go. We are also allowed to miss a turn. Construct a mathematical model for all possible movements and series of movements.

8. Three small coloured rods are tied together in the form of a three-dimensional '+' sign thus:

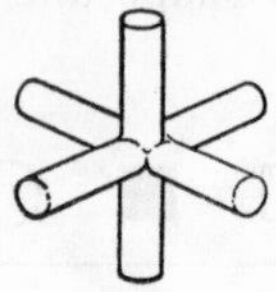

FIG. 13

If we take any rod between our thumb and forefinger and spin the rods through 180° they are apparently unmoved. Form a mathematical model of the inter-relationships of all such motions and list ways in which your model differs from that of Question 7 or Question 4.

9. A curious arithmetic consists of the numbers 1, 7, 9 and 15 only. A new form of multiplication, which we write as $\otimes$, consists of multiplying two numbers together in the usual way and knocking off as many 16's as possible! Thus:

$$7 \times 9 = 63 = 48 + 15 = 3 \times 16 + 15$$

Therefore $7 \otimes 9 = 15.$

Complete the '$\otimes$' table in the usual way.

10. A high-powered gambler has discovered a foolproof system and decides to break the bank. He is very superstitious and therefore only stakes 1*d.*, 5*d.*, 7*d.*, or 11*d.* on each game as these are his lucky numbers. The nature of his system is such that he either gets his stake money returned or he receives five times it, seven times it, or eleven times it. Being a careful man, he always pockets the shillings and stakes the surplus pennies after each win. Analyse the results of all possible investments in the game as far as his next investment is concerned. (Hint: use the technique of Question 9.)

2. AN INFINITY OF CURIOUS ARITHMETICS

2.1 Another Mathematical Structure

We now return to the original research topic and examine the series of steps which cause Scottish dancers to move in a circle. These may be variously described according to the way in which the movement is executed. Mathematically speaking we are interested in the result of the rotation rather than its mode of execution and, as before, we reduce the necessary number of processes to four.

Process *I*. The dancers stand still as usual.

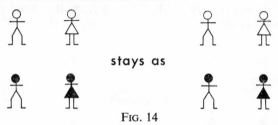

Fig. 14

Process *X*. The dancers move round one place clockwise (or three anticlockwise).

Fig. 15

Process *Y*. The dancers move round two places clockwise (or two anticlockwise).

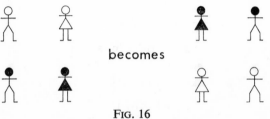

Fig. 16

Process *Z.* The dancers move round three places clockwise (or one place anti-clockwise).

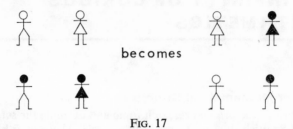

FIG. 17

Process *I* is of course the same in the circling system above as it is in the swapping system of Chapter 1. A check back to the definitions of *A*, *B* and *C* in the swapping system (p. 2) will show that process *Y* has the same effect as process *C*. For the sake of tidiness of notation we retain *Y* for the moment.

The next step is obvious. We combine processes by 'f' where 'f' means 'followed by' as before. Try *X*f *Y*. Starting from the initial position, this means 'one place clockwise' followed by 'two places clockwise'. Thus

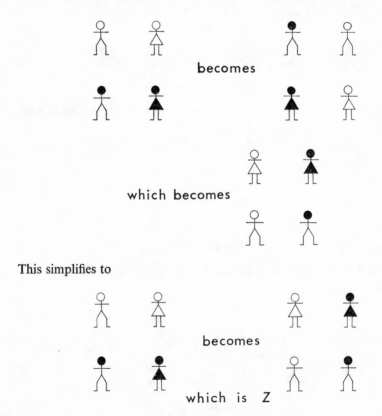

Examples 2a

Complete the table:

second process

	f	*I*	*X*	*Y*	*Z*
	I	.	.	.	.
first	*X*	.	.	*Z*	.
process	*Y*	.	.	.	.
	Z	.	.	.	.

The result is

f	*I*	*X*	*Y*	*Z*
I	*I*	*X*	*Y*	*Z*
X	*X*	*Y*	*Z*	*I*
Y	*Y*	*Z*	*I*	*X*
Z	*Z*	*I*	*X*	*Y*

Circling

TABLE 6

f	*I*	*A*	*B*	*C*
I	*I*	*A*	*B*	*C*
A	*A*	*I*	*C*	*B*
B	*B*	*C*	*I*	*A*
C	*C*	*B*	*A*	*I*

Swapping

TABLE 1 (repeated)

By comparing this with the swapping table we see at once that the two systems are not identical. Even if we consider the two tables in the abstract form of Chapter 1 there are still differences.

*	*e*	*a*	*b*	*c*
e	*e*	*a*	*b*	*c*
a	*a*	*b*	*c*	*e*
b	*b*	*c*	*e*	*a*
c	*c*	*e*	*a*	*b*

Circling

TABLE 7

*	*e*	*a*	*b*	*c*
e	*e*	*a*	*b*	*c*
a	*a*	*e*	*c*	*b*
b	*b*	*c*	*e*	*a*
c	*c*	*b*	*a*	*e*

Swapping

TABLE 4 (repeated)

The elements in the rows of the circling table move one place to the left each time with the spare man joining on at the end. This does not apply to the swapping table. The swapping table has *e*'s running down the leading

(N.W.–S.E.) diagonal which does not apply to the circling table. Comparing results individually we find that those based on e and b are the same for both tables. If we cross them out we are left with

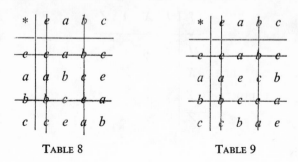

	TABLE 8			TABLE 9

This shows that the tables are identical except that the elements which give the same results in each table have changed places.

Thus our research project has so far produced two new mathematical structures. Both have four elements only, but different rules of behaviour.

Examples 2b

1. Repeat Question 1 of Examples 1d (p. 12) taking your results from Table 7 instead of Table 4. Compare your list of short cuts with those for Table 4 and abstract those which are common to both. Keep your list for future reference.

2. From the initial position of Fig. 14 first man moves to first lady, first lady moves to second lady, second lady moves to second man, and second man moves to where first man was. Then first man changes places with second lady and second man changes places with first lady. Finally, first man moves to second man, second man moves to second lady, second lady moves to first lady, and first lady moves to where first man was. Follow this through as best you may with diagrams, coins or other aids and then translate the movements into I's, X's, Y's and Z's and check your result.

Construct a new mathematical model using the 'standing still' movement and the three movements listed at the beginning of the question. Compare this with the original version. See Question 2 of Examples 1d. Is your result surprising or are we still wasting time? Again keep your results and decide later.

3. Repeat the relevant parts of Question 5 of Examples 1d using Table 7 instead of Table 4. Abstract the properties common to your new pattern and that of Table 5. You may already have produced the new pattern in answering Question 5 of Examples 1d. Well done! Again keep your results for future reference.

4. Repeat Question 6 of Examples 1d using Table 7 instead of Table 4. Revise your answer to that question if necessary. Again keep your results for future reference.

2.2 Arithmetic Modulus 4

The author possesses a clock which is used for timing moves in chess matches. A notable eccentricity of this machine is that it is a four-hour clock. The clock faces (there are two of them) have only the figures 1 to 4 printed on them and the hour hand covers one-quarter of the clock face every hour instead of the more fashionable twelfth. The minute hand behaves normally. The clock face looks like this

FIG. 18

and has its own private arithmetic.

Three hours on from one o'clock brings us to four o'clock or, more neatly, $3+1 = 4$. Three hours on from two o'clock brings us to one o'clock or $3+2 = 1$. This is less digestible but logical enough.

Examples 2c

Complete the table:

+	4	1	2	3
4	.	.	.	.
1	.	.	.	.
2	.	.	.	.
3	.	4	1	.

+	4	1	2	3
4	4	1	2	3
1	1	2	3	4
2	2	3	4	1
3	3	4	1	2

Clock

TABLE 10

f	*I*	*X*	*Y*	*Z*
I	*I*	*X*	*Y*	*Z*
X	*X*	*Y*	*Z*	*I*
Y	*Y*	*Z*	*I*	*X*
Z	*Z*	*I*	*X*	*Y*

Circling

TABLE 6 (repeated)

A comparison with the circling table shows that the two have the same form and that, once again, the same abstract mathematical structure can be used in each case.

It is embarrassing to have to use the numbers in the order 4, 1, 2, 3 instead of the more natural 1, 2, 3, 4 so as to get the two tables into the same pattern. We must realize however that 4 has a curiously hybrid set of properties in this context. It behaves like 4 in that $2+2 = 4$ and $3+1 = 4$. At the same time it behaves like 0 in that $1+4 = 1$, $2+4 = 2$, $3+4 = 3$, $4+4 = 4$. It is therefore just as reasonable to represent the first number in the table by 0 as by 4, so that the table could become

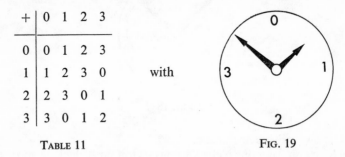

+	0	1	2	3
0	0	1	2	3
1	1	2	3	0
2	2	3	0	1
3	3	0	1	2

with

TABLE 11   FIG. 19

as the amended clock face. The symbolism does not matter, the ideas behind it do. We shall stick to 4, 1, 2, 3 at the moment since we are dealing with clock faces, but change to 0, 1, 2, 3 whenever it is convenient to do so.

The crux of this whole mathematical structure is 'four'. There are four members in the set. Four has the twin properties of 4 and 0. We can even use four to work out the table without counting our way laboriously round the clock face. $3+3 = 6$ in normal arithmetic. This is 2 hours past 4 and is therefore 2 in this system. Therefore $3+3 = 2$. We can extend this idea.

$$3+3+2+3+1+1 = 13 \text{ in normal arithmetic}$$

$$= 3 \times 4 + 1.$$

The answer is three times round the clock and one more, which brings us to one o'clock.

Thus the answer to any addition in four-hour clock arithmetic is obtained by working the sum out in orthodox arithmetic and knocking off as many fours as necessary. Four is called the modulus of this system and the system itself is arithmetic modulus four (mod 4 for short). The conscientious reader will already have come across multiplication mod 16 and mod 12 in Questions 9 and 10 of Examples 1d.

Examples 2d

1. Add the following in arithmetic mod 4:

    (a) $2+4+3+1+4+3$,

    (b) $3+1+2+4+4$,

(c) $1+4+3+2+2$,

(d) $2+4+4+2+3+1$,

(e) $4+4+2+2+3+1+1+3+2+2+4+3+1+2+2$.

There are several better methods of tackling this type of question than the one given in the text. Using only the short cuts that you have justified for this particular pattern in Question 1 of Examples 2b (p. 18), find as many ways of doing these questions as you can.

2. List all the two number additions in arithmetic mod 4 that give apparently the same answer as in orthodox arithmetic. Do this for both the Table 10 and the Table 11 versions.

3. Consider the possibilities of 'subtraction' in arithmetic mod 4. Devise a suitable definition for it and give it a physical interpretation on the four-hour clock. Keep your results for future reference.

4. Solve the following equations in arithmetic mod 4:

(a) $2+1 = x$,

(b) $3+2 = x$,

(c) $3+x = 4$,

(d) $x+2 = 1$,

(e) $x+x = 2$ (two solutions!).

2.3   Other Modulus Arithmetics

There is no reason why we should restrict ourselves to arithmetic mod 4. A six-hour version of the chess clock of the previous section is also in existence and looks like this:

giving

rise to

+	6	1	2	3	4	5
6	6	1	2	3	4	5
1	1	2	3	4	5	6
2	2	3	4	5	6	1
3	3	4	5	6	1	2
4	4	5	6	1	2	3
5	5	6	1	2	3	4

FIG. 20   TABLE 12

as an addition table for arithmetic mod 6. It is inevitable that we should eventually achieve orthodoxy with the usual clock face and arithmetic mod 12. A comparison of the three modulus tables shows that even between mathematical structures of differing sizes there can be much in common.

+	4	1	2	3
4	4	1	2	3
1	1	2	3	4
2	2	3	4	1
3	3	4	1	2

+	6	1	2	3	4	5
6	6	1	2	3	4	5
1	1	2	3	4	5	6
2	2	3	4	5	6	1
3	3	4	5	6	1	2
4	4	5	6	1	2	3
5	5	6	1	2	3	4

Mod 4 Mod 6

TABLE 10 (repeated) TABLE 12 (repeated)

+	12	1	2	3	4	5	6	7	8	9	10	11
12	12	1	2	3	4	5	6	7	8	9	10	11
1	1	2	3	4	5	6	7	8	9	10	11	12
2	2	3	4	5	6	7	8	9	10	11	12	1
3	3	4	5	6	7	8	9	10	11	12	1	2
4	4	5	6	7	8	9	10	11	12	1	2	3
5	5	6	7	8	9	10	11	12	1	2	3	4
6	6	7	8	9	10	11	12	1	2	3	4	5
7	7	8	9	10	11	12	1	2	3	4	5	6
8	8	9	10	11	12	1	2	3	4	5	6	7
9	9	10	11	12	1	2	3	4	5	6	7	8
10	10	11	12	1	2	3	4	5	6	7	8	9
11	11	12	1	2	3	4	5	6	7	8	9	10

TABLE 13

In each case the modulus number (4, 6 or 12) has the twin properties of itself and zero. Also each row of any table repeats the numbers of the row above but it is moved one to the left with the odd number joining on at the end. These two facts enable us to write down the addition table for modulus arithmetics very quickly without the labour of calculating individual results.

The reader may have noticed that the three modulus arithmetics so far (4, 6, and 12) are all factors of 12. This is due to the connexions with clock faces. There is no need to restrict modulus arithmetics either to factors of twelve or to clock-face problems.

Examples 2e

1. Write down rapidly and without effort the addition tables for
    (a) Arithmetic mod 2,
    (b) Arithmetic mod 3,
    (c) Arithmetic mod 5,
    (d) Arithmetic mod 7,
    (e) Arithmetic mod 8

after the style of Tables 10, 12, and 13. Keep your results for future reference.

2. Inevitably all these new tables have patterns. Look back at Question 5 of Examples 1d and Question 3 of Examples 2b and carefully list all properties you can find common to all the new arithmetics we have examined so far. If you do this well enough you need not read the next three chapters!

3. Using only the short cuts you can justify, calculate the following:
    (a) $3+4+5+4+2$ in arithmetics mod 5, mod 6, mod 7, mod 8 and mod 12;
    (b) $2+4+7+5+6$ in arithmetics mod 7, mod 8 and mod 12;
    (c) $1+2+3+2+1$ in arithmetics mod 3, mod 4, mod 5, mod 6, mod 7, mod 8 and mod 12.

4. Solve the following equations:
    (a) $5+4 = x$ in arithmetics mod 5, mod 6, mod 7, mod 8 and mod 12;
    (b) $3+x = 7$ in arithmetics mod 7, mod 8 and mod 12;
    (c) $x+5 = 1$ in arithmetics mod 5, mod 6, mod 7, mod 8 and mod 12;
    (d) $x+x = 4$ in arithmetics mod 4, mod 5, mod 6, mod 7, mod 8 and mod 12 (sometimes two solutions).

5. Sometimes the addition of two numbers in a modulus arithmetic gives the same result as the corresponding addition in orthodox arithmetic. Formulate a rule for deciding when this is the case.

6. 'Addition in orthodox arithmetic is merely addition in a modulus arithmetic with infinity as modulus.' Discuss this using your answer to Question 2 as a guide.

2.4 The Days of the Week

If today is the 4th of May and is a Saturday what day will it be on the 29th of May? Scorning the use of calendars and diaries we may argue that, since the 4th is a Saturday, the 11th, 18th and 25th will also be Saturdays.

Therefore the 26th will be a Sunday, the 27th a Monday, the 28th a Tuesday and the 29th a Wednesday.

The modulus arithmetician would be more inclined to say that the 29th is 25 days on from the 4th and 25 is 4 mod 7 (mod 7 because the day names repeat themselves every seven days in the same way that the hour numbers repeated themselves every 4, 6, or 12 hours).

If we represent Sun. Mon. Tues. Wed. Thur. Frid. Sat.

by   1   2   3   4   5   6   7 respectively

TABLE 14

we may say that 7 (the number representing today—Saturday) and 4 (the number of days that we must count on) make 4 (in arithmetic mod 7) which represents Wednesday. This gives us the correct answer and, with a little experience and without the explanation, is rather quicker.

We already have a complete addition table for arithmetic mod 7 from Question 1, Examples 2e.

+	7	1	2	3	4	5	6
7	7	1	2	3	4	5	6
1	1	2	3	4	5	6	7
2	2	3	4	5	6	7	1
3	3	4	5	6	7	1	2
4	4	5	6	7	1	2	3
5	5	6	7	1	2	3	4
6	6	7	1	2	3	4	5

TABLE 15

Examples 2f

1. What day will it be

   (a) 3 days on from Tuesday,

   (b) 5 days on from Thursday,

   (c) 17 days on from Friday,

   (d) 58 days on from Wednesday,

   (e) 184 days on from Sunday,

   (f) 365 days on from Monday,

   (g) 5384 days on from Saturday?

2. What month will it be

(a) 6 months on from February,

(b) 12 months on from April,

(c) 16 months on from June,

(d) 27 months on from November,

(e) 2 years, 8 months on from December?

3. Seven fathers with large cars organize a roster to drive their children to school five days a week. They take it in strict rotation and father A starts on Thursday, which is the first day of term. The term is exactly twelve weeks long. On what days is he duty chauffeur?

He finds he is down for a Monday and these are always inconvenient for him. Show that whichever day he started on he would be equally unlucky.

Reassess the situation if the children were working a six-day week and two fathers leave the district before term starts.

2.5 A Geometrical Example

If we take a regular pentagon ⬠ we may easily make a five-point star

from it by joining up all the diagonals and then removing the lines of

the original pentagon ☆. The resulting figure is called a pentagram and was

the Pythagorean emblem of good health. In mediaeval witchcraft it was believed to have the power to fend off evil. We are only interested in its geometrical properties here.

Let us name the five points of the pentagram A, B, C, D and E. We are unable to differentiate in appearance between

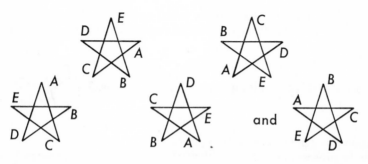

FIG. 21

To label these positions more conveniently we may use the fact that each

may be obtained from 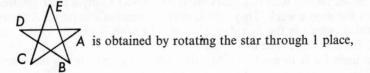 by rotating it clockwise through a

certain number of places. Thus

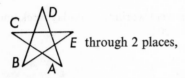 is obtained by rotating the star through 1 place,

 through 2 places,

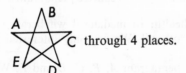 through 3 places, and

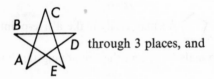 through 4 places.

FIG. 22

Five places brings us back to the initial position again and is apparently the same as no rotation at all. This of course is a situation for arithmetic

mod 5 and in this case it is logical to represent the position as a

rotation through O rather than 5 places.

By the process of reasoning with which we are now familiar we may rotate the star clockwise through, say, 4 places and then 3 places, which has the same effect as rotating it through 2 places only. The now almost inevitable addition table follows.

+	0	1	2	3	4
0	0	1	2	3	4
1	1	2	3	4	0
2	2	3	4	0	1
3	3	4	0	1	2
4	4	0	1	2	3

TABLE 16

The same arithmetic applies to the rotations of the original pentagon since we still have the five corners and the five identical positions that may be obtained by rotating the pentagon about its centre. Similarly we may extend this geometrical approach and apply arithmetic mod 4 to the rotations of a square, arithmetic mod 3 to the rotations of an equilateral triangle, or, in more general terms, arithmetic mod n to the rotations of a regular n-agon.

Examples 2g

1. Verify that △ may be used to generate the arithmetic mod 3 table, ▢ the arithmetic mod 4 table, and ⬡ the arithmetic mod 6 table.

2. Which modulus arithmetic tables may be generated by rotating the following designs in their plane?

(a) 　　(b) 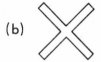　　(c)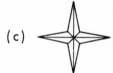

(d) 　　(e) 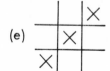　　(f)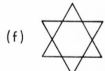

(g) 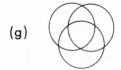　　(h) 　　(i)

FIG. 23

3. Use the following figure to generate three different modulus arithmetics according to whether we
  (a) ignore the shadings and just consider the shape of the figure,
  (b) consider the figure to be composed of just shaded and unshaded areas,
  (c) consider the figure to be composed of plain, lightly shaded and heavily shaded areas.

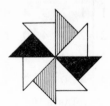

FIG. 24

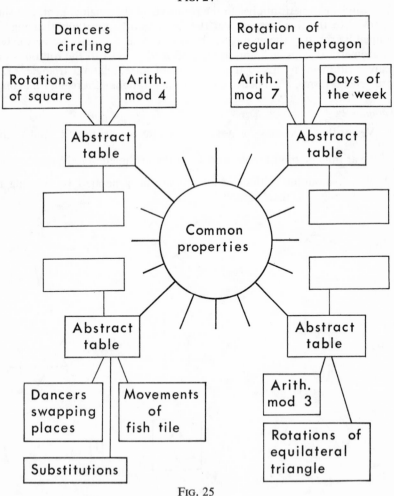

FIG. 25

2.6 Summary

In Chapter 1 we showed how a simple mathematical structure could be constructed and applied to various diverse situations. In this chapter we have examined a whole family of mathematical structures and some of the problems that we can solve with them.

We now therefore extend Fig. 11 (p. 11) and see that the original new arithmetic is just one of a far wider series.

We have of necessity listed only a few abstract tables and a few examples of each in action. In the course of this chapter we have tended to use the modulus arithmetics as archetypal patterns for the new structures as they are most easily registered in this form. However, this does incline us towards the clock-face idea and so we revert here to the more correct e, a, b, c, ... and put modulus arithmetics in their proper place as special cases. The diagram shows the new structures having properties in common. The reader has already had the chance to collect these in Question 2 of Examples 2e and we shall devote the next few chapters to correcting his answers.

3. PROPERTIES OF THE NEW SYSTEMS

3.1 Calculating

We now revert to the original research topic. In Chapter 1 the dancers' swapping places gave rise to the table

f	I	A	B	C
I	I	A	B	C
A	A	I	C	B
B	B	C	I	A
C	C	B	A	I

TABLE 1 (repeated)

and we were careful to work out $A f B f A f B$ as $\{(A f B) f A\} f B$. In other words we calculated A followed by B and followed the result of that by A again and the result of that by B again. This is reasonable in that the whole essence of Scottish dancing is that the steps follow in a certain sequence. Any alteration in the sequence produces a different dance or chaos. However, the same limitations may not apply to the mathematical model, which merely reflects certain aspects of Scottish dancing. Also an ability to alter the order of working may speed up the calculating process considerably. To relate this to more familiar fields, can we treat our I's, A's, B's and C's as normal numbers under addition where

$$3+6+7+4 = 20$$

whether we treat it as

$$\{(3+6)+7\}+4,$$

$$(3+6)+(7+4),$$

or

$$(3+7)+(6+4),$$

or any other permutation of the four numbers we can think of? Or, on the other hand, are we restricted to the original order as we would be with normal numbers under subtraction where

$$12-7-3-1 = \{(12-7)-3\}-1 = 1$$

and any alternative such as

$$(12-7)-(3-1)$$

produces a different result?

A tentative probe should give some indication. We worked out $AfBfAfB$ as $\{(AfB)fA\}fB$.

$$\{(AfB)fA\}fB = (CfA)fB$$
$$= BfB$$
$$= I \qquad \text{(see p. 4).}$$

Let us now keep the elements in the same order, but associate the second A with the second B instead of with the result of the (AfB) at the beginning. Thus we treat $AfBfAfB$ as $(AfB)f(AfB)$.

$$(AfB)f(AfB) = CfC \quad \text{since} \quad AfB = C$$
$$= I.$$

This gives the same result as before, but rather more quickly.

We will now alter the order of the elements so that we treat $AfBfAfB$ as $\{(AfA)fB\}fB$.

$$\{(AfA)fB\}fB = (IfB)fB$$
$$= BfB$$
$$= I.$$

Again the same result.

Finally, we alter both the order and the way of associating the elements so that we treat $AfBfAfB$ as $(AfA)f(BfB)$.

$$(AfA)f(BfB) = IfI$$
$$= I.$$

Again the same result.

We get the same result whichever of the four ways we work out our calculation. It therefore seems reasonable to examine further the possibility that we may treat our new system with the same careless rapture that we treat normal numbers under addition. Please note that we have not proved this. We have only tested the idea for one particular example and found that it worked. We must go further to prove our point.

Examples 3a

1. Write down as many dance sequences as possible using the three movements A, B and C once each and see if each threesome has the same effect. Keep your results for future reference.

2. Repeat Question 1 using the movements X, Y and Z of Table 6 (p. 17). Again keep your results.

3. Again repeat Question 1 for the mixtures of movements following. Use coins, chessmen or other aids to work out the new combinations and do not be surprised if unfamiliar positions appear. Again keep your results.
   (a) A, X and Z;
   (b) A, C and Z;
   (c) A, Y and C;
   (d) X, B and Z.

4. Verify that any three different numbers taken from the arithmetic mod 3 table combine under '+' in any order to give the same result.

5. Take any three numbers from arithmetic mod 5 and examine how they combine
    (a) Under '+',
    (b) Under '−'. (You defined '−' in Question 3 of Examples 2d (p. 21).)

6. Take any three numbers from orthodox arithmetic and examine how they combine
    (a) Under '×',
    (b) Under '÷'.

3.2   The Associative and Commutative Laws

Mercifully the flexibility which we hope to achieve follows from just two very simple ideas. These ideas are so universal in mathematics old and new that their truth or falsity is worth considering in any mathematical situation which may arise. In view of their importance we will define them in perfectly abstract symbols which we can amend to fit any given situation.

Let us assume that we have a set of elements, which may be linked by the combining operation '∗'. We say that the Associative Law is true for the system if

$$(x * y) * z = x * (y * z),$$

where x, y and z are any members of the set (in the same way that we use x, y and z to represent any numbers in normal algebra). This indicates that if we have any three elements linked together by the same combining operation we may associate the middle one with either the first or the last without altering the result. We frequently assume this law in everyday arithmetic.

$13+8+2$ strictly speaking means '8 added to 13 and 2 added to the result', i.e. $(13+8)+2$. Since we assume the Associative Law, the brackets become irrelevant and we may well work out the expression by saying '$8+2 = 10$, $13+10 = 23$', i.e. $13+(8+2)$.

On the other hand, $13-8-2$ definitely means '8 subtracted from 13 and 2 subtracted from the result', i.e. $(13-8)-2$. If we were to apply the Associative Law in this expression we would get $(13-8)-2 = 13-(8-2)$ which is certainly not true and therefore the Associative Law does not apply in the case of subtraction.

It is one of the more depressing aspects of this type of mathematics that we can prove that a law does not always work merely by producing one example where it falls down. On the other hand, we shall soon discover that proving a law does always work is one of the more exasperating pastimes of the modern mathematician. William James once said that it only required one white crow to disprove the statement that all crows were black, which suggests that he was having much the same trouble. We may remember certain painful occasions in our childhood when we unconsciously tried to apply the Associative Law to subtractions and were told off for 'not changing the signs when we removed brackets'.

The second law is even more straightforward. Going back to our abstract set again, we say that the Commutative Law is true for the system if

$$x * y = y * x,$$

where x and y are any members of the set. In this case we consider the order in which the elements appear as opposed to the way they are linked together. Again our experience tells us that the law holds good for normal addition and we are perfectly prepared to say that $5+9 = 9+5$. This is a fact that was not readily apparent to us as children and was one which we had to ingest at an early age.

Again subtraction provides a counter-example. $5-3$ does not equal $3-5$ and many of us as children must have considerably reduced our popularity with teacher by deciding that since in

$$\begin{array}{r} 23 \\ -17 \\ \hline \end{array}$$

we could not take 7 from 3 it was far more convenient to take 3 from 7, thus unconsciously applying a Commutative Law that does not work!

3.3 The Laws in Action

It is now necessary to establish that the Associative and Commutative Laws are sufficient to provide the flexibility in calculation that we require. Let us again examine $3+6+7+4$ which initially means $\{(3+6)+7\}+4$. The easiest way of adding these four numbers is to put them in the form $(3+7)+(6+4)$ which our experience tells us is perfectly permissible and respectable. We will now demonstrate that this type of reorganization is dependent on the two laws alone. If we can do this successfully it suggests that, whatever mathematical system we may be handling, we have only to prove our two laws to be able to treat its elements under their combining operation in the same way that we treat normal numbers under addition.

$$3+6+7+4 \quad \text{means} \quad \{(3+6)+7\}+4.$$

But

$$\{(3+6)+7\}+4 = \{3+(6+7)\}+4$$

by associating the 6 with the 7 instead of the 3;

$$= \{3+(7+6)\}+4$$

by making the 7 and 6 change places according to the Commutative Law;

$$= \{(3+7)+6\}+4$$

by associating the 7 with the 3 instead of the 6;

$$= (3+7)+(6+4)$$

by associating the 6 with the 4 instead of the $(3+7)$.

From this we may say that if the Associative and Commutative Laws are true for normal numbers under addition then

$$\{(3+6)+7\}+4 = (3+7)+(6+4).$$

Similarly by a judicious application of the two laws we could alter the order of calculation to anything we liked. Furthermore, we could extend the process to any number of numbers under addition and, of course, since we have used no property of numbers or addition except these two laws we may treat any mathematical situation which obeys these two laws in an equally cavalier manner.

Examples 3b

1. Three elements p, q and r of a mathematical system may be combined by an operation '$*$'. Combine the three in as many different orders as possible and show that one can get from $p*q*r$ to any of the other forms by using the Associative and Commutative Laws only.

2. Repeat Question 1 using the letter 'p' twice and work from the form $p*p*q*r$.

3. In Question 3 of examples 3a (p. 31) check whether the Associative and Commutative Laws work for the three elements in each of the four examples.

3.4 Proving the Commutative Law for the Swapping System

The remainder of this chapter is pure mathematical technique and covers the proof of the two laws for the swapping system. This enables us to alter the elements around as we feel inclined without altering the result. The techniques we have at the moment are limited and therefore our proofs are clumsy. We shall learn more sophisticated methods in later chapters, but brute force and ignorance has a certain primitive appeal and at the same time illustrates various basic principles very clearly. We tackle the Commutative Law first because it is easier to prove and because we can then use it to help prove the Associative Law.

The Commutative Law states that whichever pair of elements we choose we shall get the same result whichever way round we combine them. The most direct way to prove this is to take every possible pair of elements, combine them both ways, and check from the table that the results are the same. This is tedious, crude, but effective.

We will agree that If I, AfA, BfB, and CfC all remain unaltered if we put the second element first and the first element second. There remain for our consideration the following pairs: IfA, AfI; IfB, BfI; IfC, CfI; AfB, BfA; AfC, CfA; BfC, CfB.

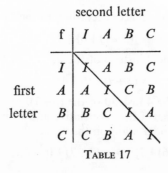

second letter

f	I	A	B	C
I		A	B	C
A	A		C	B
B	B	C		A
C	C	B	A	

first letter

TABLE 17

From the table we see that

$$If A = A = AfI,$$

$$If B = B = BfI,$$

$$If C = C = CfI,$$

$$AfB = C = BfA,$$

$$AfC = B = CfA,$$

$$BfC = A = CfB.$$

Thus we have established that the Commutative Law is true for every possible pair of elements that we may choose and is therefore true for the swapping system as a whole. In other words,

$$xfy = yfx,$$

where x and y are any of I, A, B and C.

The reader may have noticed that a broken line has been introduced into the swapping table along the leading diagonal (N.W.–S.E.). By mentally (or physically if necessary) folding the table along this diagonal we can see that all the A's fit onto A's, B's onto B's, C's onto C's, and I's onto I's (self-corresponding in this case). A little thought will show that this is a quick way of justifying the Commutative Law since, for example, the A in the first row and second column is the result of IfA and this fits onto the A in the second row and first column which is the result of AfI. The same line of thought may be followed all the way through and the reader may well have discovered it for himself from working Question 5 of Examples 1d (p. 13).

A small point which needs emphasizing and which will be reinforced in the proof of the Associative Law is that when we say $xfy = yfx$ where x and y are any of I, A, B and C we also include the possibility that x and y may be the same (just as in normal algebra in a given problem x and y may both be equal to 3, say). This we dismiss here as being trivial since IfI, AfA, BfB and CfC are singularly unaffected by the Commutative Law, but we must be aware of the situation in order to avoid pitfalls in more complex cases.

Examples 3c

1. Prove or disprove the Commutative Law for the following systems:
   (a) The dancers' circling system (Table 6, p. 17),
   (b) Arithmetic mod 3 under '+',
   (c) Arithmetic mod 3 under '−'.
2. Use your general experience to decide whether the Commutative Law is true or not for the following systems:
   (a) The set of positive whole numbers under '+',
   (b) The set of all whole numbers under '×',
   (c) The set of all rational numbers (whole numbers and fractions) under '÷',
   (d) The set of all positive numbers under 'to the power of' (e.g. 2^3, 4^9, $(3 \cdot 2)^{2 \cdot 37}$).

3.5 Proving the Associative Law for the Swapping System

Does $(x f y) f z = x f(y f z)$ where x, y and z are any of I, A, B and C? In other words can we, with justification, drop the brackets and refer to the expression as just $x f y f z$? The proof here is an extension of the one used in the previous section in which we examined each case separately. We first of all consider the cases where all the elements are the same.

Does

$$(I f I) f I = I f(I f I),$$

$$(A f A) f A = A f(A f A),$$

$$(B f B) f B = B f(B f B),$$

and

$$(C f C) f C = C f(C f C)?$$

These are all immediately seen to be true by the Commutative Law.

The next series of cases are those where two elements are the same. We shall restrict ourselves for the sake of space and sanity to the cases based on two A's and a B. For a complete proof it would, of course, be necessary to cover also the versions based on two I's and an A, two A's and an I, two I's and a B, two B's and an I, two I's and a C, two C's and an I, two B's and an A, two A's and a C, two C's and an A, two B's and a C and two C's and a B. If there are those who find fascination in such manipulation and who feel inclined to tackle the proof *in toto*, we suggest that they wait until the end of the next chapter when some further aids to calculation will have been examined.

Considering two A's and a B the following permutations arise: $A f A f B$, $A f B f A$, and $B f A f A$. To establish the Associative Law for these three we must prove that

$$A f(A f B) = (A f A) f B, \tag{i}$$

$$(A f B) f A = A f(B f A), \tag{ii}$$

$$(B f A) f A = B f(A f A). \tag{iii}$$

Equation (ii) is easily proved.

$$(A f B) f A = (B f A) f A \quad \text{by the Commutative Law,}$$

$$= A f(B f A) \quad \text{by the Commutative Law again.}$$

This proof is independent of any special properties of A and B so that it is true for all threesomes where two are the same and the odd one is in the middle.

Equation (i) can easily be turned into equation (iii) by applying the Commutative Law twice to $A f(A f B)$ to give the left-hand side of (iii) and once to $(A f A) f B$ to give the right-hand side of (iii). We therefore only have to prove equation (i).

$$A f B = C. \quad \text{Therefore} \quad A f(A f B) = A f C = B.$$

Similarly

$$A f A = I. \quad \text{Therefore} \quad (A f A) f B = I f B = B.$$

$$\text{Therefore} \quad A f(A f B) = (A f A) f B.$$

We have previously shown that equation (i) can easily be converted into equation (iii) since the Commutative Law is true and that equation (ii) is true anyway. Therefore we have established the Associative Law for these three statements. Whilst doing this we have also established that the truth of equation (ii) is independent of the symbols employed and depends only on the Commutative Law. Similarly we have established that equations (i) and (iii) are identical whatever symbols may be used as long as the Commutative Law is true. Therefore we have already gone a considerable way towards verifying the proof of the Associative Law for other threesomes which have two elements the same.

All that is left now is the series where all three elements are different. These will involve $I, A, B; I, A, C; I, B, C$ and A, B, C. Again for economy of effort we only tackle the versions based on A, B and C. These give us the following variations:

$$A\,f\,B\,f\,C, \quad A\,f\,C\,f\,B, \quad B\,f\,C\,f\,A, \quad B\,f\,A\,f\,C, \quad C\,f\,A\,f\,B, \quad C\,f\,B\,f\,A.$$

This means that we must prove that

$$A\,f(B\,f\,C) = (A\,f\,B)\,f\,C, \tag{i}$$

$$A\,f(C\,f\,B) = (A\,f\,C)\,f\,B, \tag{ii}$$

$$B\,f(C\,f\,A) = (B\,f\,C)\,f\,A, \tag{iii}$$

$$B\,f(A\,f\,C) = (B\,f\,A)\,f\,C, \tag{iv}$$

$$C\,f(A\,f\,B) = (C\,f\,A)\,f\,B, \tag{v}$$

$$C\,f(B\,f\,A) = (C\,f\,B)\,f\,A. \tag{vi}$$

These expressions separate themselves into three distinct varieties according to whether A, B or C is the element outside the brackets. We can prove easily, for example, that all expressions with A outside the bracket are equal by repeated application of the Commutative Law. Thus

$$A\,f(B\,f\,C) = A\,f(C\,f\,B) = (C\,f\,B)\,f\,A = (B\,f\,C)\,f\,A.$$

The same is true for all expressions with B outside the brackets and for those with C outside the brackets. Thus we only have to prove that representatives of the three types all give the same result in order to prove the Associative Law in these circumstances. Again this part of the reasoning is independent of the nature of A, B and C and will therefore carry over to the other similar versions. Let us take $A\,f(B\,f\,C)$, $B\,f(A\,f\,C)$ and $C\,f(A\,f\,B)$ as the representatives of their sets.

$$A\,f(B\,f\,C) = A\,f\,A = I,$$

$$B\,f(A\,f\,C) = B\,f\,B = I,$$

$$C\,f(A\,f\,B) = C\,f\,C = I.$$

Thus all three are equal. Therefore the twelve expressions of equations (i) to (vi) are all equal which proves the Associative Law in these circumstances. By repeating this proof for the other cases involving three different elements and also repeating the proofs in the previous sections where necessary, we could then cover every possibility and be sure that the Associative Law was true in every possible case.

The reader will doubtless agree that this is a very lengthy and involved procedure. As we said previously, there are other quicker methods which we will demonstrate later. However at least an outline proof of the two laws is desirable at this stage so that we may build on fairly sound foundations. Also an examination of the two proofs does help clarify one's ideas on the subject a little.

Examples 3d

1. Prove or disprove the Associative Law for the following systems:
   (a) Arithmetic mod 2 under '+',
   (b) Arithmetic mod 3 under '+',
   (c) Arithmetic mod 3 under '−'.
2. Give an outline of the proof of the Associative Law for
   (a) The dancers' circling system (Table 6, p. 17),
   (b) Arithmetic mod 5 under '+'.
3. Use your general experience to decide whether the Associative Law is true or not for the mathematical systems in Question 2 of Examples 3c (p. 35).

3.6 Summary

As a result of this chapter we are now on nodding terms with two very basic laws in mathematics:

$$\text{the Associative Law} \quad x*(y*z) = (x*y)*z$$

and

$$\text{the Commutative Law} \quad x*y = y*x,$$

where x, y and z are any members of the set.

If the two laws hold good for a system then that system may be handled in much the same way as we handle normal numbers under addition.

We have also at least outlined the proofs for our swapping system and a thorough investigation of the proofs would show that in fact the two laws do hold good. The method of proof is equally valid for any of the systems which we have discussed so far in Chapters 1 and 2. In fact it is most unlikely that we shall deal seriously with any system in which the Associative Law is not true as it is then very difficult to make progress at all. However, situations where the Commutative Law is not true are more fashionable and we shall meet another example of this in the next chapter.

Finally, a summary of what we have done so far lest we lose ourselves in the details. In the course of the last three chapters we have taken the reader through a complicated piece of logical reasoning. We have been faced with a practical problem (Scottish dancing). We have analysed some of its properties and turned them into our own private mathematical system. Now we are examining aids to calculation which we may employ in this system. In the next chapter we shall continue this process.

4. FURTHER PROPERTIES

4.1 Neutral Element

The reader may well have noticed (Question 2, Examples 2e, p. 23) that every new system we have met has contained an element, usually but not necessarily represented by I or e, which, when combined with any of its fellows, leaves them unaltered. Thus, in our now familiar swapping system

f	I	A	B	C
I	I	A	B	C
A	A	I	C	B
B	B	C	I	A
C	C	B	A	I

TABLE 1 (repeated)

If $A = A$, If $B = B$, If $C = C$ and similarly, by the Commutative Law or from the table, $A f I = A$, $B f I = B$, $C f I = C$. This is reasonable enough in this case since I represents the process of standing still. Such an element is called the neutral or identity element and has the great merit that if we find it combined with anything else in our calculations we can cross it out and forget about it.

We must be careful to note that a neutral element usually acts for one particular combining operation only. Thus I is the neutral element for 'f' but if we conjured up another combining operation 'g' for the same set of elements then it would be most unlikely that I would be the neutral element for 'g' as well. We are familiar with this situation in orthodox arithmetic. Normal numbers have two identity elements, 0 and 1. 0 is the identity element for '+' and 1 is the identity element for '×'. $0 + a = a$ and $1 \times a = a$ where a is any number. Note that 0 is not an identity element for '×' and 1 is not an identity element for '+' since $0 \times a$ is not a and neither is $1 + a$.

Examples 4a

1. What is the neutral element for arithmetic mod 3 under '+'?

2. What is the neutral element for arithmetic mod 5 under '+'?

3. Is there a neutral element for the set of all rationals (whole numbers and fractions) under '÷'? Be careful!

4

4. Is there a neutral element for the set of all whole numbers under '−'? Be equally careful!

5. Is there a neutral element for arithmetic mod 2 under '−'?

6. Is there a neutral element for arithmetic mod 4 under '−'?

4.2 Inverse Elements

Two elements of a set are said to be inverses of each other if the two combine to form the neutral element of that set. In the swapping system each element is its own inverse since

$$If I = I, \quad A f A = I, \quad B f B = I \quad \text{and} \quad C f C = I.$$

This is an eccentricity of this system and is not usually so. If we examine the circling system instead

f	I	X	Y	Z
I	I	X	Y	Z
X	X	Y	Z	I
Y	Y	Z	I	X
Z	Z	I	X	Y

TABLE 6 (repeated)

we see that $If I = I$, $Z f X = I$ and $Y f Y = I$. Thus I and Y are their own inverses and X and Z are inverses of each other. The action of the inverse in any system is to restore the *status quo*. In the Scottish dancing examples the inverses gently but firmly shepherd the dancers back to their initial positions. Thus if any pair swap places then the same pair must swap places back again to return to their starting positions and each process is its own inverse. In the circling system, on the other hand, we must remember that moving round through four places is effectively the same as standing still. Thus the inverse of X (moving round one place) can be taken as either moving round three more places or back one place, both of which are called Z. I is its own inverse once again since if we stand still in the initial position, the best way of staying there is to stand equally still, whilst once you are half-way round (Y) you can go either half-way back or half-way forward to return to base (Y again).

It is a feature of the systems that we have examined so far that every element of every system has an inverse. To check this is a little tedious but the quickest way is to see that every row and every column has an I (or whatever symbol is being used for the neutral element) in it. This means that whatever element we take of any system there must be an element somewhere in the system that combines with it to give the neutral element and is therefore its inverse. A quick examination of the tables for swapping and circling will show that this is so.

f	I	A	B	C
I	I	.	.	.
A	.	I	.	.
B	.	.	I	.
C	.	.	.	I

TABLE 18

f	I	X	Y	Z
I	I	.	.	.
X	.	.	.	I
Y	.	.	I	.
Z	.	I	.	.

TABLE 19

With the ideas of Associativity, Commutativity and neutral and inverse elements we are now able to simplify calculation as much as possible. If we take our usual example from the swapping system

$$A f B f A f B$$

we know from Chapter 3 that we can link any element with any other element in any order we like. We therefore link inverses together giving

$$(A f A) f (B f B).$$

Each expression in the brackets gives I since A and B are self-inverses and therefore

$$(A f A) f (B f B) = I f I = I,$$

which is the quickest solution. This, of course, we have done before but with our now greater experience we know how to go straight to the easiest method. We need not even bother about rewriting the expression at all since, on seeing

$$A f B f A f B$$

and knowing that the Associative and Commutative Laws are true, we can immediately obliterate the two A's as self-inverses and also the two B's. Thus

$$A f B f A f B = \cancel{A} f \cancel{B} f \cancel{A} f \cancel{B} = I.$$

A purely random jumble of symbols, unconnected with any dance known to the author, will illustrate the matter further.
$$A f B f C f C f B f A f I f A f C f B f I f C$$

$$= A f B f C f C f B f A f A f C f B f C \quad \text{since the } I\text{'s have no effect,}$$

$$= A f B \quad \text{obliterating pairs of self-inverses,}$$

$$= C \quad \text{from the table.}$$

If this process disconcerts let us again turn to normal arithmetic. The inverse of any number with respect to addition is the negative of that number. Thus the inverse of 3 is -3 since $3 + (-3) = 0$, the neutral element for addition. We usually write $3+(-3)$ as $3-3$ and, with a long string of figures such as

$$3+4-3+5-4-2+2-5+0+6-0-6,$$

we would have no compunction at all in first of all forgetting the 0's and then crossing out all pairs of additive inverses, so that we get

$$\cancel{3}+\cancel{4}-\cancel{3}+\cancel{5}-\cancel{4}-\cancel{2}+\cancel{2}-\cancel{5}+\cancel{6}-\cancel{6}$$

which reduces to 0.

This process is exactly parallel to the one we did in the swapping system.

In the previous section we established that a neutral element acts only for a particular combining operation. Since inverse elements are closely linked with neutral elements the same restrictions apply here. The additive inverse (negative) of 3 is -3 since $3+(-3)=0$, the neutral element for addition. On the other hand, the multiplicative inverse of 3 (normally called its reciprocal) is $1/3$ since $3\times 1/3=1$, the neutral element for '×'. We are probably even more familiar with the handling of multiplicative inverses than additive ones, since most of us in our school-days gave vent to our spite on expressions such as

$$\frac{1}{3}\times\frac{3}{7}\times\frac{2}{5}\times\frac{14}{4}$$

by doing

$$\frac{1}{\cancel{3}}\times\frac{\cancel{3}}{\cancel{7}}\times\frac{\cancel{2}}{5}\times\frac{\cancel{14}}{\cancel{4}}$$

to it and getting $1/5$ as the result.

Examples 4b

1. Locate the inverse of each element in

   (a) Arithmetic mod 3 under '+',

   (b) Arithmetic mod 6 under '+'.

2. Look back to your list of short cuts in calculation (Question 1, Examples 2b, p. 18) and amend if necessary to include all the latest improvements.

3. Look back to Question 1, Examples 2d, p. 20 and rework the examples by the slickest possible methods.

4. Repeat the above with Question 3, Examples 2e, p. 23.

5. Rapidly work out

   (a) $Bf Cf Af Af Bf C$,

   (b) $Xf Yf Zf Zf Zf Zf Xf Yf$,

(c) $A f C f B f C f A f I f B f C$,

(d) $X f I f X f Z f I f Y f Y f X f X f Y f Z f I$,

(e) $1+3+2+4+5+3+2+1$ in arithmetic mod 6,

(f) $1+2+3+2+1+2+3+2+1+2+3+2+1$ in arithmetic mod 3.

4.3 Closure and Uniqueness

The topics of this section are apparently so trivial as to be unworthy of us. We have already more or less taken them for granted throughout the first part of this chapter. Let us examine a simple calculation in a purely abstract system

$$x * y.$$

There are three possibilities here: no result, one result, or many results. We hope that there is just one result and in all the systems we have examined so far this is true.

'Closure' is straightforward. If we have a set of elements and a combining operation, the set is said to be closed under the combining operation if, whichever pair of elements of the set we combine, we always get a member of the set as a result. In the swapping system, whenever we combine I's, A's, B's, or C's by 'f', we know, from the table, that we shall always get an I, an A, a B, or a C as the result. Again normal numbers under addition seem to obey the closure rule. If we add any two numbers, as far as we know, we always get another number. If however we decide to take the set of whole numbers and have '÷' as our combining operation the set is not closed under division. If we evaluate $6 \div 3$ we get 2 which certainly belongs to the set of all whole numbers. On the other hand, $6 \div 4$ gives $1\frac{1}{2}$ which is not a whole number. Therefore the set of whole numbers is not closed under division. (It only takes one white crow to disprove the statement that all crows are black.) In the new systems so far, closure is always true and can be checked easily by examining the relevant tables and making sure that no symbol appears that is not listed along the top and side.

Uniqueness of result gives the other side of the picture. The idea is that if we have a solution in the set, we wish to make sure that it is the only solution in the set. In other words, subject to human error, we only want one solution per calculation. This is such a basic notion and one that we take so much for granted that it is difficult to find a counter-example. However a series of quadratic equations, although not strictly pertinent to the present investigations, illustrate the concepts of closure and uniqueness well enough.

We define the 'quadroot' of two positive whole numbers as follows: multiply the first by x, add the second to the result, subtract the result of this from x^2, and put the lot equal to zero. The quadroots of the two numbers are the roots of the quadratic equation thus formed. '4 q 12', for example, is the abbreviation for 'the quadroots of four and twelve' and may be evaluated by solving the quadratic equation

$$x^2 - 4x - 12 = 0.$$

This has solutions $x = 6$ and $x = -2$ so that $4\,q\,12 = 6$ and -2. Uniqueness of result specifies that each calculation has but one result and, if we permit answers in the set of all integers, we have two. Closure specifies that the results should be elements of the original set. If we restrict ourselves to the set of positive integers only, the negative answer is out of court. We therefore have a far-fetched but non-the-less legitimate example where both the closure and uniqueness rules may break down.

Examples 4c

1. Which of the following sets are closed under '$+$', '$-$', '$\times$', or '$\div$':

   (a) Positive whole numbers,

   (b) All whole numbers,

   (c) Positive rationals (positive whole numbers and fractions),

   (d) All rationals (excluding 0),

   (e) All real numbers?

2. Test the set of positive whole numbers under 'quadrootion' for:

   (a) Associativity,

   (b) Commutativity,

   (c) The existence of a neutral element,

   (d) The existence of inverses.

3. If we extend the process of quadrootion to include negative whole numbers we avoid the difficulty about closure for the example given in the text. Is the set of all whole numbers closed under quadrootion? Try also the set of all rationals and the set of all real numbers.

4. We can avoid the uniqueness difficulty for the example in the text by redefining quadrootion as the taking of the positive roots of the quadratics only. Will this guarantee not more than one solution for any quadrootion of positive whole numbers? Will this guarantee at least one solution in the set of positive real numbers?

4.4   The Logical Extension of the Dancing Research

For the sake of simplicity we have restricted our mathematical model of Scottish dancing to two 'f' tables, the swapping and the circling ones. This has left our poor dancers either furiously swapping places or whirling round in a circle until they go dizzy. To make an adequate and enjoyable dance we need a pleasing blend of both types of step and our intention now is to combine the swapping and the circling processes into one big table.

Before we do this it may be as well for us to list again our symbols so that we know where we are.

I left the dancers in their initial positions.

1st man   1st lady

2nd man   2nd lady

A moved them from the initial position to (change places crossways).

B moved them from the initial position to (change places up and down).

C moved them from the initial position to (change places diagonally).

X moved them from the initial position to (all move round one place clockwise).

Y has a similar effect to *C* and can now be ignored (all move round two places clockwise).

Z moved them from the initial position to (all move round three places clockwise).

Fig. 26

Let us now bundle the processes together and see what happens.

second process

f	I	A	B	C	X	Z
I	I	A	B	C	X	Z
A	A	I	C	B	.	.
B	B	C	I	A	.	.
C	C	B	A	I	Z	X
X	X	.	.	Z	C	I
Z	Z	.	.	X	I	C

first process (labels at left for rows I, A, B, C, X, Z)

TABLE 20

We can complete the table except for the places where the eight dots appear since we have calculated the results previously in the separate tables. Notice that we have completely replaced Y by C in this table as Y is now *persona non grata*. However, since C and Y have the same effect we can quote $C f X$, $C f Z$, $X f C$ and $Z f C$ from the corresponding results for Y from the original circling table. We now compute the remaining results (using chessmen, or other aids if required).

$A f X$ means that from the initial position the dancers change places crossways and all move one place clockwise. This brings us to

FIG. 27

which unfortunately has not appeared before. Therefore the closure rule is not true in the combined case. Let us however call this **process P** and continue. We may describe P as *top left and bottom right change places*.

$A f Z$ means change places crossways and everyone moves three places clockwise. This brings us to

FIG. 28

Again this has not appeared before. Call this **process** *Q* and continue. *Q* is equivalent to *top right and bottom left changing places.*

*B*f*X* means changing places up and down followed by all moving one place clockwise producing

Good, *Q* again.

*B*f*Z* means changing places up and down followed by all moving three places clockwise producing

which is *P* again. This completes the little square of empty spaces at top right of the table. It would be pleasant to be able to quote the Commutative Law here to fill in the remaining blanks, but unfortunately we cannot be certain that the Commutative Law is true in the whole of the combined system although we know that it is true in a large number of cases. We therefore continue.

*X*f*A* means all move one place clockwise followed by changing places crossways. This produces

which is *Q*. Since *A*f*X* gave us *P* this means that the Commutative Law is not true and our suspicions were therefore justified (see Question 3, Examples 3a, p. 31).

$X f B$ means a one place rotation followed by changing places up and down which gives

which is P. Similarly, to save labouring the point, $Z f A$ gives P and $Z f B$ gives Q.

We have now completed the table but, unfortunately, for the first time in our research it is not closed. The only thing that we can do is to extend our system by putting extra rows and columns for P and Q along the bottom and right-hand side of the table and again compute our results. This may produce more unnamed processes. In this case the closure rule would again not hold good and again we would have to extend our table. There are however only a limited number of ways of arranging four dancers (24 in all, see Chapter 8) so that we must come to an end eventually!

second process

f	I	A	B	C	X	Z	P	Q
I	I	A	B	C	X	Z	.	.
A	A	I	C	B	P	Q	.	.
B	B	C	I	A	Q	P	.	.
C	C	B	A	I	Z	X	.	.
X	X	Q	P	Z	C	I	.	.
Z	Z	P	Q	X	I	C	.	.
P	.	.	.	.	.	.	.	.
Q	.	.	.	.	.	.	.	.

first process (labels to the left: first, process)

TABLE 21

The table is now becoming enormous and so is the computation. We will shoot through it as quickly as we can. I, the process of standing still, when combined with either of the new processes will still leave them alone. P and Q both involve two dancers swapping places. Therefore P and Q, when they happen twice, will cancel themselves out. In other words $P f P = I$ and $Q f Q = I$, i.e. each are self-inverses.

$P f Q$ and $Q f P$ both result in a complete change of places diagonally which is C.

We now examine $Pf X$, $Pf C$ and $Pf Z$, i.e. the effect of rotating the dancers through one, two and three places once P has been done. These give us

,   and   respectively

which are B, Q, and A. The rest we leave to the reader.

Examples 4d

Complete the table!

second process

f	I	A	B	C	X	Z	P	Q
I	I	A	B	C	X	Z	P	Q
A	A	I	C	B	P	Q	X	Z
B	B	C	I	A	Q	P	Z	X
C	C	B	A	I	Z	X	Q	P
X	X	Q	P	Z	C	I	A	B
Z	Z	P	Q	X	I	C	B	A
P	P	Z	X	Q	B	A	I	C
Q	Q	X	Z	P	A	B	C	I

first process (B, C rows), process label on left

TABLE 22 (combined table)

4.5 An Examination of the New Table

With the introduction of the two new processes P and Q we have managed to produce a closed system which is capable of handling a fair number of the usual patterns of Scottish country dances. We are, of course, restricted to dances based on two couples where the dancers remain more or less in square formation. Even with this reduction we have not taken into account every possible pattern. As we have said previously, there are twenty-four of these in all and we suffered some considerable anguish during the computation of the above table in case it was necessary to include the full twenty-four versions before closure was achieved.

Barring accidents, the same sequence of steps still produces the same result each time we do it so that uniqueness of result still holds good.

We suggest that the reader accepts our word that the Associative Law is true. He has the means of proof at his disposal but he is a brave man if he is prepared to tackle it. As we said previously, we shall produce a quicker method in a later chapter.

I behaves as the perfect identity element for all elements of the table but the question of inverses causes trouble. If it is no longer always true that $L\,f\,M = M\,f\,L$, where L and M are any of I, A, B, C, X, Y, P, or Q, we must of necessity distinguish between combining on the left and combining on the right. In view of this it does not necessarily seem to be true that if L^{-1} is a right inverse of L (i.e. if $L\,f\,L^{-1} = I$) then L^{-1} is also a left inverse of L (i.e. $L^{-1}\,f\,L = I$). In other words, $L\,f\,L^{-1}$ does not apparently have to be equal to $L^{-1}\,f\,L$ and if the equality does not hold good then L^{-1} cannot be both a left and a right inverse. This is very simple but most difficult for the mind to grasp. We are so used to saying that $4 \times \frac{1}{4} = \frac{1}{4} \times 4$ that the thought of a situation where such a happy state does not occur seems almost a heresy. However, such topics are more the affair of the next chapter than this one and we merely note with some relief that six of the eight elements are their own inverses and therefore unaffected by the Commutative Law and that the other two, X and Z, are inverses of each other whichever way round we put them. In other words, $X\,f\,Z = Z\,f\,X = I$.

4.6 An Example of Computation

Having evolved a system of mathematics that is capable of handling various Scottish dances for two couples it would be well to see it in action before finishing this chapter. The dance 'The Merry Oddfellows'—an eminently suitable title—goes as follows:

'The Merry Oddfellows'

Tune: any good jig   Time 6/8

Bars

1–4	1st and 2nd couples advance towards partners and retire. 4 skip change of step.
5–8	They dance half right and left to change places. 4 skip change of step.
9–12	1st lady and 2nd man, joining right hands, turn each other $1\frac{1}{2}$ times to finish back in their original places.
13–16	1st man and 2nd lady do the same.
17–24	1st man leads his partner down the middle and up again.
25–32	1st and 2nd couples change places with poussette.
	1st couple repeat dance with next couple.†

For those who are not familiar with the esoteric symbolism of Scottish country dancing the following translation may help.

† J. C. Milligan, *101 Scottish Country Dances* (Collins).

Bars 1-4   No change of relative positions

Bars 5-8

AfB

Bars 9-12

$QfQfQ$

Bars 13 - 16

As above but with ☆and☆ in action

resulting in

$PfPfP$

Bars 17 - 24

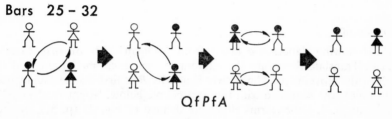

BfB

Bars 25 - 32

$QfPfA$

FIG. 29

(Although this demonstration of the poussette is accurate enough for our research, the purist would justifiably protest that this was not a correct representation of the movement. In fact the couples circle around each other as they change their relative positions. This idea is not allowed for in our mathematical model as it does not affect the relative positions of the dancers.)

The result of all this is

$$If(AfB)f(QfQfQ)f(PfPfP)f(BfB)f(QfPfA).$$

We can ignore the I at the beginning. We know that Q, P and B are self-inverses so that we can replace QfQ, PfP and BfB by I and thus ignore them. We can also omit the brackets since we are assuming the Associative Law to be true. Thus the expression reduces to

$$AfBfQfPfQfPfA.$$

We cannot immediately pair off the A's at the beginning and at the end as this would entail the use of the Commutative Law in getting one of the A's past the Q's and P's in the middle and we know that the law is not true for AfP and AfQ. However, we can by the Associative Law link each Q with the following P. $QfP = C$ so that the expression reduces to

$$AfBfCfCfA.$$

The Commutative Law now applies since we are restricted to members of the original swapping system so that the two A's and the two C's reduce to I apiece which leaves us with B as the answer. This means that the dancers have moved from

1st couple   to

2nd couple

which is correct since the first couple go on to dance the sequence with a third couple who would usually be standing just below the second at the beginning of the dance.

Examples 4c

The following dances are taken from Milligan's *101 Scottish Country Dances*. Translate them into the relevant mathematical model and find the result of the movements. The answer is usually B as first couple usually goes on to repeat the sequence with the next couple below. 'Rights and Lefts' is defined on p. 4. Other terms either are defined in Fig. 29 (p. 51), notated in the dances, or self-explanatory.

1.   'Rory O'More'

Tune: original   Time 6/8

Bars

1–4   1st and 2nd couples advance towards partners and retire. 4 skip
       change of step.

5–8   They cross over to change places, ladies passing under the arch made
       by the men. 4 skip change of step.

9–16   They repeat all this back to places, the men passing under the arch
       made by the ladies. 8 skip change of step.

17–24 1st man leads his partner down the middle and up again.

25–32 1st and 2nd couples change places with poussette.
       1st couple repeat dance with next couple.

2.   'Ha! Ha! The Wooin' O' It'

Tune: *Duncan Gray* or any good reel   Time 4/4

Bars

1–4   1st and 2nd ladies advance towards partner—2 skip change of step,
       and set—2 pas de basque (*process I*).

5–8   They retire—2 skip change of step, and set (*process I*).

9–16   1st and 2nd men do the same.

17–24 1st man leads his partner down the middle and up again.

25–32 1st and 2nd couples change places with poussette.
       1st couple repeat dance with next couple.

3.   'Roxburgh Castle'

Tune: original or any good reel   Time 4/4

Bars

1–8   1st and 2nd couples dance round following each other in a square.
       2 skip change of step to each side of the square.

9–16   1st and 2nd couples, giving right hands across to make a wheel, dance
       round for 4 skip change of step. They give left hands across and
       dance back to places.

17–24 1st man leads his partner down the middle and up again.

25–32 1st and 2nd couples change places with poussette.
       1st couple repeat dance with next couple.

4.   'The River Cree'

Tune: any good jig   Time 6/8

Bars

1–4   1st man and 2nd lady, giving right hand in passing, cross over to
       change places. 4 skip change of step.

5–8   1st lady and 2nd man do the same.

9–12   Joining nearer hands, the 2 ladies and the 2 men advance towards
       partners with 2 skip change of step and retire for 2.

13–16   1st and 2nd couples dance ½ right and left back to places. 4 skip
       change of step.

17–24   1st man leads his partner down the middle and up again.

25–32   1st and 2nd couples change places with poussette.
       1st couple repeat dance with next couple.

5. 'High Road to Wigton'

Tune: any good reel   Time 4/4

Bars

  1–4   1st and 2nd couples cross over to change places, the men passing
       between the two ladies. 4 skip change of step.

  5–8   They cross back to own places, the ladies passing between the 2
       men.

 9–16   1st and 2nd couples, giving right hands across in a wheel, dance
       round 4 skip change of step. They give left hands across and dance
       back to places.

17–24   1st man leads his partner down the middle and up again.

25–32   1st and 2nd couples change places with poussette.
       1st couple repeat dance with next couple.

6. 'The Linton Ploughman'

Tune: *The Muckin' o' Geordie's Byre*   Time 4/4

Bars

  1–8   1st and 2nd couples make a circle and dance 8 slip steps round to
       the left and 8 back.

 9–16   1st and 2nd couples, giving right hands across to make a wheel, dance
       4 skip change of step round, then give left hands across and dance
       4 back again.

17–24   1st couple dance down the middle and up.

25–32   1st and 2nd couples change places with poussette.
       1st couple repeat dance with next couple.

7. 'The Lass O' Livingston'

Tune: original or any good reel tune   Time 4/4

Bars

  1–4   1st man and 2nd lady, joining right hands, turn each other round once
       and return to places. 4 skip change of step.

  5–8   1st lady and 2nd man do the same.

 9–16   1st man leads his partner down the middle and up again.

17–24   1st and 2nd couples change places with poussette.

25–32   1st and 2nd couples dance rights and lefts across the dance and back
       again.
       1st couple repeat dance with next 2 couples.

8.   'Knit the Pocky'

Tune: any good reel   Time 4/4

Bars
1–4   1st lady and 2nd man advance towards each other and retire. 4 skip change of step.
5–8   They turn each other, giving both hands, and return to place. 4 skip change of step.
9–16   1st man and 2nd lady do the same.
17–20   1st man leads his partner down the middle followed by the 2nd couple. They turn and now 2nd couple are in front.
21–24   2nd man leads his lady up the middle to the top place, while 1st couple follow and finish in 2nd place.
25–32   1st and 2nd couples dance rights and lefts across the dance and back again.
        1st couple repeat dance with next couple.

9.   'Clydeside Lassies'

Tune: *Clydesdale Lassies* or any good reel   Time 4/4

Bars
1–8   1st and 2nd couples make a circle and dance 8 slip steps round to the left and 8 to the right.
9–16   1st man leads his partner down the middle and up again. They finish facing each other at the top ready for poussette.
17–24   1st and 2nd couples poussette.
25–32   1st and 2nd couples dance rights and lefts across and back again.
        1st couple repeat dance with next couple.

10.   'Grant's Reel'

Tune: any good strathspey   Time 4/4

Bars
1–4   1st man and 2nd lady set to each other with 2 strathspey setting steps. They give both hands and turn each other, and return to places—2 strathspey travelling steps.
5–8   1st lady and 2nd man do the same.
9–16   1st man leads his partner down the middle and up again.
17–20   1st couple set to each other, then cast off one place on their own sides of the dance (*process B*).
21–24   1st couple dance back to back, passing right shoulders then left. 4 strathspey travelling steps.
25–32   1st and 2nd couples dance rights and lefts across the dance and back again.
        1st couple repeat dance with next couple.

5

For the following dances the dancers take up the position

FIG. 30

of Fig. 30 at the beginning of the dance. Make what amendments are necessary to the mathematical model and proceed as before.

| 11. | 'Waltz Country Dance' |

Tune: original or any good Scottish waltz   Time 3/4

Bars
1–2   All set to the dancers facing them—men set to opposite ladies. 2 pas de basque moving forward and back (*process I*).

3–4   They change places with the dancers to whom they have set, passing by the right. The men dance straightforward but the ladies do a full waltz turn.

5–8   All dance these 4 bars with partner and finish facing the same opposite man or lady.

9–16   Repeat all this back to original places.

17–18   All four make a circle and do the same two steps forward and backward.

19–20   The men, dancing on the spot, give both hands to the opposite lady and bring her across to their right hand.

21–24   They make a circle again, set, and bring their own partners back to place.

25–32   They repeat these last 8 bars.

33–40   Couples change places with poussette. The men begin the poussette by pushing their partners backwards.

The dance is repeated until couples meet those with whom they began, or as many times as you will.

| 12. | 'My Love She's but a Lassie yet' |

Tune: original   Time 4/4

Bars
1–4   All set to the opposite dancer, 2 pas de basque, and change places, passing right shoulder with 2 skip change of step. They finish facing partners.

5–8   Partners set to each other, then change places passing right again and face opposite couple.

9–16   They repeat all this back to original places.

17–24   Each 4 give right hand across in a wheel and dance round for 4 steps, then, giving left hands across, dance back for 4.

25–32   All poussette to pass the couple with whom they have been dancing and meet the next couple coming towards them. To begin this poussette the men push their partners backwards—those going clockwise towards the middle of the circle, the other couple towards the outside of the circle.

        Repeat with next couple.

5. GROUP THEORY

5.1 The Group

The mathematical systems we examined in the first four chapters are but a few of the many we have at our disposal. It would be inconvenient to deal with each separately and also unnecessary since the systems have so much in common. The modern mathematician therefore attacks this situation from the opposite point of view. His attitude is that he will concentrate only on those mathematical systems which consist of a set of elements and a combining operation and which obey the following rules or axioms:

1. the set is closed under the combining operation and uniqueness of result holds good;
2. the Associative Law is true;
3. there is an identity element;
4. each element has an inverse.

Any system that satisfies these axioms is called a group. Furthermore, if also

5. the Commutative Law is true,

the group is called commutative or, more usually, Abelian after the famous Norwegian mathematician Abel.

All the new structures examined so far satisfy the group axioms and all except the last one satisfy the Commutative Law. The term 'group' can therefore be used as a family name for the new systems of the first four chapters. We shall go on to deduce properties from the group axioms and, since these are true for all the new systems, the deduced properties will also be true. Thus each of the systems will have the properties common to all groups and also some due to its own individual nature. In the same way members of a human family show certain family traits whilst at the same time keeping their own individuality.

Any reputable mathematician would accuse us of sharp practice if we left the group axioms as they stand. We craftily slid the Commutative Law out of its original position and put it in at the end as a free bonus. This is hardly cricket since we used the Commutative Law frequently in discussing the Associative Law, identities, and inverses. If the Commutative Law is not necessarily true then we must be careful about the order in which we combine elements. In particular we must be careful about identities and inverses. Is an identity element an identity element on the left as well as on the right and is an inverse from the left also an inverse from the right? These questions may be answered readily enough in specific cases and where the associated table is small, but would our deductions be true for all groups or are they true only in individual cases? We have much to examine here and our axioms must be tackled with far greater precision. We are going to have difficulty with language as the last few sentences have shown and this will require much writing. The mathematician is by nature a lazy but ingenious animal and therefore adopts his own shorthand. The next task is to achieve a certain proficiency at this. We shall then be able to tidy up our group axioms.

5.2 Mathematical Shorthand

We have used the term 'set' frequently in this book without attempting to define it. This we will continue to do, but make the point that the whole essence of a set is that it has or has not certain elements as members. We must therefore be precise in naming a set so as to include those elements we intend to include and exclude those less favoured by us. Thus 'the set of people in this room' is a precise enough definition if no one is hovering on the threshold. We may run into trouble however with 'the set of people in this room having fair hair', since the dividing line between dark and fair tends to be a function of the mousiness of one's own hair rather than a precisely defined measure.

Sets of mathematical entities are usually better behaved and we usually specify a set by writing its defining characteristics between two curly brackets. Thus $\{1, 2, 3\}$ means the set that consists of the three numbers 1, 2 and 3. We do not always have to be quite so precise. {All positive integers}, which means the set of all positive integers, is clear enough. Do not, however, fall into the frequent error of {the set of all positive integers} which is rather like referring to the county of Devonshire. Finally, with sublime logic we say that { } represents a set with no members at all which gives rise to interesting philosophical speculations.

Since we shall talk incessantly of belonging or not belonging to sets we shall take

$$\in \quad \text{to mean} \quad \text{'belongs to'}$$

and

$$\notin \quad \text{to mean} \quad \text{'does not belong to'}.$$

Thus

$$1 \in \{1, 2, 3\};$$

$$1 \in \{\text{all positive integers}\};$$

$$1 \notin \{\ \};$$

$$5 \notin \{1, 2, 3\};$$

$$5 \in \{\text{all positive integers}\};$$

$$I \in \{I, A, B, C\};$$

$$X \notin \{I, A, B, C\}.$$

We have frequently had to state generalized rules such as

$$x\,\mathrm{f}\,y = y\,\mathrm{f}\,x,$$

where x and y are any of I, A, B, or C. This is clumsy enough here but becomes insufferable with a larger set. The tidier way is to let $\{I, A, B, C\}$ be the set S.

We then rewrite the rule as

$$x f y = y f x \quad \text{for all } x, y \in S$$

which means the same thing. The expressions 'for all', 'for each', 'for every', 'for any' occur frequently and are usually abbreviated to $\forall$. The rule now reads

$$x f y = y f x \quad \forall \ x, y \in S.$$

Other symbols we use are

$\exists$ meaning 'there is' or 'there exists',

$|$ meaning 'such that',

$\Rightarrow$ meaning 'implies',

and $\Leftrightarrow$ meaning 'if and only if'.

The first two are straightforward enough but the last two require comment. $\Leftrightarrow$ is $\Leftarrow$ and $\Rightarrow$ stuck together. Or, if you prefer, 'if and only if' means the same as 'implies' both ways. This could not be more obscure but an example may help.

We will agree that

$$x - 4 = 0 \quad \Rightarrow \quad x = 4.$$

We will also agree that

$$x = 4 \quad \Rightarrow \quad x - 4 = 0.$$

Therefore $x = 4$ and $x - 4 = 0$ imply each other and therefore

$$x = 4 \quad \Leftrightarrow \quad x - 4 = 0.$$

In other words, $x = 4$ is equivalent to $x - 4 = 0$, or $x = 4$ if and only if $x - 4 = 0$. $\Rightarrow$ is very fashionable these days and deservedly so but the poor thing must not be worked to death. One use is as a replacement for the less tidy 'if...then'. Thus 'If two triangles are congruent then corresponding sides are equal.' may be replaced by 'Two triangles are congruent $\Rightarrow$ corresponding sides are equal.'

Both $\Rightarrow$ and $\Leftrightarrow$, or their colleagues $\Downarrow$ and $\Updownarrow$ where statements on different lines are involved, can help clarify ideas in orthodox algebra. To solve $x + \sqrt{(x+2)} = 4$ we write

$$\Downarrow \quad x + \sqrt{(x+2)} = 4$$
$$\Downarrow \quad \sqrt{(x+2)} = 4 - x$$
$$\Downarrow \quad x + 2 = (4-x)^2$$
$$\Downarrow \quad x + 2 = 16 - 8x + x^2$$
$$\Downarrow \quad x^2 - 9x + 14 = 0$$
$$\Downarrow \quad (x-2)(x-7) = 0$$
$$\Downarrow \quad \text{either} \quad x = 2 \quad \text{or} \quad x = 7.$$

The algebraist of cunning will doubtless have observed that, although we have two answers to the equation, if we take the positive value of $\sqrt{(x+2)}$, only $x = 2$ checks in the original equation and that by squaring in line three we have collected the extra value. In terms of $\Rightarrow$ this means that we can work the implications backwards from 'either $x = 2$ or $x = 7$' to '$x+2 = (4-x)^2$', but it would not be true to say that

$$x+2 = (4-x)^2 \quad \Rightarrow \quad +\sqrt{(x+2)} = 4-x$$

since the implication may well be in the direction of $-\sqrt{(x+2)} = 4-x$ instead. Thus the implication does not work both ways at this stage and a more precise solution of the equation would be

$$x+\sqrt{(x+2)} = 4$$
$$\Updownarrow$$
$$\sqrt{(x+2)} = 4-x$$
$$\Downarrow$$
$$x+2 = (4-x)^2$$
$$\Updownarrow$$
$$x+2 = 16-8x+x^2$$
$$\Updownarrow$$
$$x^2-9x+14 = 0$$
$$\Updownarrow$$
$$(x-2)(x-7) = 0$$
$$\Updownarrow$$
$$\text{either} \quad x = 2 \quad \text{or} \quad x = 7.$$

The fact that the second implication does not necessarily reverse gives us the clue that our final solutions may be at fault and indicates that we should make the necessary check. This is a favourite blunder and is a mistake in logic rather than algebra. $\Rightarrow$ and $\Leftrightarrow$ belong to the realm of symbolic logic and will be dealt with more fully in a later volume. We merely appeal to the reader's common sense at this stage to agree that if we have a series of statements so linked that the first implies the second which in turn implies the third which implies the fourth and so on then we can finally say that the first implies the last. Thus, in the example given,

$$x+\sqrt{(x+2)} = 4 \quad \Rightarrow \quad \text{either} \quad x = 2 \quad \text{or} \quad x = 7.$$

We must fully understand that mathematical shorthand is there for our own convenience and must not be allowed to run away with itself. For example,

$$\{y \mid y \in \{\text{positive integers}\}\}$$

which looks highly professional means 'the set of all y's such that y belongs to the set of positive integers' which is rather better expressed as {positive integers}, 'the set of positive integers'. Similarly to define the set S as

$$\{x \mid x \in \{\text{positive integers}\} \quad \text{and} \quad 0 < x < 3\}$$

which means 'the set of all x's such that x is a positive integer and lies between 0 and 3' is more conveniently and comprehensibly written as $\{1, 2\}$. We will try to avoid this sort of thing but it is something of an occupational hazard.

Vocabulary

$\{a, b, c, d, \ldots\}$	'the set containing $a, b, c, d, \ldots$'.
$\in$	'belongs to'.
$\notin$	'does not belong to'.
$\forall$	'for all', 'for each', 'for every', 'for any'.
$\exists$	'there is', 'there exists'.
$\mid$	'such that'.
$\Rightarrow$	'implies' or 'if ... then'.
$\Leftrightarrow$	'if and only if' or 'is equivalent to'.

Examples 5a

1. Translate into English:
   (a) My heart $\in$ daddy,
   (b) {positive even numbers less than 5},
   (c) $\exists$ a tavern in the town,
   (d) One $\forall$ and all for one,
   (e) $\{x \mid x^2 = 4\}$,
   (f) $\{x \mid x^2 = 9\}$,
   (g) $\{y \mid x^2 = 16\}$,

   (h)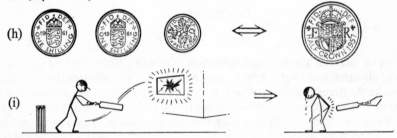

   (i)

   (j) $\exists\, x \mid 2x = 4$,
   (k) $\forall\, y \in \{\text{integers}\};\; 2\,y \in \{\text{integers}\}$.

2. Define more simply the following sets:
   (a) $\{x \mid x^2 - 3x + 2 = 0\}$,
   (b) {red, amber, green},
   (c) $\{x \mid 10 \leqslant x \leqslant 20 \text{ and } x \text{ is a whole number}\}$,
   (d) $\{y \mid y = a/b \text{ where } a > b \text{ and } 0 \leqslant y \leqslant 1\}$,
   (e) $\{z \mid (z-3)^2 = 9\}$.

3. Consider the following statements.
   All equilateral triangles are isosceles.
   All isosceles triangles have at least two sides equal.
   Therefore all equilateral triangles have at least two sides equal.
   These may be summarized as
      Triangles: equilateral $\Rightarrow$ isosceles;
                         isosceles $\Rightarrow$ at least two sides equal.
   By the argument of p. 61 this reduces to
      equilateral $\Rightarrow$ isosceles $\Rightarrow$ at least two sides equal.
   or   equilateral $\Rightarrow$ at least two sides equal.

Using the same techniques draw the relevant conclusions, if any, from the following statements.

    (a) All mathematicians are idiots.

       Idiots waste their time.

    (b) All mathematicians are idiots.

       The author is an idiot.

    (c) All mathematicians are idiots.

       The reader is no mathematician.

    (d) All mathematicians are idiots.

       The reader is wasting his time.

    4. Translate into symbols, in the simplest way you can find, as much as possible of the following phrases or sentences.

    (a) The set of all positive whole numbers less than 10 which are divisible by 3.

    (b) If the square of a number is 9 the number is either 3 or -3.

    (c) The set of all fractions such that the denominator is one more than the numerator.

    (d) You can always find a real number that is one more than any given real number.

    (e) The set of roots of the equation

$$x^2 - 5x + 4 = 0.$$

5.3 Revised Group Axioms

Our heads buzzing with symbols, we now make a determined assault on the group axioms. We assume that we have a set of elements called G and a combining operation called $*$. Then for a group:

    1. *The set is closed under the combining operation $*$ and uniqueness of result holds good.*

This means that whenever we combine a pair of elements of G by $*$ we get just one element of G as the result. Expressed as symbols this means that

$$\forall \ x, y \in G; \quad \exists \ \text{a unique element } x * y \in G.$$

    2. *The Associative Law is true.*

This means that if we take any three elements of G and combine them by $*$ then the result is the same whichever way we bracket the elements together. In symbols,

$$(x * y) * z = x * (y * z) \quad \forall \ x, y, z \in G.$$

    3. *There is an identity element.*

By this we mean that there is a member of G, e say, which, when combined by $*$ with any other element, leaves that element unaltered. To avoid having to consider multiplying on the left and on the right due to the possible absence of the Commutative Law we include both possibilities in the axiom and say

$$\exists \ e \in G \mid e * x = x * e = x \quad \forall \ x \in G.$$

The reader may well question our right to avoid an inconvenience by saying that it does not happen. However, it is perfectly reasonable for a mathematician to produce any set of axioms he likes. As long as they do not contradict each other, he will have constructed a perfectly good abstract mathematical system. It may well be that his new system has no practical application but this certainly does not affect its validity. If we check we shall find that the group axioms as we now list them are still satisfied by all the systems of the first four chapters. The Associative Law may be proved by the method already adopted without using the Commutative Law, although it will take longer. All the identities and inverses that we have met so far work from both sides and later in the chapter we shall deduce that all left inverses must be right inverses and all left identities must be right identities and vice versa. Therefore our alterations are perfectly justified from an abstract mathematician's point of view and the new version is still justified by all practical situations we have met so far.

4. *Each element has an inverse.*

Again we avoid Commutative Law trouble by postulating that inverses work both on the left and on the right. Thus, in symbols,

$$\forall\, x \in G; \quad \exists\, x^{-1} \in G \mid x^{-1} * x = x * x^{-1} = e.$$

In other words, 'for every element x of G there is another element that we shall call x^{-1} which also belongs to G and which when combined with x from either side gives the neutral element'.

If the group is an Abelian group then

5. *the Commutative Law is true.*

This we have examined already (p. 59). It translates into

$$x * y = y * x \quad \forall\, x, y \in G.$$

We now list the group axioms in their more professional form so that we may refer to them in future.

A set of elements G with a combining operation $*$ forms a group if and only if

1. $\forall\, x, y \in G; \quad \exists$ a unique element $x * y \in G$,
2. $(x * y) * z = x * (y * z) \quad \forall\, x, y, z \in G$,
3. $\exists\, e \in G \mid e * x = x * e = x \quad \forall\, x \in G$,
4. $\forall\, x \in G, \quad \exists\, x^{-1} \in G \mid x^{-1} * x = x * x^{-1} = e$.

If, further,

5. $x * y = y * x \quad \forall\, x, y \in G$ then the group is called a commutative or Abelian group.

Examples 5b

1. Assuming the Associative Law in each case, prove that the following are Abelian groups by verifying that they satisfy the list of axioms above.

   (a) The dancers' swapping system (Table 1, p. 4),
   (b) The dancers' circling system (Table 6, p. 17),
   (c) Arithmetic mod 3 under '+',
   (d) Arithmetic mod 6 under '+'.

2. Multiplication for modulus arithmetics was defined in Question 9 of Examples 1d (p. 14). Complete the multiplication tables for the following and see whether or not they form a group.

(a) Arithmetic mod 3,
(b) Arithmetic mod 6.

3. The one non-commutative system we have so far is the combined dancing system of Table 22 (p. 49). Assuming the Associative Law, see whether this combined system forms a group. Notice in particular whether the identity element is both a left and a right identity and whether the inverses are both left and right inverses.

4. In Question 2 of Examples 1d (p. 12) an alternative method of defining the movements of the dancers swapping places was indicated. Combine this with the usual circling system (Table 6, p. 17) and check whether the new combined table is the same as Table 22 (p. 49) and also whether it forms a group.

5.4 The Cancellation Rule

If we construct a set of axioms for a mathematical system, we must make sure that they do not contradict each other. The simplest way of doing this is to find a practical situation that fits them. If there is a contradiction it will come to light in the fitting since practical situations are, of necessity, consistent. Since we have many practical examples of our group axioms in the first four chapters we may therefore reasonably assume that these do not contradict each other.

Once we have proved the consistency of our axioms we may deduce theorems from them in much the same way that we did in school geometry. Lest this should dismay any of our readers who suffered a traumatic experience in this direction, we hasten to add that the technique is far easier in this case as we have only four simple axioms to remember and these, with a little common sense, should see us through.

THEOREM 1. *The Cancellation Rule*
In any group G with combining operation $*$

$$a*x = a*y \Rightarrow x = y$$
and
$$x*a = y*a \Rightarrow x = y$$
$$\forall\, a, x, y \in G.$$

We must include both versions since the Commutative Law is not necessarily true. We hope that our readers will have become sufficiently conditioned by this time not to talk in terms of 'dividing both sides by a'. It is true that, in general, if in normal algebra we are given

$$ax = ay$$

we can divide both sides by a and get

$$x = y.$$

It is equally true that if the combining operation were '+' then

$$a+x = a+y \Rightarrow x = y,$$

but in this case we must subtract a from both sides to give the required result. Our general theorem would cover both the '$\times$' and the '$+$' case if we have proved that normal numbers formed a group under '$+$' or '$\times$'—which we have not—so that there is no real reason at this stage why we should attempt to generalize about group structures from normal arithmetic.

We must also point out that the rule is definitely stated to be true 'for all a, x, y belonging to G' but we should certainly be at fault were we to write down

$$0 \times x = 0 \times y \;\Rightarrow\; x = y$$

in normal arithmetic. From now on, however difficult it may be, the reader must try to limit his mathematical experience to the four, or possibly five, axioms with the systems of the first four chapters as practical examples. We shall prove later that certain subsets of normal numbers do provide examples of group structures, but these are only examples and it is unwise to try to generalize from them.

To prove: $a * x = a * y \;\Rightarrow\; x = y \;\; \forall\, a, x, y \in G.$

Proof. a has an inverse, a^{-1}, say.   *Axiom 4*

$$a * x = a * y.$$

Pre-$*$ both sides by a^{-1}.

$$a^{-1} * (a * x) = a^{-1} * (a * y)$$
$\Downarrow$
$$(a^{-1} * a) * x = (a^{-1} * a) * y \qquad\qquad \textit{Associative Law; Axiom 2}$$
$\Downarrow$
$$e * x = e * y \qquad\qquad\qquad \textit{Inverse property; Axiom 4}$$
$\Downarrow$
$$x = y \qquad\qquad\qquad\qquad \textit{Identity property; Axiom 3.}$$

Hence $a * x = a * y \;\Rightarrow\; x = y$ as required.

The second half of the theorem could be quoted immediately if the Commutative Law were true. Since this is not necessarily so the proof must be done again, this time post-$*$-ing by a^{-1} instead of pre-$*$-ing. The reader is asked to follow this through for himself. The result of this theorem is that whenever we come across

$$a * x = a * y \quad \text{or} \quad x * a = y * a$$

we may immediately say that $x = y$ in either case. We shall use this rule frequently in the next section.

5.5 Groups of Order 4

We have two abstract groups of order 4 represented by Tables 7 and 4 (repeated) on p. 17. With the four axioms and one theorem we can now prove that these are in fact the only two possibilities, thus giving a satisfactory answer to Question 5 of Examples 1d (p. 13).

Firstly, we are restricted to four distinct elements, one of which must be the identity, by Axiom 3. Therefore we take G to be $\{e, a, b, c\}$ where e is the identity element. We shall use $*$ as the combining operation as usual. The table is now

$*$	e	a	b	c
e	e	a	b	c
a	a	.	.	.
b	b	.	.	.
c	c	.	.	.

TABLE 23

because of e's properties as a neutral element.

The next step is to prove that the same element may not occur twice in any row or column. Suppose that we wanted to fill the first vacant space with an a. This would imply that

$$a * a = a$$

but $\qquad e * a = a \qquad$ *from the table*

$\Downarrow$

$$e * a = a * a$$

$\Downarrow$

$$e = a \qquad \text{*by the Cancellation Rule (Th. 1).*}$$

However $e \neq a$ since, if it were, G would have only three elements. Therefore $a * a \neq a$.

By a similar line of thought we may prove that a repeat of any letter in any line or column produces a contradiction. Try for example $b * c = e$ and $b * a = e$. This implies that

$$b * c = b * a$$

$\Downarrow$

$$c = a \qquad \text{*by the Cancellation Rule (Th. 1),*}$$

which is again impossible. We must therefore restrict ourselves to using each element once and once only in each row or column. Reverting to Table 23 therefore we find that the first vacant space must be filled by either b, c, or e. Try b but remember we made an arbitrary choice.

$*$	e	a	b	c
e	e	a	b	c
a	a	b	.	.
b	b	.	.	.
c	c	.	.	.

TABLE 24

We are now left with c and e to fit in the third and fourth columns. c cannot go in the fourth as there is one there already. Therefore we can complete the second row of the table to give

*	e	a	b	c
e	e	a	b	c
a	a	b	c	e
b	b	.	.	.
c	c	.	.	.

TABLE 25

Now the fourth space of row three cannot be c or e as these already appear in the fourth column. Similarly it cannot be b as b is already in the third row. Therefore it must be a. This leaves c and e for the middle two places. c is already used in the third column and must therefore go in the second, so that the table now reads:

*	e	a	b	c
e	e	a	b	c
a	a	b	c	e
b	b	c	e	a
c	c	.	.	.

TABLE 26

and the fourth row may be filled in by the only letters not already used in each column. This gives us Table 7 again.

Notice that we have not proved that the table is that of a group. It has been constructed using the properties of closure, uniqueness, identity element and the Cancellation Rule only. However, it is not necessary for us to prove the group properties here as the reader will already have done this in Question 1(b), Examples 5b (p. 64).

We now revert to Table 23 and try again with c.

*	e	a	b	c
e	e	a	b	c
a	a	c	.	.
b	b	.	.	.
c	c	.	.	.

TABLE 27

We are now left with b and e which must fit in as e and b.

*	e	a	b	c
e	e	a	b	c
a	a	c	e	b
b	b	.	.	.
c	c	.	.	.

TABLE 28

The first empty place in the third row must be filled by e which leaves c and a in that order and the last row follows automatically to give

*	e	a	b	c
e	e	a	b	c
a	a	c	e	b
b	b	e	c	a
c	c	b	a	e

TABLE 29

This is apparently a new table but this is not so. If we put c third and b fourth in the table after the style of Question 6, Examples 1d (p. 13) it becomes

*	e	a	c	b
e	e	a	c	b
a	a	c	b	e
c	c	b	e	a
b	b	e	a	c

TABLE 30

and if we call 'b' 'c' and 'c' 'b' we get

*	e	a	b	c
e	e	a	b	c
a	a	b	c	e
b	b	c	e	a
c	c	e	a	b

TABLE 7 (repeated)

which is back to Table 7 again! Thus we have merely constructed another version of the same system.

We leave the rest of this argument to the reader. If he fills in the first empty space in Table 23 by *e* he should get two versions. One of these will be yet another version of Table 7 which can be converted by the process outlined above and the other will give Table 4.

As a result of all this we know that there are but two possible groups of order 4. This will save us much time in future since the testing of a system of four elements for group properties merely reduces to a comparison of the relevant table with those of this section.

Now that we are achieving some measure of sophistication in group theory it is as well to call these familiar structures by their official titles. The generalized form of the swapping system (Table 4) is called the Klein four-group (after the famous German mathematician Felix Klein) and the generalized form of the circling system (Table 7) is called the cyclic four-group. The name cyclic is appropriate in that if we write the four elements involved round a circle we get

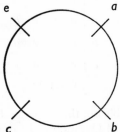

By reading round the circle starting from *e* we get *e*, *a*, *b*, *c* which is the first row of the cyclic table. We start the next row with the next letter round the circle, i.e. *a*, giving *a*, *b*, *c*, *e*. Similarly the other two rows also move round the circle starting with *b* and *c* respectively. We can produce a cyclic group of any finite order as we explained in Chapter 2. We shall meet cyclic groups frequently in later chapters.

Examples 5c

1. Complete the argument of this section by filling in

*	e	a	b	c
e	e	a	b	c
a	a	e	.	.
b	b	.	.	.
c	c	.	.	.

TABLE 31

in two different ways so as to give results corresponding to Tables 4 and 7.

2. Deduce that there is only one possible group pattern
   (a) of order 2,
   (b) of order 3,
   (c) of order 5,
and show that they are all cyclic groups.

5.6 Uniqueness of Identity and Inverses

The group axioms specify that each group has an identity element and that each element of a group has its inverse element. From the axioms we may easily prove that each group has just one identity element and that each element has just one inverse. The method employed in each case is much used in this type of work. We assume the contrary of what we wish to prove and then establish that this produces a contradiction.

THEOREM 2. *Any group has just one identity element.*

Proof. Let us assume that a group G with combining operation $*$ has two identity elements e_1 and e_2, say.

$$\begin{cases} e_1 * x = x \quad \forall\ x \in G & \textit{since } e_1 \textit{ is an identity element} \\ e_2 * x = x \quad \forall\ x \in G & \textit{since } e_2 \textit{ is an identity element} \end{cases}$$
$$\Downarrow$$
$$e_1 * x = e_2 * x$$
$$\Downarrow$$
$$e_1 = e_2 \qquad \textit{by the Cancellation Rule (Th. 1).}$$

Therefore if we assume that there are two distinct identity elements we may prove that they are the same and that our assumption was wrong. Therefore there is only one identity element.

THEOREM 3. *Any element of any group has just one inverse.*

Proof. Let us assume that an element $x \in G$ has two inverses x_1^{-1} and x_2^{-1}.

$$\begin{cases} x_1^{-1} * x = e & \textit{since } x_1^{-1} \textit{ is an inverse of } x \\ x_2^{-1} * x = e & \textit{since } x_2^{-1} \textit{ is an inverse of } x \end{cases}$$
$$\Downarrow$$
$$x_1^{-1} * x = x_2^{-1} * x$$
$$\Downarrow$$
$$x_1^{-1} = x_2^{-1} \quad \textit{by the Cancellation Rule (Th. 1).}$$

Therefore, by the same reasoning as before, each element of the group has just one inverse.

5.7 A Final Version of Group Axioms

The first criterion for a set of well-behaved axioms is that they do not contradict each other. The second is that no axiom should be unnecessary. Suppose, for example, that we were to include Theorem 1, the Cancellation Rule, as No. 5 of the group axioms. It would be redundant since we could deduce it from the first four. In the present section we examine our group axioms and try to simplify them still further, throwing out any redundancies which may have occurred.

6

The targets for attack are Axioms 3 and 4. In each case, because of the lack of the Commutative Law, we were forced to postulate that a left identity was also a right identity and that a left inverse was also a right inverse. We will now prove that this was not necessary. Let us suppose that Axioms 3 and 4 are amended as follows:

Axiom 3. $\qquad\qquad \exists\, e \in G \mid e * x = x \quad \forall\, x \in G.$

Axiom 4. $\qquad\qquad \forall\, x \in G; \quad \exists\, x^{-1} \in G \mid x^{-1} * x = e.$

These postulate the existence of a left identity and left inverses only. We now deduce from these and from Axioms 1 and 2 that the left identity must also be a right identity and that left inverses must also be right inverses. This makes the other halves of the old Axioms 3 and 4 redundant.

THEOREM 4. *To prove, via the amended group axioms, that*

$$x^{-1} * x = e \quad \Rightarrow \quad x * x^{-1} = e \quad \forall\, x \in G$$

Proof.

$\qquad\qquad x^{-1} * x = e$

$\Downarrow$

$\qquad\qquad (x^{-1} * x) * x^{-1} = e * x^{-1} \qquad$ *post-multiplying by* x^{-1}

$\Downarrow$

$\qquad\qquad x^{-1} * (x * x^{-1}) = x^{-1} \qquad\qquad$ *by the Associative Law (Ax. 2) and*
$\qquad\qquad\qquad\qquad\qquad\qquad\qquad\qquad$ *identity property (Ax. 3 amended).*

$x^{-1} \in G$ and therefore x^{-1} has a left inverse y, say. Pre-multiply by y

$\qquad\qquad y * \{x^{-1} * (x * x^{-1})\} = y * x^{-1}$

$\Downarrow$

$\qquad\qquad (y * x^{-1}) * (x * x^{-1}) = y * x^{-1} \quad$ *by the Associative Law (Ax. 2)*

$\Downarrow$

$\qquad\qquad e * (x * x^{-1}) = e \qquad\qquad\quad$ *by the inverse property (Ax. 4 amended)*

$\Downarrow$

$\qquad\qquad\qquad x * x^{-1} = e \qquad\qquad\quad$ *by the identity property (Ax. 3 amended).*

Thus if x is a left inverse it is also a right inverse.
The second proof is much simpler.

THEOREM 5. *To prove, via the amended group axioms, that*

$$e * x = x \quad \Rightarrow \quad x * e = x \quad \forall\, x \in G.$$

Proof.

$\qquad\qquad x * e = x * (x^{-1} * x) \qquad$ *by Ax. 4 amended*

$\qquad\qquad\quad = (x * x^{-1}) * x \qquad$ *by Ax. 2*

$\qquad\qquad\quad = e * x \qquad\qquad\quad$ *by Th. 4*

$\qquad\qquad\quad = x \qquad\qquad\qquad$ *by Ax. 3 amended.*

Thus if e is the left identity it is also the right identity.

As a result of the last two theorems we have proved that the amended versions of Axioms 3 and 4 imply the fuller versions and may adequately replace them. There is a certain mathematical pride in keeping the axioms as simple as possible but there are practical considerations as well. If we wish to prove that a structure is a group we now have only to prove the existence of a left identity and left inverses which takes half the time required to prove the properties for both sides. In future therefore we shall use the amended versions of Axioms 3 and 4 instead of the more complex versions given previously.

5.8 An Alternative Approach to the Group Structure

As long as a set S is closed and has uniqueness of result under a combining operation $*$, we may say that

$$\forall\ a,b \in S; \quad \exists \quad \text{a unique} \quad x \in S \mid a*b = x.$$

In other words, closure and uniqueness of result are the minimal conditions for the tidy solution of the equation

$$a*b = x.$$

The next step requires the solution of equations such as

$$a*x = b$$

or

$$y*a = b.$$

The minimal conditions here are those laid down by the group axioms. Let us examine

$$a*x = b.$$

To solve this we must pre-$*$ by a^{-1}, the inverse of a, giving

$$a^{-1}*(a*x) = a^{-1}*b.$$

This presupposes the existence of inverses.

To move further we must now apply the Associative Law to get

$$(a^{-1}*a)*x = a^{-1}*b.$$

This now simplifies to

$$e*x = a^{-1}*b.$$

$$x = a^{-1}*b$$

using the property of the identity element.

Closure and uniqueness are necessary for us to be able to work at all so that we have used all four group axioms in the solution of this equation. Therefore the group is the minimal mathematical structure in which such equations may always be solved. The second equation is solved in much the same way. Some mathematicians prefer to define a group as a structure in which closure and uniqueness of result are true, the Associative Law holds good, and the equations

$$a * x = b \quad \text{and} \quad y * a = b$$

always have a solution, or more formally

$$\left.\begin{array}{l} \forall \, a, b, \in G; \quad \exists \, x \mid a * x = b \\ \forall \, a, b, \in G; \quad \exists \, y \mid y * a = b \end{array}\right\}.$$

Examples 5d

1. Prove that in a group there is just one element x with the property that $x * x = x$ (such an element is said to be idempotent).

2. We abbreviate $x * x * x \dots n$ times to x^n. If $x^n = e$ and n is the smallest positive whole number for which this happens, n is called the order of x. Prove that if x is of order n, $x^{kn} = e$ where k is any whole number.

3. Prove that an element and its inverse are of the same order.

4. Prove that the order of any power of an element is not greater than the order of the element itself.

5. Prove that, if x is of order 4, x, x^2, x^3, and e are all distinct elements and show that they form a group. Such a group is said to be 'generated' by x. Extend your arguments to elements of other orders.

6. In this section we showed that it was possible to solve the equations $a * x = b$ and $y * a = b$ in any group structure. We also stated that the solvability of these equations was sometimes postulated instead of the identity and inverse axioms in the definition of a group. If the two definition systems are equivalent then each must be deducible from the other. We have already deduced the solvability of the equations from the first. Now deduce the existence of identities and inverses from the second.

7. Yet another definition system for a finite group replaces the identity and inverse axioms by the Cancellation Rule. In other words,

$$\forall \, a, b, x \in G, \quad a * x = b * x \quad \Rightarrow \quad a = b$$

$$\text{and} \quad x * a = x * b \quad \Rightarrow \quad a = b$$

Show that the two definition systems are equivalent.

5.9 Group Theory and Normal Arithmetic

We have on numerous occasions used normal numbers to illustrate various principles in group theory. We therefore feel honour bound to devote at least a little space to making a survey of orthodox arithmetic with regard to the four usual combining operations '+', '−', '×', and '÷'.

We are faced with an extra problem compared with what we have done so far in that we are now dealing with an infinite number of elements instead of the usual three, four, or eight. This means that we must rely on common sense and experience to see us through the proofs of the various axioms. Unfortunately common sense is a dangerous commodity. We ourselves have called it to our aid in the course of this book when more formal methods would have proved too tedious, but we were gripped with pangs of conscience as we did so and these were only allayed by the thought that the reader could refer to more enlightened texts when the essentials were more firmly in his mind. The following example will perhaps demonstrate the difficulty. We can write down the set of positive whole numbers

$$1 \quad 2 \quad 3 \quad 4 \quad 5 \quad 6 \quad 7 \quad 8 \quad 9 \quad 10 \quad ...$$

and we can write down the set of even positive whole numbers

$$2 \quad 4 \quad 6 \quad 8 \quad 10 \quad 12 \quad 14 \quad 16 \quad 18 \quad 20 \quad ...$$

All the evens appear in the series of positive whole numbers together with all the odds. Therefore there are more positive whole numbers than even positive whole numbers which is only common sense.

Now each positive whole number has a double. Therefore the numbers

	1	2	3	4	5	6	7	8	9	10	...
each have	↕	↕	↕	↕	↕	↕	↕	↕	↕	↕	
a double	2	4	6	8	10	12	14	16	18	20	...

and we may pair them off by arrows as shown. Therefore there must be the same number of even positive whole numbers as there are positive whole numbers. But we have already proved that this is not so. Therefore we are in trouble.

Playing with the infinite is a fascinating but frustrating game. The solution to the above is quite simple. Our experience with arithmetic enables us to handle very large numbers. It does not however equip us to deal with 'infinity' whatever that might be. Either the set of positive whole numbers stops or it does not. If it does not stop then we can go on writing down doubles for ever and there will be the same number of numbers top and bottom. There is no question of 'knowing' what happens. Mathematicians usually postulate the second alternative as being the more convenient. However, this is more of a topic for Volume II than for the present work.

Since '−' and '÷' obey neither the Associative nor the Commutative Laws they are best treated as inverse operations to '+' and '×'. We shall therefore restrict our investigations to '+' and '×'.

The classification of normal numbers is more tricky. We may split them up into

A. The set of positive whole numbers (integers) $\{1\,2\,3\,4\,5\,...\}$.

B. The set of all integers $\{0 \pm 1 \pm 2 \pm 3 \pm 4 \pm 5\,...\}$.

C. The set of positive rationals (numbers of the form a/b where a and $b \in A$).

D. The set of all rationals (numbers of the form a/b where a and $b \in B$ except that $b \neq 0$ although a may be).

E. The set of positive real numbers, which is C amplified by all the positive irrational numbers such as π, $\sqrt{2}$, and all the many others.

F. The set of all real numbers, which is D amplified by all irrationals irrespective of sign.

We first of all examine the group properties of all of these when combined by '+'. We may exclude A, C and E on the grounds that additive inverses are not available. The additive inverse of 5 is -5 since $5 + (-5) = 0$ and -5 and his comrades do not appear in A, C, or E.

A quick survey will show that, according to our experience, all the group axioms for '+' are satisfied in the three remaining sets B, D and F. As far as we know two integers add to another integer, two rationals add to another rational, and two reals add to another real. We always assume that any addition gives only one answer.

We use the Associative Law as the mood takes us with any of the sets we have mentioned. 0 is the neutral element for '+' and belongs to each of the three sets. Each member of B, D and F has its negative (its additive inverse) in B, D, or F respectively. Also normal numbers always commute under '+' so that the sets B, D and F are all Abelian groups under the combining operation '+'.

The situation is more complicated under '×'. A and B are out because the multiplicative inverse of any number is its reciprocal. The reciprocal of 5 is $1/5$ and $1/5$ is not in A or B. C and E are all right in this case since as far as we can tell reciprocals are always available. D and F cause trouble however, since 0 has no inverse, i.e. there is no number which, when multiplied with 0, gives 1. We can however manage things by missing out 0 altogether.

The other axioms are then easily satisfied. Positive rationals multiply to give positive rationals, positive or negative rationals multiply to give other positive or negative rationals, and the same applies to corresponding real sets. The omission of the 0 element mercifully does not affect things since, if two numbers multiply to give zero, then at least one of them must be zero and we have automatically excluded that possibility.

Uniqueness of result we take for granted as we do the Associative and Commutative Laws. 1, the multiplicative identity, belongs to C, D, E and F so that these four are all Abelian groups under '×' if we omit 0 from D and F.

The results of this section so far show that any general deductions from the group axioms apply equally well to normal numbers in their separate group situations. Of particular interest are D and F which form double group structures, one for '+' with 0 and one for '×' without it. We shall return to this point in the last chapter.

5.10 Summary

It is difficult but necessary to summarize the amount of information in this chapter. The vital point is the approach to the axiomatic way of thought. The axioms may be chosen at random as long as they do not contradict each other.

They are more usually chosen with some particular situation or series of situations in mind, but there is no need for this to be so. Once we have some idea of our axioms we may simplify them to eliminate redundancies. Then from our axioms we may deduce theorems and they will apply to all mathematical systems which fit these axioms. In particular the group axioms are satisfied by many versions of normal numbers and any theorems we have deduced will similarly be satisfied by them. There is a certain paucity in what we have deduced from these axioms so far, but this is essentially a beginners' book and we are still near the beginning of it. We shall learn more as we go on and more lengthy and formal treatises should provide more enlightenment.

We shall make much use of the group axioms as we proceed and their frequent appearances, together with those of the matrices of the next few chapters, will, we hope, form a connecting link between the many and diverse situations which we have met and will continue to meet.

6. MATRICES

6.1 The General Idea

A matrix is a list of numbers laid out in a rectangular pattern so that each number has its own special place and the whole is tied together neatly by a pair of square brackets. We frequently use this idea without noticing in normal non-mathematical life. A bowler's achievements at cricket may be scored as

Overs	Maidens	Runs	Wickets
22	7	63	5

The keen enthusiast would certainly not stop to look at the headings to the columns. He would know what each number represented by its position in the list and, if asked how he got on by an equally enthusiastic friend, would be quite prepared to say, '22 7 63 5' which would be perfectly comprehensible to both. The mathematician would wrap the numbers up in a bracket thus

$$[22 \ 7 \ 63 \ 5]$$

and call the whole a 1×4 matrix. This means that the matrix has one row and four columns. If the reader remembers that the order is columns–rows alphabetically and rows–columns matrixwise he will number them correctly.

The housewife who uses a printed shopping list from the dairy is also guilty of playing with matrices.

Milk	14 pints
Butter	2 lb
Eggs	12
Cheese	3 lb
Yoghourt	1 carton

represents the sum total of an errand. Familiarity with the order of the printed list leaves us with the matrix

$$\begin{bmatrix} 14 \\ 2 \\ 12 \\ 3 \\ 1 \end{bmatrix}$$

where each number again has its own specific meaning. This is a 5×1 matrix.

The first of these matrices is called a row matrix since it is just one row of numbers, while the second is called a column matrix. There is no need to restrict ourselves to these shapes. Three bowlers in a team may produce the results

	Overs	Maidens	Runs	Wickets
Smith	22	7	63	5
Jones	24	6	98	3
Robinson	14	3	11	2

The 3×4 matrix

$$\begin{bmatrix} 22 & 7 & 63 & 5 \\ 24 & 6 & 98 & 3 \\ 14 & 3 & 11 & 2 \end{bmatrix}$$

specifies the information clearly enough.

The representation of data in this manner is extremely convenient and matrices appear frequently in many branches of mathematics and also in physics, chemistry, biology, statistics, psychology, and, of course, business methods and computing. Even in elementary graphical work the use of $(3, 2)$ to represent the point 'three along and two up' from the origin uses the matrix principle. It is only in our early days that we try to express it as 'three up and two along'!

The reader would not expect us to leave such a potent weapon as the matrix without subjecting it to the full mathematical treatment. The next step therefore is to think up suitable combining operations and then, inevitably, we test for group properties.

Example 6a

1. Find five situations where we unconsciously use matrix ideas. Write down your lists of numbers in matrix form, indicate the size of the matrices, and, if they are of the form $1 \times n$ or $n \times 1$, try to combine several such lists to form more exotic shapes.

6.2 The Addition of Matrices

Our mathematical housewife, who presents her shopping list in matrix form, is undoubtedly interested in the quantities of each commodity which she purchases each month. In the four weeks of the month in question she submits this list to the dairy.

Milk	14	14	16	14
Butter	2	2	1	3
Eggs	12	6	18	12
Cheese	3	4	2	6
Yoghourt	1	2	1	1

Note that we may equally well represent our data in four separate 5×1 matrices as in one large 5×4 matrix. It still means the same thing. To find the total amount of milk bought in the month all that is necessary is to add together the top numbers in each of the four matrices giving a total of $14 + 14 + 16 + 14 = 58$ pints. The amounts of other food bought may be found by similar tactics. Only a minor strain on the imagination is necessary to extend this process to the addition of whole matrices and to say that if we add together a series of column matrices we merely add together the corresponding numbers. Thus

$$\begin{bmatrix} 14 \\ 2 \\ 12 \\ 3 \\ 1 \end{bmatrix} + \begin{bmatrix} 14 \\ 2 \\ 6 \\ 4 \\ 2 \end{bmatrix} + \begin{bmatrix} 16 \\ 1 \\ 18 \\ 2 \\ 1 \end{bmatrix} + \begin{bmatrix} 14 \\ 3 \\ 12 \\ 6 \\ 1 \end{bmatrix} = \begin{bmatrix} 14+14+16+14 \\ 2+ 2+ 1+ 3 \\ 12+ 6+18+12 \\ 3+ 4+ 2+ 6 \\ 1+ 2+ 1+ 1 \end{bmatrix} = \begin{bmatrix} 58 \\ 8 \\ 48 \\ 15 \\ 5 \end{bmatrix}.$$

We are extending the '+' sign a little in using it as a symbol for both the addition of numbers and the addition of collections of numbers and perhaps we really ought to use a symbol such as '$\oplus$' to which we can give a similar meaning but which looks a little different. However, there is never any confusion as to whether we are 'adding' numbers or matrices so that we shall retain the normal '+'. Later we shall examine more closely the connexions between matrices and numbers which will justify our decision still further.

There is one point where we must be careful in the addition of matrices. Suppose, for example, that the order to the dairy after the first week was just 14 pints of milk, 12 eggs, and 3 pounds of cheese. It could then be represented by

$$\begin{bmatrix} 14 \\ 0 \\ 12 \\ 3 \\ 0 \end{bmatrix} \quad \text{or} \quad \begin{bmatrix} 14 \\ 12 \\ 3 \end{bmatrix}.$$

Either would do as long as we knew the convention in which we were working. If however we try to add them to the previous week's order,

$$\begin{bmatrix} 14 \\ 2 \\ 12 \\ 3 \\ 1 \end{bmatrix} + \begin{bmatrix} 14 \\ 0 \\ 12 \\ 3 \\ 0 \end{bmatrix} = \begin{bmatrix} 28 \\ 2 \\ 24 \\ 6 \\ 1 \end{bmatrix}$$

is perfectly respectable whereas

$$\begin{bmatrix} 14 \\ 2 \\ 12 \\ 3 \\ 1 \end{bmatrix} + \begin{bmatrix} 14 \\ 12 \\ 3 \end{bmatrix}$$

gives gibberish. We therefore make a point of adding only matrices of the same size and shape and judiciously build up outsiders with 0's to make them fit.

We need not restrict addition to single column matrices. Consider the drinking habits of three undergraduates; Smith, Jones and Robinson in four successive weeks.

| | 1st week | | | 2nd week | | | 3rd week | | | 4th week | | |
	S.	J.	R.	S.	J.	R.	S.	J.	R.	S.	J.	R.
Beer	7	14	21	12	18	5	13	11	12	2	1	3
Whisky	5	3	2	6	9	3	4	8	7	0	1	1
Rum	4	9	5	5	2	11	3	9	2	1	2	0
Gin	6	2	1	3	8	4	4	1	5	0	3	1
Cocoa	0	0	0	0	0	0	0	0	0	18	36	25

(end of the month).

The total amount consumed in the month by these pillars of sobriety is given by the sum of the four matrices which is

$$\begin{bmatrix} 7+12+13+\ 2 & 14+18+11+\ 1 & 21+\ 5+12+\ 3 \\ 5+\ 6+\ 4+\ 0 & 3+\ 9+\ 8+\ 1 & 2+\ 3+\ 7+\ 1 \\ 4+\ 5+\ 3+\ 1 & 9+\ 2+\ 9+\ 2 & 5+11+\ 2+\ 0 \\ 6+\ 3+\ 4+\ 0 & 2+\ 8+\ 1+\ 3 & 1+\ 4+\ 5+\ 1 \\ 0+\ 0+\ 0+18 & 0+\ 0+\ 0+36 & 0+\ 0+\ 0+25 \end{bmatrix} = \begin{bmatrix} 34 & 44 & 41 \\ 15 & 21 & 13 \\ 13 & 22 & 18 \\ 13 & 14 & 11 \\ 18 & 36 & 25 \end{bmatrix}$$

and our idea of addition still works.

To summarize this section, in order to add two matrices they must be of the same size and shape. If they are we may add them by adding together corresponding numbers and forming a matrix of the results which has the same size and shape as the originals.

Examples 6b

1. Add where possible the following matrices:

(a) $\begin{bmatrix} 2 & 3 \\ 1 & 4 \end{bmatrix}$, $\begin{bmatrix} 5 & 0 \\ 0 & 2 \end{bmatrix}$, $\begin{bmatrix} 2 & 3 \\ 0 & 2 \end{bmatrix}$

(b) $\begin{bmatrix} 3 \\ -2 \\ 4 \end{bmatrix}$, $\begin{bmatrix} -2 \\ 1 \\ 0 \end{bmatrix}$, $\begin{bmatrix} 4 \\ -1 \\ -3 \end{bmatrix}$

(c) $\begin{bmatrix} 2{\cdot}3 & 5{\cdot}7 \\ 3{\cdot}8 & 2{\cdot}5 \\ 1{\cdot}4 & 0 \end{bmatrix}$, $\begin{bmatrix} 7{\cdot}8 & 6{\cdot}2 \\ 1{\cdot}3 & 1{\cdot}0 \\ 2{\cdot}4 & 3{\cdot}6 \end{bmatrix}$, $\begin{bmatrix} 5{\cdot}7 & 2{\cdot}4 \\ 6{\cdot}3 & 1{\cdot}2 \end{bmatrix}$

(d) $\begin{bmatrix} 6 & 2 & 1 \\ 3 & 0 & 4 \end{bmatrix}$, $\begin{bmatrix} 2 & 3 & 4 \\ 1 & 6 & 5 \end{bmatrix}$, $\begin{bmatrix} 6 & 2 & 2 \\ 3 & 1 & 5 \end{bmatrix}$ (In this case the numbers belong to arithmetic mod 7.)

2. Owing to a sudden invasion of doting aunties, Junior has three choc. ices, two crunchy bars and a lollypop on Monday; two crunchy bars, a bag of peppermint creams and a choc. ice on Tuesday; two bags of peppermint creams and a crunchy bar on Wednesday; four lollypops, three crunchy bars and a choc. ice on Thursday; six choc. ices on Friday. He had the week-end off. Represent this gastronomic feat in matrix form and calculate the sum total of his achievements.

3. On Monday Albert wore a red tie, blue socks and black shoes. Bernie wore a green tie, pink socks and brown shoes. Charlie wore a pink tie, green socks and grey shoes. Desmond wore black shoes, a green tie and red socks.

On Tuesday Albert wore grey shoes, a red tie and green socks. Bernie wore a green tie, pink socks and black shoes. Charlie wore red socks, a pink tie and brown shoes. Desmond wore black shoes, a grey tie and yellow socks.

On Wednesday Albert wore brown shoes, pink socks and a green tie. Bernie was sick and stayed in bed. Charlie wore red socks, a green tie and grey shoes. Desmond wore black shoes, a red tie and green socks.

Translate these data into assorted matrices and decide which colour of each article was the most popular.

4. All four bridge players after a rubber bemoan the fact that they never have any good cards. In the first hand the cards were as follows:

N. ♠ xxxx, ♥ xx, ♦ Jxx, ♣ Qxxx; E. ♠ Jxx, ♥ xxx, ♦ AKxx, ♣ Jxx; S. ♠ AKQx, ♥ AKQ, ♦ xx, ♣ AKxx; W. ♠ xx, ♥ Jxxxx, ♦ Qxxx, ♣ xx.

In the second hand: N. ♠ QJx, ♥ Kxxx, ♦ A, ♣ Kxxxx; E. ♠ Axxx, ♥ QJxx, ♦ Jxxxx, ♣ –; S. ♠ xxxx, ♥ Ax, ♦ Kxxx, ♣ QJx; W. ♠ Kx, ♥ xxx, ♦ Qxx, ♣ Axxxx.

In the third hand: N. ♠ Axx, ♥ xx, ♦ Qxxxx, ♣ xxx; E. ♠ KQxxx, ♥ Kx, ♦ xx, ♣ KQxx; S. ♠ Jxx, ♥ Jxxx, ♦ xxx, ♣ Jxx; W. ♠ xx, ♥ AQxxx, ♦ AKJ, ♣ Axx.

In the fourth hand: N. ♠ AKxx, ♥ J, ♦ Kxxx, ♣ QJxx; E. ♠ Qx, ♥ AQxxx, ♦ Axx, ♣ xxx; S. ♠ xxxxx, ♥ x, ♦ QJxx, ♣ xxx; W. ♠ Jx, ♥ Kxxxxx, ♦ xx, ♣ AKx.

Counting 4 points for an ace, 3 for a king, 2 for a queen, and 1 for a jack, use matrix methods to sort out the above data and decide whether N.–S. or E.–W. held the better cards.

6.3 Matrices under Addition and the Group Axioms

We now examine matrices under addition in the light of the group axioms so painfully evolved over the first five chapters. The first axiom requires that there must be just one answer to any calculation based on the relevant combining operation. We know from the previous section that only matrices of the same size and shape can be added and therefore all matrices do not form a group under '+' since we cannot always add them. We shall therefore restrict ourselves to 2×2 matrices. Parallel arguments apply to other sizes and shapes but 2×2's are small and easily handled and illustrate the principles readily enough.

Let G be the set of all 2×2 matrices and let the combining operation be '+' as defined in the previous section.

To prove Axiom 1. $\forall\, x, y \in G;\quad \exists$ a unique $x + y \in G$.

Here x and y are 2×2 matrices and we must prove that any two 2×2 matrices add to give a third 2×2 matrix. We are not in a position to add every possible pair of elements here as we were in earlier examples since there are an infinite number of them but we are lucky in being able to write down typical 2×2 matrices such as

$$\begin{bmatrix} a & b \\ c & d \end{bmatrix} \quad \text{and} \quad \begin{bmatrix} e & f \\ g & h \end{bmatrix},$$

where a, b, c, d, e, f, g and h belong to the set of real numbers.

If we now add these we get

$$\begin{bmatrix} a & b \\ c & d \end{bmatrix} + \begin{bmatrix} e & f \\ g & h \end{bmatrix} = \begin{bmatrix} a+e & b+f \\ c+g & d+h \end{bmatrix}$$

which is another 2×2 matrix. The result depends upon the four additions of numbers $a+e$, $b+f$, $c+g$, $d+h$, each of which has just one result. Thus the sum of the 2×2 matrices is just one 2×2 matrix subject to the assumption of closure and uniqueness for real numbers under addition. When dealing with matrices we shall assume the group properties for the various subsets of real numbers which we discussed at the end of Chapter 5 (p. 75). Subject to our assumption, therefore, Axiom 1 is proved.

To prove Axiom 2. The Associative Law.

$$(x+y)+z = x+(y+z) \quad \forall\, x, y, z \in G.$$

This time we write down three general 2×2 matrices

$$\begin{bmatrix} a & b \\ c & d \end{bmatrix}, \quad \begin{bmatrix} e & f \\ g & h \end{bmatrix} \quad \text{and} \quad \begin{bmatrix} i & j \\ k & l \end{bmatrix}$$

and endeavour to prove that

$$\left\{ \begin{bmatrix} a & b \\ c & d \end{bmatrix} + \begin{bmatrix} e & f \\ g & h \end{bmatrix} \right\} + \begin{bmatrix} i & j \\ k & l \end{bmatrix} = \begin{bmatrix} a & b \\ c & d \end{bmatrix} + \left\{ \begin{bmatrix} e & f \\ g & h \end{bmatrix} + \begin{bmatrix} i & j \\ k & l \end{bmatrix} \right\},$$

where $a, b, c, d, e, f, g, h, i, j, k$ and l belong to the set of real numbers. Now

$$\left\{\begin{bmatrix} a & b \\ c & d \end{bmatrix} + \begin{bmatrix} e & f \\ g & h \end{bmatrix}\right\} + \begin{bmatrix} i & j \\ k & l \end{bmatrix} = \begin{bmatrix} a+e & b+f \\ c+g & d+h \end{bmatrix} + \begin{bmatrix} i & j \\ k & l \end{bmatrix}$$

by the definition of '+' for matrices,

$$= \begin{bmatrix} (a+e)+i & (b+f)+j \\ (c+g)+k & (d+h)+l \end{bmatrix} \quad \text{by the definition of '+' for matrices,}$$

$$= \begin{bmatrix} a+e+i & b+f+j \\ c+g+k & d+h+l \end{bmatrix} \quad \text{by the Associative Law for real numbers.}$$

We can now argue that $a+e+i$ for example is independent of the way in which we added the three matrices together and similarly for the other three sums. Thus, since the matrix itself is composed of these four separate sums, it also is independent of the way in which its component matrices are added. For those to whom this philosophical note is a disharmony we repeat the whole process for the other version and get that

$$\begin{bmatrix} a & b \\ c & d \end{bmatrix} + \left\{\begin{bmatrix} e & f \\ g & h \end{bmatrix} + \begin{bmatrix} i & j \\ k & l \end{bmatrix}\right\} = \begin{bmatrix} a & b \\ c & d \end{bmatrix} + \begin{bmatrix} e+i & f+j \\ g+k & h+l \end{bmatrix}$$

$$= \begin{bmatrix} a+(e+i) & b+(f+j) \\ c+(g+k) & d+(h+l) \end{bmatrix}$$

$$= \begin{bmatrix} a+e+i & b+f+j \\ c+g+k & d+h+l \end{bmatrix}$$

which is the same as the alternative version. Thus the Associative Law is true for 2×2 matrices under '+'.

To prove Axiom 3. Identity element.

$$\exists\, 0 \in G \,|\, 0+x = x \quad \forall\, x \in G.$$

(Earlier in the proofs we used e as a real number. 0 is usual for '+' anyway.)

Here we require a 2×2 matrix that will add to any other 2×2 matrix $\begin{bmatrix} a & b \\ c & d \end{bmatrix}$ from the left and leave it unaltered. The only reasonable candidate is $\begin{bmatrix} 0 & 0 \\ 0 & 0 \end{bmatrix}$ which duly behaves since

$$\begin{bmatrix} 0 & 0 \\ 0 & 0 \end{bmatrix} + \begin{bmatrix} a & b \\ c & d \end{bmatrix} = \begin{bmatrix} 0+a & 0+b \\ 0+c & 0+d \end{bmatrix} = \begin{bmatrix} a & b \\ c & d \end{bmatrix}.$$

To prove Axiom 4. Inverse elements.

$$\forall\, x \in G; \quad \exists\, (-x) \,|\, (-x)+x = 0$$

(when '+' is the combining operation we use $(-x)$ for the inverse of x).

In other words, given any 2×2 matrix $\begin{bmatrix} a & b \\ c & d \end{bmatrix}$, can we find another that we may add to it from the left to give $\begin{bmatrix} 0 & 0 \\ 0 & 0 \end{bmatrix}$?

Again we are lucky since

$$\begin{bmatrix} -a & -b \\ -c & -d \end{bmatrix} + \begin{bmatrix} a & b \\ c & d \end{bmatrix} = \begin{bmatrix} -a+a & -b+b \\ -c+c & -d+d \end{bmatrix}$$

$$= \begin{bmatrix} 0 & 0 \\ 0 & 0 \end{bmatrix}.$$

as required.

Thus we can find an additive inverse for each 2×2 matrix merely by changing the sign of all the numbers included in that matrix.

Since the four axioms are duly satisfied by 2×2 matrices under addition we may safely say that they form a group. We now test the Commutative Law.

To prove Axiom 5. The Commutative Law.

$$x+y = y+x \quad \forall \; x,y \in G.$$

Take our usual two general 2×2 matrices. This time we wish to prove that

$$\begin{bmatrix} a & b \\ c & d \end{bmatrix} + \begin{bmatrix} e & f \\ g & h \end{bmatrix} = \begin{bmatrix} e & f \\ g & h \end{bmatrix} + \begin{bmatrix} a & b \\ c & d \end{bmatrix}.$$

Now

$$\begin{bmatrix} a & b \\ c & d \end{bmatrix} + \begin{bmatrix} e & f \\ g & h \end{bmatrix} = \begin{bmatrix} a+e & b+f \\ c+g & d+h \end{bmatrix},$$

similarly

$$\begin{bmatrix} e & f \\ g & h \end{bmatrix} + \begin{bmatrix} a & b \\ c & d \end{bmatrix} = \begin{bmatrix} e+a & f+b \\ g+c & h+d \end{bmatrix}$$

$$= \begin{bmatrix} a+e & b+f \\ c+g & d+h \end{bmatrix}$$

by the Commutative Law for real numbers under '+'.

Therefore the Commutative Law is true and 2×2 matrices under addition form an Abelian group. As we explained previously, this means that we may handle their addition in much the same way that we handle the addition of normal numbers.

Examples 6c

1. Prove that the set of matrices of the form $\begin{bmatrix} a \\ b \end{bmatrix}$, where a and b are any real numbers, forms a group under matrix addition.

2. Prove that the set of matrices of the form $\begin{bmatrix} a & b & c \\ d & e & f \end{bmatrix}$, where $a, b, c, d,$ $e,$ and f are any real numbers, forms a group under matrix addition.

The following set of matrices may or may not form groups under addition. Try and see.

3. $\left\{ \begin{bmatrix} a & 0 \\ 0 & a \end{bmatrix} \right\}$ where a is a real number.

4. $\left\{ \begin{bmatrix} a & 0 \\ 2a & 0 \end{bmatrix} \right\}$ where a is a positive integer.

5. $\left\{ \begin{bmatrix} a & 0 & b \\ b & 0 & a \end{bmatrix} \right\}$ where a and b are integers.

6. $\left\{ \begin{bmatrix} 2 & 2 \\ 2 & 2 \end{bmatrix}, \begin{bmatrix} 0 & 0 \\ 0 & 0 \end{bmatrix} \right\}$ where 2 and 0 are from arithmetic mod 4.

6.4 Matrix Multiplication

We return to the machinations of our mathematical housewife. In the first week she bought from the dairy

Milk	14 pints
Butter	2 lb
Eggs	12
Cheese	3 lb
Yoghourt	1 carton

and her main consideration will undoubtedly be the cost of the order. Let us assume that milk costs 1*s.* a pint, butter 1*s.* 3*d.* a pound, eggs 6*d.* each, cheese 1*s.* 6*d.* a pound, and yoghourt 1*s.* a carton, where the prices reflect the natural antipathy of the author towards arithmetic rather than the present economic trends in dairy farming. For convenience we shall work in threepences so that milk costs 4 threepences, butter 5, eggs 2, cheese 6, and yoghourt 4 per unit measure. The whole may be written as a cost matrix

Milk	Butter	Eggs	Cheese	Yoghourt
4	5	2	6	4

To find the total amount spent we must multiply the amount of each commodity purchased by the cost per pint, per pound or whatever the unit of measurement happens to be. We then add the lot up. The whole process is best tabulated as follows.

Commodity	Cost in threepences	Amount	Total
Milk	4 per pint	14 pints	56
Butter	5 per lb	2 lb	10
Eggs	2 each	12	24
Cheese	6 per lb	3 lb	18
Yoghourt	4 per carton	1 carton	4

$$Total \quad 112$$
threepences
$$= \text{£1. } 8s.$$

The process of multiplying lists of numbers together is of frequent occurrence as we shall see during the next few chapters and is of such importance that we use it as our process for 'multiplying' matrices together. Thus we write

$$[4 \quad 5 \quad 2 \quad 6 \quad 4] \begin{bmatrix} 14 \\ 2 \\ 12 \\ 3 \\ 1 \end{bmatrix} = [4 \times 14 + 5 \times 2 + 2 \times 12 + 6 \times 3 + 4 \times 1]$$

$$= [112].$$

This is a nasty shock and requires much justification. First of all the process we call matrix multiplication seems even less like orthodox multiplication than matrix addition is like orthodox addition. Again we argue that there is no confusion as to whether we are multiplying matrices or numbers and the matrix process has close connexions with number multiplication. Again we crave the reader's indulgence (or perhaps demand would be a better word) and ask him to wait until Chapter 9 where even closer links will be forged between the two processes. Another legitimate double query is, 'Why is the cost matrix horizontal and the quantities matrix vertical and why does the cost matrix come first and the quantities matrix second?' The answer at this stage is that it does not matter in the slightest which way up or which way round the matrices are used. However, a degree of consistency is necessary and we adopt the present form as having the most useful application in other fields. We could have written the quantities matrix first and the cost matrix second and obtained the same result if we had written the quantities matrix horizontally and the cost matrix vertically. We shall examine this point in greater detail later.

Perhaps the most pertinent query is, 'How on earth are we going to compute these wretched things—especially if they are going to get any more complicated?' The answer here is to build up the right habits for matrix multiplication now so that the more complex examples will follow automatically when the time comes. This will be the task of the next few paragraphs.

Note that the answer to the example given is a 1×1 matrix. A 1×1 matrix is, of course, just a single number and we were merely being pedantic in putting square brackets round it. We wanted to emphasize however that the product of two matrices is, in fact, another matrix. We shall omit the brackets in future in similar cases.

The best way of getting the numbers in the two matrices paired off correctly is to twist the horizontal one clockwise through a right-angle, slide it along, and drop it down so that

$$[4 \ 5 \ 2 \ 6 \ 4] \begin{bmatrix} 14 \\ 2 \\ 12 \\ 3 \\ 1 \end{bmatrix} \quad becomes \quad \begin{bmatrix} 4 \times 14 \\ 5 \times 2 \\ 2 \times 12 \\ 6 \times 3 \\ 4 \times 1 \end{bmatrix}$$

and the required pairings may be read off without difficulty. This apparently childish process will save many a headache in more complex examples and may be done mentally or physically with the aid of a pencil and rubber according to the powers of visualization of the reader. Please note that in order to be able to multiply two matrices together it is necessary that there should be the same number of columns in the first matrix as there are rows in the second. Otherwise the two will not fit and we get the same trouble that we had in matrix addition.

We now examine our housewife's purchases over the whole month. These can be represented by the 5×4 matrix

	1st	2nd	3rd	4th
Milk	14	14	16	14
Butter	2	2	1	3
Eggs	12	6	18	12
Cheese	3	4	2	6
Yoghourt	1	2	1	1

If we require the cost of each week's purchases we may again use matrix multiplication and proceed in the same way as before only more often. Thus the product is

$$\overset{Cost}{[4 \ 5 \ 2 \ 6 \ 4]} \overset{Quantities}{\begin{bmatrix} 14 & 14 & 16 & 14 \\ 2 & 2 & 1 & 3 \\ 12 & 6 & 18 & 12 \\ 3 & 4 & 2 & 6 \\ 1 & 2 & 1 & 1 \end{bmatrix}}$$

which we may evaluate by treating each column of the second matrix as a separate matrix.

By sliding the cost matrix into position for the first column we get

$$\begin{array}{c} 4 \\ 5 \\ 2 \\ 6 \\ 4 \end{array} \begin{bmatrix} 14 & 14 & 16 & 14 \\ 2 & 2 & 1 & 3 \\ 12 & 6 & 18 & 12 \\ 3 & 4 & 2 & 6 \\ 1 & 2 & 1 & 1 \end{bmatrix}$$

giving us $4 \times 14 + 5 \times 2 + 2 \times 12 + 6 \times 3 + 4 \times 1 = 112$ as before. Moving the cost matrix along one we get

$$\begin{bmatrix} 14 & 4 \times 14 & 16 & 14 \\ 2 & 5 \times 2 & 1 & 3 \\ 12 & 2 \times 6 & 18 & 12 \\ 3 & 6 \times 4 & 2 & 6 \\ 1 & 4 \times 2 & 1 & 1 \end{bmatrix}$$

which gives us $4 \times 14 + 5 \times 2 + 2 \times 6 + 6 \times 4 + 4 \times 2 = 110$ as the answer to the second column. Proceeding similarly for the other two columns we get 121 and 135 respectively which the reader would do well to check. The result of all this labour is four numbers, one for each column, which we represent as the totals matrix.

1st   2nd   3rd   4th

[112   110   121   135]

which gives the amount in threepences spent each week.

So far we have restricted ourselves to multiplication where the first was a single row matrix. There is no need for this. Let us suppose that a super-market has opened and that our housewife has decided that, whilst keeping her custom with the original dairy, she will carefully compare prices with those at the new supermarket. She discovers that they charge 9*d*. a pint for milk, 1*s*. 6*d*. a pound for butter, 3*d*. each for eggs, 1*s*. 9*d*. a pound for cheese and 6*d*. a carton for yoghourt. These give a second cost matrix of

[3   6   1   7   2]

in threepences for the supermarket. Alternatively we may write a combined cost matrix of

$$\begin{bmatrix} 4 & 5 & 2 & 6 & 4 \\ 3 & 6 & 1 & 7 & 2 \end{bmatrix}$$

where the first row represents the dairy's costs and the second those of the supermarket. The results of the now quite large and complicated matrix multiplication

$$\begin{bmatrix} 4 & 5 & 2 & 6 & 4 \\ 3 & 6 & 1 & 7 & 2 \end{bmatrix} \begin{bmatrix} 14 & 14 & 16 & 14 \\ 2 & 2 & 1 & 3 \\ 12 & 6 & 18 & 12 \\ 3 & 4 & 2 & 6 \\ 1 & 2 & 1 & 1 \end{bmatrix}$$

should give us two totals for each column, the first row being for the dairy and the second for the supermarket, in all a 2×4 matrix. We know the process for getting the first of these rows as it is identical with what we have done already. To obtain the second row in the answer matrix we repeat the process using the second row of the first matrix. Thus the first number in the second row is obtained by sliding

the $\begin{bmatrix} 3 & 6 & 1 & 7 & 2 \end{bmatrix}$ next to the $\begin{bmatrix} 14 \\ 2 \\ 12 \\ 3 \\ 1 \end{bmatrix}$ column

and multiplying and adding as before. The remaining columns are obtained similarly. The final result of all this is

$$\begin{bmatrix} 4 & 5 & 2 & 6 & 4 \\ 3 & 6 & 1 & 7 & 2 \end{bmatrix} \begin{bmatrix} 14 & 14 & 16 & 14 \\ 2 & 2 & 1 & 3 \\ 12 & 6 & 18 & 12 \\ 3 & 4 & 2 & 6 \\ 1 & 2 & 1 & 1 \end{bmatrix} = \begin{bmatrix} 112 & 110 & 117 & 135 \\ 89 & 92 & 88 & 116 \end{bmatrix}$$

where the first row gives the totals obtained already and the second row gives the totals obtained by using supermarket prices.

We have learnt already that in order for us to be able to multiply two matrices together there must be the same number of columns in the first matrix as there are rows in the second. An examination of results that we have obtained so far shows that the product of

a 1×5 and a 5×1 is a 1×1,

a 1×5 and a 5×4 is a 1×4,

and

a 2×5 and a 5×4 is a 2×4.

This pattern is true for all matrix multiplication and we may generalize and say that if we have an $l \times m$ matrix and an $m \times n$ matrix we may multiply them together, since there are the same number of columns in the first as there are rows in the second, and that the result will be an $l \times n$ matrix. Since matrix multiplication can be a little confusing, it is as well to decide what size and shape the answer will be before multiplying so as to avoid a possible source of error. The process is not as complicated as it may seem and may soon be mastered with a little perseverance. The reader would do well to gain some fluency at matrix multiplication since we shall use it frequently in future.

Worked example I

$$\text{Evaluate} \quad \begin{bmatrix} 2 & 1 & 0 \\ 3 & 6 & 2 \end{bmatrix} \quad \begin{bmatrix} 1 & 4 \\ 2 & 0 \\ 4 & 2 \end{bmatrix}$$

The first is a 2×3 matrix and the second a 3×2 matrix. We may therefore multiply them to give a 2×2 matrix. First take the [2 1 0] of the first matrix and mentally place it in turn against the two columns of the second matrix. This gives us

$$[2 \times 1 + 1 \times 2 + 0 \times 4 \quad 2 \times 4 + 1 \times 0 + 0 \times 2]$$

as the first row of the result. Note that this depends upon the first row of the first matrix. Now repeat the process for [3 6 2] to give the second row. The complete result is

$$\begin{bmatrix} 2 \times 1 + 1 \times 2 + 0 \times 4 & 2 \times 4 + 1 \times 0 + 0 \times 2 \\ 3 \times 1 + 6 \times 2 + 2 \times 4 & 3 \times 4 + 6 \times 0 + 2 \times 2 \end{bmatrix}$$

where the second row depends upon the second row of the first matrix. Also we may notice that the first column of the result depends upon the first column of the second matrix and the second on the second. We may therefore say that the number which appears in, say, the second row of the first column is going to depend upon the second row of the first matrix and the first column of the second matrix, i.e.

$$[3 \quad 6 \quad 2] \quad \text{and} \quad \begin{bmatrix} 1 \\ 2 \\ 4 \end{bmatrix}$$

This gives us

$$3 \times 1 + 6 \times 2 + 2 \times 4$$

which we can see is correct from the completed product. This enables us where necessary to work out any required number in the middle of a matrix product without having to work out the whole result. Simple arithmetic tidies up the completed matrix to give

$$\begin{bmatrix} 4 & 8 \\ 23 & 16 \end{bmatrix}$$

A result far easier to get than to explain.

Worked example II

Evaluate $\begin{bmatrix} 1 & 0 \\ 2 & 3 \\ 4 & 1 \end{bmatrix} \begin{bmatrix} 2 & 1 & 4 & 6 \\ 3 & 0 & 1 & 2 \end{bmatrix}.$

The first is a 3×2 matrix and the second a 2×4 matrix. We may therefore multiply them and the answer will be a 3×4 matrix. First take the $[1 \quad 0]$ of the first matrix and mentally place it in turn against the various columns of the second matrix. This gives us

$$[1 \times 2 + 0 \times 3 \quad 1 \times 1 + 0 \times 0 \quad 1 \times 4 + 0 \times 1 \quad 1 \times 6 + 0 \times 2]$$

as the first row of the result.

Now repeat the process for $[2 \quad 3]$ and $[4 \quad 1]$, the second and third rows of the first matrix, to give the second and third rows of the result. The complete result is now

$$\begin{bmatrix} 1 \times 2 + 0 \times 3 & 1 \times 1 + 0 \times 0 & 1 \times 4 + 0 \times 1 & 1 \times 6 + 0 \times 2 \\ 2 \times 2 + 3 \times 3 & 2 \times 1 + 3 \times 0 & 2 \times 4 + 3 \times 1 & 2 \times 6 + 3 \times 2 \\ 4 \times 2 + 1 \times 3 & 4 \times 1 + 1 \times 0 & 4 \times 4 + 1 \times 1 & 4 \times 6 + 1 \times 2 \end{bmatrix}$$

Simple arithmetic tidies up the completed matrix to give

$$\begin{bmatrix} 2 & 1 & 4 & 6 \\ 13 & 2 & 11 & 18 \\ 11 & 4 & 17 & 26 \end{bmatrix}$$

Examples 6d

1. Calculate the size and shape of the following matrix products and then work out the results.

(a) $\begin{bmatrix} 2 & 3 \\ 0 & 1 \end{bmatrix} \begin{bmatrix} 1 & 0 \\ 2 & 4 \end{bmatrix}$
(b) $\begin{bmatrix} 2 & 0 \\ 0 & 3 \end{bmatrix} \begin{bmatrix} 0 & 2 \\ 0 & 0 \end{bmatrix}$
(c) $\begin{bmatrix} 1 & 0 \\ 0 & 0 \end{bmatrix} \begin{bmatrix} 0 & 0 \\ 2 & 0 \end{bmatrix}$

(d) $[2 \quad 1] \begin{bmatrix} 5 \\ 6 \end{bmatrix}$
(e) $[5 \quad 6] \begin{bmatrix} 1 \\ 2 \end{bmatrix}$
(f) $\begin{bmatrix} 6 & 1 & 2 \\ 3 & 2 & 1 \end{bmatrix} \begin{bmatrix} 3 \\ 1 \\ 2 \end{bmatrix}$

(g) $[1 \quad 2 \quad 4] \begin{bmatrix} 5 \\ 9 \\ 1 \end{bmatrix}$
(h) $[5 \quad 9 \quad 1] \begin{bmatrix} 1 \\ 2 \\ 4 \end{bmatrix}$
(i) $\begin{bmatrix} 1 \\ 2 \\ 4 \end{bmatrix} [5 \quad 9 \quad 1]$

(j) $\begin{bmatrix} 5 \\ 9 \\ 1 \end{bmatrix} [1 \quad 2 \quad 4]$
(k) $\begin{bmatrix} 3 & 2 & 1 \\ 9 & 0 & 1 \end{bmatrix} \begin{bmatrix} 1 & 3 & 1 \\ 0 & 1 & 0 \\ 1 & 2 & 2 \end{bmatrix}$

(l) $\begin{bmatrix} 1 & 6 & 5 \\ 2 & 0 & 1 \\ 2 & 1 & 1 \end{bmatrix} \begin{bmatrix} 2 & 0 & 7 \\ 1 & 1 & 3 \\ 2 & 1 & 4 \end{bmatrix}$

2. From an examination of the three matrix products

$$\begin{bmatrix} a & b \\ c & d \end{bmatrix} \begin{bmatrix} e & f \\ g & h \end{bmatrix}, \quad [a \ b \ c] \begin{bmatrix} d & g \\ e & h \\ f & i, \end{bmatrix} \quad \text{and} \quad \begin{bmatrix} a & b & c \\ d & e & f \end{bmatrix} \begin{bmatrix} g & h \\ i & j \end{bmatrix}$$

and others of your own choosing deduce what you may about closure and uniqueness for matrices under matrix multiplication.

3. By working out

$$\begin{bmatrix} 2 & 1 \\ 3 & 4 \end{bmatrix} \begin{bmatrix} 1 & 5 \\ 3 & 7 \end{bmatrix} \begin{bmatrix} 4 & 9 \\ 1 & 3 \end{bmatrix}$$

in two separate ways test the validity of the Associative Law for this particular case.

4. Locate, if possible, an identity element for

$$\left\{ \begin{bmatrix} a & b \\ c & d \end{bmatrix} \right\}$$

under matrix multiplication where a, b, c, d are real numbers.

5. Locate, if possible, an inverse element for each of the following matrices:

$$\begin{bmatrix} 1 & 0 \\ 0 & 1 \end{bmatrix}, \quad \begin{bmatrix} 3 & 1 \\ 5 & 2 \end{bmatrix}, \quad \begin{bmatrix} 2 & 2 \\ 2 & 4 \end{bmatrix}, \quad \begin{bmatrix} 3 & 1 \\ 5 & 1 \end{bmatrix}, \quad \begin{bmatrix} 6 & 3 \\ 4 & 2 \end{bmatrix}$$

and hence evolve a general procedure for finding such inverses for 2×2 matrices.

6. Is the Commutative Law true for matrix multiplication in general and 2×2 matrices in particular?

7. In the answer to the following matrix product

$$\begin{bmatrix} 1 & 2 & 9 & 4 & 8 \\ 2 & 4 & 3 & 7 & 4 \\ 4 & 6 & 2 & 12 & 1 \\ 0 & 2 & 4 & 9 & 2 \\ 3 & 1 & 3 & 3 & 2 \end{bmatrix} \begin{bmatrix} 2 & 9 & 4 & 9 & 6 & 10 & 4 \\ 4 & 3 & 3 & 0 & 2 & 12 & 4 \\ 3 & 2 & 8 & 0 & 4 & 6 & 3 \\ 2 & 7 & 4 & 3 & 0 & 2 & 2 \\ 1 & 2 & 1 & 2 & 3 & 1 & 5 \end{bmatrix}$$

what number appears in
   (a) The first row of the first column,
   (b) The third row of the fourth column,
   (c) The fifth row of the seventh column,
   (d) The fourth row of the third column,
   (e) The sixth row of the seventh column?

6.5 Further Matrix Multiplication

The examples of the last section were introduced in order to demonstrate the principles of matrix multiplication and many of our readers probably reached the solution of even the most complicated problem without bothering to use matrices. It must be admitted however that the data we were using were very neatly presented in matrix form and that once this had been done the rest of the work was automatic and could easily have been done by an adequately conditioned office girl or computer.

The reader will find it useful to think in terms of whole matrices rather than individual numbers. The cost of a number of articles at a given price is obtained in normal arithmetic by multiplying the cost per article by the number of articles. In matrices the same idea prevails. The total cost of a number of different articles at various prices is obtained by multiplying the cost matrix by the quantities matrix. Once the matrices have been set up correctly there is no need to worry about each number being multiplied by its correct partner as matrix multiplication will do this automatically for us.

We now show matrices in action in a more complicated example. The situation has been much over-simplified to keep the size of matrix and the numbers involved sufficiently small for ease of working, but the principles still apply and are even more helpful in more complex situations. Let us assume that we are the owners of a small factory that makes articles from just one raw material. The only other factors that we need consider are transport and labour. Let us assume that there are four different articles made: E, F, G, and H. E needs 6 lb of raw material, takes 1 man 5 hours to make and takes up 3 cubic feet of space on a lorry. F, on the other hand, takes 8 lb of raw material, takes 2 men 3 hours to make and requires 4 cubic feet of lorry space. G takes 10 lb of raw material, takes 3 men 2 hours to make it and it requires 6 cubic feet of lorry space. Finally, H requires 7 lb of raw material, takes 1 man 4 hours to make and takes up 5 cubic feet of lorry space. A tender is requested by a large firm for the delivery of 100 of type E, 50 of type F, 60 of type G, and 30 of type H to depot I, and 200 of type E, 100 of type F, 50 of type G and 80 of type H to depot J. We wish to make a profit of 10 per cent on the transaction. What should our tender be for each depot if raw material costs 15s. per pound, labour 10s. per man-hour and lorry space on average 6s. per cubic foot?

The data are too involved for us to absorb what is going on and therefore tabulating or matricizing is the obvious solution. Let us first of all form an amounts matrix A, which tells us the amounts of raw material, man-hours, and lorry space required for the various articles.

	E	F	G	H	
Raw material	6	8	10	7	pounds
Labour	5	6	6	4	man-hours
Lorry space	3	4	6	5	cubic feet.

With this we may associate a cost matrix C.

Raw material	Labour	Lorry space	
[15	10	6]	shillings.

We write C this way round instead of $\begin{bmatrix} 15 \\ 10 \\ 6 \end{bmatrix}$, which would express the same information just as well, as we are bound to require the products of the individual costs and the amounts. With C in the horizontal form we can calculate the product CA easily enough since C has the same number of columns as A has rows but this would not be possible if C were in the vertical form.

The last pieces of information which we are given are the details of the two orders. We shall call them Q, the quantities matrix, and write either as

$$\begin{array}{c} \\ \text{Depot } I \\ \text{Depot } J \end{array} \begin{array}{cccc} E & F & G & H \\ \begin{bmatrix} 100 & 50 & 60 & 30 \\ 200 & 100 & 50 & 80 \end{bmatrix} \end{array}$$

or

$$\begin{array}{c} \\ E \\ F \\ G \\ H \end{array} \begin{array}{cc} \text{Depot } I & \text{Depot } J \\ \begin{bmatrix} 100 & 200 \\ 50 & 100 \\ 60 & 50 \\ 30 & 80 \end{bmatrix} \end{array}.$$

To decide which we prefer we must think again of the object of these calculations. We require the total cost of manufacture and transport. This means that we must multiply together the cost per article and the number of articles. The cost per article is based on the product of the matrices C and A so that we want to arrange Q so that it can multiply the result of C and A. Now C is a 1×3 matrix and A is a 3×4 matrix so that CA is a 1×4 matrix. Thus we must make Q the 4×2 matrix

$$\begin{bmatrix} 100 & 200 \\ 50 & 100 \\ 60 & 50 \\ 30 & 80 \end{bmatrix}$$

so as to be able to form the matrix multiplication CAQ. The grand estimate (to be increased by 10 per cent for profit) is now given by

$$CAQ = \begin{bmatrix} 15 & 10 & 6 \end{bmatrix} \begin{bmatrix} 6 & 8 & 10 & 7 \\ 5 & 6 & 6 & 4 \\ 3 & 4 & 6 & 5 \end{bmatrix} \begin{bmatrix} 100 & 200 \\ 50 & 100 \\ 60 & 50 \\ 30 & 80 \end{bmatrix}$$

since the product of the first two will give a 1×4 matrix listing the costs of each of the four articles and the product of that with the quantities matrix will give a 1×2 matrix listing the total costs for the two orders.

Amongst other things, notions of an unproved Associative Law should be wrinkling the reader's brow at this stage. We shall prove the Associative Law for 2×2 matrices when we play with the Group Axioms again later in this chapter. It is reasonable that the Associative Law should be true since we should get the same results by finding the total amounts of raw material, labour, and lorry space used (AQ) and costing the whole lot $C(AQ)$ as by costing each article (CA) and then multiplying by the total number of articles ordered. To make assurance doubly sure we work it out both ways.

$$\left\{ \begin{bmatrix} 15 & 10 & 6 \end{bmatrix} \begin{bmatrix} 6 & 8 & 10 & 7 \\ 5 & 6 & 6 & 4 \\ 3 & 4 & 6 & 5 \end{bmatrix} \right\} \begin{bmatrix} 100 & 200 \\ 50 & 100 \\ 60 & 50 \\ 30 & 80 \end{bmatrix}$$

$$= \begin{bmatrix} 158 & 204 & 246 & 175 \end{bmatrix} \begin{bmatrix} 100 & 200 \\ 50 & 100 \\ 60 & 50 \\ 30 & 80 \end{bmatrix}$$

$$= \begin{bmatrix} 46010 & 78300 \end{bmatrix}.$$

Add 10 per cent to each result for profit and the tenders become 50611s. and 86130s. respectively or £2530. 11s. and £4306. 10s.

The reader may object to the sordid amount of arithmetic involved but that is a function of the problem rather than matrices themselves. The arithmetic would still have to be done whatever type of solution was employed. Again we make the point that the work is automatic once the necessary sorting of data has been done at the beginning. We will now work out the matrix multiplication the other way round and hope for the best.

$$\begin{bmatrix} 15 & 10 & 6 \end{bmatrix} \left\{ \begin{bmatrix} 6 & 8 & 10 & 7 \\ 5 & 6 & 6 & 4 \\ 3 & 4 & 6 & 5 \end{bmatrix} \begin{bmatrix} 100 & 200 \\ 50 & 100 \\ 60 & 50 \\ 30 & 80 \end{bmatrix} \right\}$$

$$= \begin{bmatrix} 15 & 10 & 6 \end{bmatrix} \begin{bmatrix} 1810 & 3060 \\ 1280 & 2220 \\ 1010 & 1700 \end{bmatrix}$$

$$= \begin{bmatrix} 46010 & 78300 \end{bmatrix}$$

which is mercifully the same as before.

Examples 6e

1. In the example given in the text (p. 94) the cost of raw materials increases by 5s. per pound, labour costs go up by 2s. per man-hour, and lorry space by

1s. per cubic foot. Another tender is requested for 70 of type *E*, 35 of type *F*, 20 of type *G*, and 30 of type *H* to be delivered to depot *I*. Allowing the usual 10 per cent profit, what should the tender be?

2. Junior goes to a party and wins 4 toy soldiers and 7 oranges. His sister wins 2 small dolls and 3 oranges. His friend wins 7 oranges. The soldiers cost 1s. each, the oranges 6d. each and the dolls 5s. each. Junior goes to 5 more parties this season. His sister goes to 2 more and his friend goes to 1 more. They manage to do equally well at their other parties. What is the total value of all their booty?

3. Three very special machines are designed to measure the amount of woffle written in text-books. They are called the 'Dewoffleiser' Mark I, Mark II and Mark III. The chief components of these machines are 'plings', 'quangs', 'gunks' and 'sploogiks'. Mark I requires 3 plings, 4 quangs, 5 gunks and a sploogik. Mark II, a special heavy-duty model, requires 2 extra quangs and another sploogik, whilst Mark III, economy size, requires a pling and a gunk less than the Mark I model and no sploogik at all!

Plings cost 10s. each, quangs £1, gunks 2s. 6d. and sploogiks £2. Orders are received from Publisher A for 2 of Mark I, 3 of Mark II and 1 of Mark III, whilst Publisher B requires 6 of Mark II and 1 of Mark III. What is the total cash value of the components supplied to each customer?

4. See Question 2 of Examples 6b (p. 82). Choc. ices cost 6d. each, crunchy bars 8d., lollypops 4d. and peppermint creams 1s. per bag. How much was spent on Junior?

Aunty Jane took Junior out on Monday, Aunty Jean took him on Tuesday, Aunty Joan on Wednesday, Aunty June on Thursday, and Aunty Hetty on Friday. They always buy Junior the same sweets and nobody else ever buys him any. In the course of a month Aunty Jane comes to stay for a week, Aunty Jean for three days, Aunty Joan does not come at all, Aunty June comes for a fortnight and Aunty Hetty for a day. What is the sum total of Junior's gastronomic achievements and what did it all cost?

6.6 Matrices under Multiplication and the Group Axioms

We cannot form a group of all matrices under matrix multiplication for the very good reason that not all pairs of matrices can be multiplied together. Also we must restrict ourselves to square matrices for if we take a pair of

matrices such as $[1 \quad 2 \quad 3]$ and $\begin{bmatrix} 2 & 1 \\ 4 & 3 \\ 6 & 5 \end{bmatrix}$

these multiply as $[1 \quad 2 \quad 3] \begin{bmatrix} 2 & 1 \\ 4 & 3 \\ 6 & 5 \end{bmatrix}$ to give $[28 \quad 22]$

but do not fit as $\begin{bmatrix} 2 & 1 \\ 4 & 3 \\ 6 & 5 \end{bmatrix} [1 \quad 2 \quad 3]$

Even if we take a pair such as $\begin{bmatrix} 1 & 2 & 3 \end{bmatrix}$ and $\begin{bmatrix} 4 \\ 5 \\ 6 \end{bmatrix}$

which multiply as $\begin{bmatrix} 1 & 2 & 3 \end{bmatrix} \begin{bmatrix} 4 \\ 5 \\ 6 \end{bmatrix}$ to give $[32]$

and as $\begin{bmatrix} 4 \\ 5 \\ 6 \end{bmatrix} \begin{bmatrix} 1 & 2 & 3 \end{bmatrix}$ to give $\begin{bmatrix} 4 & 8 & 12 \\ 5 & 10 & 15 \\ 6 & 12 & 18 \end{bmatrix}$

we cannot use matrix multiplication to combine the two results

$$[32] \quad \text{and} \quad \begin{bmatrix} 4 & 8 & 12 \\ 5 & 10 & 15 \\ 6 & 12 & 18 \end{bmatrix}$$

so that the Closure Rule would not be satisfied. We shall therefore restrict ourselves to 2×2 matrices as before. The reader should notice at this stage, even if he has not done so as the result of Examples 6d, that the Commutative Law is certainly not always true for matrix multiplication although it may be under certain circumstances.

We will therefore, as before, let G be the set of all 2×2 matrices and let the combining operation be matrix multiplication.

To prove Axiom I.

$$\forall \, x, y \in G; \quad \exists \text{ a unique } xy \in G.$$

We adopt the same technique as with addition and take two general matrices $\begin{bmatrix} a & b \\ c & d \end{bmatrix}$ and $\begin{bmatrix} e & f \\ g & h \end{bmatrix}$ where a, b, c, d, e, f, g and h are real numbers. If we multiply these together we get

$$\begin{bmatrix} a & b \\ c & d \end{bmatrix} \begin{bmatrix} e & f \\ g & h \end{bmatrix} = \begin{bmatrix} ae+bg & af+bh \\ ce+dg & cf+dh \end{bmatrix}$$

which is another 2×2 matrix and the only possible result.

To prove Axiom 2. The Associative Law.

$$x(yz) = (xy)z \quad \forall \, x, y, z \in G.$$

This is sheer purgatory but must be done. Timid readers may skip the next bit. We shall merely take three general 2×2 matrices

$$\begin{bmatrix} a & b \\ c & d \end{bmatrix}, \quad \begin{bmatrix} e & f \\ g & h \end{bmatrix} \quad \text{and} \quad \begin{bmatrix} i & j \\ k & l \end{bmatrix}$$

where a, b, c, d, e, f, g, h, i, j, k and l are real numbers and multiply them together in the two possible ways. Thus

$$\left\{ \begin{bmatrix} a & b \\ c & d \end{bmatrix} \begin{bmatrix} e & f \\ g & h \end{bmatrix} \right\} \begin{bmatrix} i & j \\ k & l \end{bmatrix}$$

$$= \begin{bmatrix} ae+bg & af+bh \\ ce+dg & cf+dh \end{bmatrix} \begin{bmatrix} i & j \\ k & l \end{bmatrix}$$

$$= \begin{bmatrix} (ae+bg)i+(af+bh)k & (ae+bg)j+(af+bh)l \\ (ce+dg)i+(cf+dh)k & (ce+dg)j+(cf+dh)l \end{bmatrix}$$

$$= \begin{bmatrix} aei+bgi+afk+bhk & aej+bgj+afl+bhl \\ cei+dgi+cfk+dhk & cej+dgj+cfl+dhl \end{bmatrix}$$

By the alternative route we get

$$\begin{bmatrix} a & b \\ c & d \end{bmatrix} \left\{ \begin{bmatrix} e & f \\ g & h \end{bmatrix} \begin{bmatrix} i & j \\ k & l \end{bmatrix} \right\}$$

$$= \begin{bmatrix} a & b \\ c & d \end{bmatrix} \begin{bmatrix} ei+fk & ej+fl \\ gi+hk & gj+hl \end{bmatrix}$$

$$= \begin{bmatrix} a(ei+fk)+b(gi+hk) & a(ej+fl)+b(gj+hl) \\ c(ei+fk)+d(gi+hk) & c(ej+fl)+d(gj+hl) \end{bmatrix}$$

$$= \begin{bmatrix} aei+afk+bgi+bhk & aej+afl+bgj+bhl \\ cei+cfk+dgi+dhk & cej+cfl+dgj+dhl \end{bmatrix}$$

which is the same as before. Therefore the Associative Law is true.

To prove Axiom 3. Identity element.

$$\exists\, I \in G \,|\, Ix = x \quad \forall\, x \in G.$$

(I is the symbol usually used for the identity for matrix multiplication.)

This time the candidate is $\begin{bmatrix} 1 & 0 \\ 0 & 1 \end{bmatrix}$ which triumphantly fulfils the required conditions since

$$\begin{bmatrix} 1 & 0 \\ 0 & 1 \end{bmatrix} \begin{bmatrix} a & b \\ c & d \end{bmatrix} = \begin{bmatrix} 1 \times a+0 \times c & 1 \times b+0 \times d \\ 0 \times a+1 \times c & 0 \times b+1 \times d \end{bmatrix}$$

$$= \begin{bmatrix} a & b \\ c & d \end{bmatrix}$$

as required.

To prove Axiom 4. Inverse elements.

$$\forall\, x \in G;\ \exists\, x^{-1} \in G \,|\, x^{-1}x = I.$$

We are now in trouble. What is required is a matrix which will multiply

$\begin{bmatrix} a & b \\ c & d \end{bmatrix}$ and give $\begin{bmatrix} 1 & 0 \\ 0 & 1 \end{bmatrix}$ as the result.

If we swap over the a and the d and change the sign of the b and the c we get $\begin{bmatrix} d & -b \\ -c & a \end{bmatrix}$ which very nearly does what is required since

$$\begin{bmatrix} d & -b \\ -c & a \end{bmatrix} \begin{bmatrix} a & b \\ c & d \end{bmatrix} = \begin{bmatrix} ad-bc & 0 \\ 0 & ad-bc \end{bmatrix}.$$

We have the 0's in the right place but unfortunately we have $ad-bc$ in each case instead of 1. This is easily remedied however by dividing the numbers in the prospective inverse matrix by $ad-bc$ to give

$$\begin{bmatrix} \dfrac{d}{ad-bc} & \dfrac{-b}{ad-bc} \\ \dfrac{-c}{ad-bc} & \dfrac{a}{ad-bc} \end{bmatrix}$$

The number $ad-bc$ is of great importance and is called the determinant of the matrix $\begin{bmatrix} a & b \\ c & d \end{bmatrix}$. It is frequently written $\begin{vmatrix} a & b \\ c & d \end{vmatrix}$, or if we call $\begin{bmatrix} a & b \\ c & d \end{bmatrix}$ the matrix A, we may write the associated determinant as $\det A$ or $|A|$. Let us check that the amended version of the inverse does in fact work.

$$\begin{bmatrix} \dfrac{d}{ad-bc} & \dfrac{-b}{ad-bc} \\ \dfrac{-c}{ad-bc} & \dfrac{a}{ad-bc} \end{bmatrix} \begin{bmatrix} a & b \\ c & d \end{bmatrix}$$

$$= \begin{bmatrix} \dfrac{ad-bc}{ad-bc} & 0 \\ 0 & \dfrac{ad-bc}{ad-bc} \end{bmatrix}$$

$$= \begin{bmatrix} 1 & 0 \\ 0 & 1 \end{bmatrix}$$

which is what is required.

Unfortunately we now reach complications. Suppose we have a matrix such as $\begin{bmatrix} 3 & 6 \\ 1 & 2 \end{bmatrix}$. We obtain its inverse by swapping the 3 and the 2 and putting '$-$' signs in front of the 1 and the 6 to give $\begin{bmatrix} 2 & -6 \\ -1 & 3 \end{bmatrix}$. We now divide by the associated determinant which has the value $3 \times 2 - 6 \times 1$ which is 0. Thus the inverse becomes

$$\begin{bmatrix} \dfrac{2}{0} & \dfrac{-6}{0} \\[2ex] \dfrac{-1}{0} & \dfrac{3}{0} \end{bmatrix}$$

which is hardly helpful. We must therefore face the inevitable fact that 2×2 matrices whose determinant is 0 have no inverses and that therefore all 2×2 matrices under matrix multiplication do not form a group. We can however salvage something from the ruins by excluding all those matrices which have zero determinants from our prospective group in the same way that we excluded 0 from multiplicative groups for real numbers (p. 76). A quick gallop back through the axioms will show that we can do this without cheating. Each matrix under consideration now has an inverse. The identity element has a determinant of 1 and therefore belongs to the reduced set. Since the Associative Law is true for all 2×2's it will certainly be true for the reduced set. Uniqueness of result will still be true and the only difficulty will be with the Closure Rule. We know that all 2×2 matrices with non-zero determinants multiply to other 2×2's by the original Closure Rule, but can we prove that they multiply to other 2×2's with non-zero determinants? Let us try. Unfortunately the algebra is again not for the faint-hearted.

Assume that $\begin{bmatrix} a & b \\ c & d \end{bmatrix}$ and $\begin{bmatrix} e & f \\ g & h \end{bmatrix}$ are any 2×2 matrices with non-zero determinants. In other words, $ad - bc \neq 0$ and $eh - fg \neq 0$.

$$\begin{bmatrix} a & b \\ c & d \end{bmatrix} \begin{bmatrix} e & f \\ g & h \end{bmatrix} = \begin{bmatrix} ae + bg & af + bh \\ ce + dg & cf + dh \end{bmatrix}$$

The determinant of the result is

$$(ae + bg)(cf + dh) - (af + bh)(ce + dg)$$
$$= aecf + aedh + bgcf + bgdh - afce - afdg - bhce - bhgd$$
$$= aedh - afdg + bgcf - bhce$$
$$= ad(eh - fg) + bc(gf - he)$$
$$= ad(eh - fg) - bc(eh - fg)$$
$$= (ad - bc)(eh - fg).$$

Neither $ad - bc$ nor $eh - fg$ are zero and therefore their product is not zero. Thus the product of two 2×2 matrices with non-zero determinants is another 2×2 matrix of the same type which proves the Closure Rule in this case. The reduced set of 2×2 matrices with non-zero determinants therefore forms a group under matrix multiplication.

We have previously established that the Commutative Law is not always true for matrix multiplication. It may possibly be true however for 2×2's. We can easily check.

$$\begin{bmatrix} a & b \\ c & d \end{bmatrix} \begin{bmatrix} e & f \\ g & h \end{bmatrix} = \begin{bmatrix} ae + bg & af + bh \\ ce + dg & cf + dh \end{bmatrix}.$$

On the other hand,

$$\begin{bmatrix} e & f \\ g & h \end{bmatrix} \begin{bmatrix} a & b \\ c & d \end{bmatrix} = \begin{bmatrix} ea+fc & eb+fd \\ ga+hc & gb+hd \end{bmatrix}$$

and the two results are not, in general, the same. Thus the Commutative Law does not always hold good for 2×2 matrices.

The author's educational principles have taken yet another denting as the result of this curious process of finding inverses which we quoted but in no wise justified. The amount of explanation would far outweigh the value of the exercise at this stage however, so that we refer the interested reader to the references for solace.

Examples 6f

1. Show that $\left\{ \begin{bmatrix} 1 & 0 \\ 0 & 1 \end{bmatrix}, \begin{bmatrix} 0 & -1 \\ 1 & 0 \end{bmatrix}, \begin{bmatrix} -1 & 0 \\ 0 & -1 \end{bmatrix}, \begin{bmatrix} 0 & 1 \\ -1 & 0 \end{bmatrix} \right\}$ forms a group under matrix multiplication. Work out a complete multiplication table for them. Where have you seen this before?

2. Repeat Question 1 for

$$\left\{ \begin{bmatrix} 1 & 0 \\ 0 & 1 \end{bmatrix}, \begin{bmatrix} -1 & 0 \\ 0 & 1 \end{bmatrix}, \begin{bmatrix} -1 & 0 \\ 0 & -1 \end{bmatrix}, \begin{bmatrix} 1 & 0 \\ 0 & -1 \end{bmatrix} \right\}$$

3. Repeat Question 1 for

$$\left(\left\{ \begin{bmatrix} 1 & 0 \\ 0 & 1 \end{bmatrix}, \begin{bmatrix} \dfrac{1}{2} & -\dfrac{\sqrt{3}}{2} \\ \dfrac{\sqrt{3}}{2} & \dfrac{1}{2} \end{bmatrix}, \begin{bmatrix} \dfrac{1}{2} & \dfrac{\sqrt{3}}{2} \\ -\dfrac{\sqrt{3}}{2} & \dfrac{1}{2} \end{bmatrix} \right\} \right).$$

4. Form a combined group from the elements of Questions 1 and 2, making whatever additions are necessary. Where have you seen this one before?

5. Do $\left\{ \begin{bmatrix} a & 0 \\ 0 & a \end{bmatrix} \right\}$, where a is a real number, form a group under matrix multiplication?

6. Repeat Question 5 where a is an integer.

7. Find, where possible, the multiplicative inverses of the following matrices and check that they work from both sides.

(a) $\begin{bmatrix} 1 & 0 \\ 0 & 1 \end{bmatrix}$, (b) $\begin{bmatrix} 2 \\ 1 \\ 4 \end{bmatrix}$, (c) $\begin{bmatrix} 3 & 0 \\ 4 & 1 \end{bmatrix}$, (d) $\begin{bmatrix} 2 & 1 & 6 \\ 3 & 0 & 1 \end{bmatrix}$, (e) $[4]$,

(f) $\begin{bmatrix} 2 & 1 \\ 4 & 2 \end{bmatrix}$, (g) $\begin{bmatrix} 0 & 0 \\ 0 & 2 \end{bmatrix}$.

7. NEW WAYS WITH SIMULTANEOUS EQUATIONS

7.1 A Little Linear Programming

The most astounding developments in industrial technique over the last few years have been based on the computer. No longer is it necessary for the harassed executive to ingest pages of statistical information and regurgitate some sort of decision based on experience, instinct or sheer luck. The computer can scan such data for him in a fraction of the time and produce an answer based on an accurate evaluation. In this section we shall examine a simplified version of the type of problem the computer is adept at handling. We must, of course, simplify it virtually out of existence in order to be able to do it at all in a reasonable time but we shall illustrate some of the principles involved and at the same time extend our experience of matrices and other mathematical flora and fauna that we shall collect *en route*.

Let us examine the following situation.

A toothpaste manufacturer makes tubes of that invaluable commodity in three different sizes: 'Large', 'Super' and 'Mammoth'. He has a factory at Eastleigh and one at Westleigh. The Eastleigh factory can produce 2000 'Large' tubes, 3000 'Super' tubes and 1000 'Mammoth' tubes a day, whilst the daily production figures for Westleigh are 1000 'Large' tubes, 1000 'Super' tubes, and 2000 'Mammoth' tubes. The Eastleigh factory costs £500 a day to run and the Westleigh factory £200. The manufacturer has a regular weekly order for 5000 'Large' tubes, 6000 'Super' tubes and 4000 'Mammoth' tubes. For how many days in each week should he keep each factory working in order to minimize his costs? (We assume that it is economical to keep a factory running for part of a day only.)

The first difficulty is to separate the information from the verbiage. Listing the data in matrix form will help here. Even a cursory glance will tell us that we have 3 sizes of tube made at 2 factories and we can therefore summarize all our production figures in a simple 3×2 (or 2×3) matrix thus:

Factories

	Eastleigh	*Westleigh*	
'Large'	2000	1000	
'Super'	3000	1000	Output per day
'Mammoth'	1000	2000	

Sizes of tube

We will call the matrix $\begin{bmatrix} 2 & 1 \\ 3 & 1 \\ 1 & 2 \end{bmatrix}$ the amounts matrix A and work in units of 1000 tubes of toothpaste for the sake of arithmetic.

The most important thing about this question is the answer which requires two numbers, x and y say, to represent the number of days that Eastleigh and Westleigh shall work. We shall write them as the unknowns matrix X in the form $\begin{bmatrix} x \\ y \end{bmatrix}$ as we shall almost certainly want to form the product AX. This will give us the product of the amounts per day and the number of days per week which gives us the total amount of each type of tube manufactured per week. If we had written A as a 2×3 matrix, X would have to be $[x \quad y]$ and we would have to form the product XA.

We may note that even without reading further there are already severe limitations on the values of x and y. Negative times are, of course, impossible and it is unfashionable these days to work more than a five-day week. Thus

$$0 \leqslant x \leqslant 5$$

and

$$0 \leqslant y \leqslant 5.$$

These are officially known as constraints on the values of x and y and may also be written as $0 \leqslant X \leqslant 5$.

A necessary piece of information is the amounts of the various tubes required. This we will call the requirements matrix R and will write as $\begin{bmatrix} 5 \\ 6 \\ 4 \end{bmatrix}$

meaning that 5000 of the 'Large' tubes are required, 6000 of the 'Super' and 4000 of the 'Mammoth'. We write it as a 3×1 matrix as opposed to a 1×3 as it must bear comparison with the amounts matrix A which also lists quantities of tubes. In fact this gives us a further opportunity to list constraints on x and y since any feasible solution to the problem must satisfy the condition that the amount produced is at least as great as the amount required. We saw earlier in this section that the amount produced was given by AX and may therefore write our constraints in the matrix form $AX \geqslant R$. If we write this expression in full we get

$$\begin{bmatrix} 2 & 1 \\ 3 & 1 \\ 1 & 2 \end{bmatrix} \begin{bmatrix} x \\ y \end{bmatrix} \geqslant \begin{bmatrix} 5 \\ 6 \\ 4 \end{bmatrix}$$

or

$$\begin{bmatrix} 2x+y \\ 3x+y \\ x+2y \end{bmatrix} \geqslant \begin{bmatrix} 5 \\ 6 \\ 4 \end{bmatrix}.$$

We can write this expression out in a form that shows the separate relationships

$$2x + y \geqslant 5,$$

$$3x + y \geqslant 6,$$

$$x + 2y \geqslant 4.$$

For the reader who still finds matrices disturbing, we may arrive at these further constraints quite happily by saying, for example, that the number of 'Large' tubes we must make in a week must be at least as great as the number required, i.e. 5000. Thus 2000 for x days and 1000 for y days must produce at least 5000. More formally

$$2000x + 1000y \geqslant 5000$$

or

$$2x + y \geqslant 5.$$

The matrix method is neater, requires less effort and does all three at once.

The only bits of information unlisted are the daily running costs for the two factories. These we write as a cost matrix C in the form [5 2] where we work for ease in £100-units. We write our matrix horizontally so that we may calculate the product CX or $\begin{bmatrix} 5 & 2 \end{bmatrix} \begin{bmatrix} x \\ y \end{bmatrix}$ which will give us the product of the number of days each factory is in use and the corresponding running costs. This gives us the total cost of the whole process which we want to minimize. Almost every linear programming problem is based on minimizing costs or maximizing profits. We could here have made a first-class blunder. The product XC can be calculated and gives

$$\begin{bmatrix} x \\ y \end{bmatrix} \begin{bmatrix} 5 & 2 \end{bmatrix} = \begin{bmatrix} 5x & 2x \\ 5y & 2y \end{bmatrix}$$

which is meaningless. To avoid sources of error in this way it is a good idea to check the type of result you are aiming for. Thus CX is the product of a 1×2 matrix and a 2×1, the result being a 1×1 matrix, which is what is required for the total cost of the whole process. XC, on the other hand, is a product of a 2×1 and a 1×2. This gives a 2×2 matrix, which is not relevant and should therefore raise suspicions. After all this the reader may well have lost his bearings. We therefore have a résumé.

The problem is to

minimize

$$CX$$

subject to

$$0 \leqslant X \leqslant 5$$

and

$$AX \geqslant R$$

where

$$A = \begin{bmatrix} 2 & 1 \\ 3 & 1 \\ 1 & 2 \end{bmatrix}, \qquad R = \begin{bmatrix} 5 \\ 6 \\ 4 \end{bmatrix},$$

$$X = \begin{bmatrix} x \\ y \end{bmatrix} \quad \text{and} \quad C = [5 \quad 2].$$

The reader should now check back and make sure that this is an adequate mathematical model of the original problem. In other words, subject to the conventions about working in hundreds of pounds and thousands of tubes, does the collection of matrix inequalities given above say the same as the original problem?

Writing all these out in full we get
minimize

$$5x + 2y$$

subject to

$$0 \leqslant x \leqslant 5,$$

$$0 \leqslant y \leqslant 5,$$

$$2x + y \geqslant 5,$$

$$3x + y \geqslant 6,$$

$$x + 2y \geqslant 4.$$

The construction of a mathematical model to fit a given practical situation is the most difficult and fascinating part of any branch of applied mathematics and the reader may feel well pleased if he has battled through with us so far even in this relatively simple example. We have, of course, been fitting mathematical models to practical situations throughout the book but, surprisingly enough, this is our most involved so far even though it is based on orthodox numbers. However, we would not expect industrial mathematics to be simple. There would be no point in using computers if it were.

Examples 7a

There are many examples for solution at the end of section 7.4 (p. 114). The reader would be well advised to take Nos. 9 and 11–15 and process them as far as we have reached in the text. Familiarity with the construction of these mathematical models will help considerably with the understanding of the next two sections.

7.2 A Little Graphical Work

The simplest way to deal with the maze of inequalities in the previous section is to plot them on a graph. Once this is done it is easy enough to see what is happening. Let us consider a sheet of graph paper with a pair of axes conveniently situated in the middle.

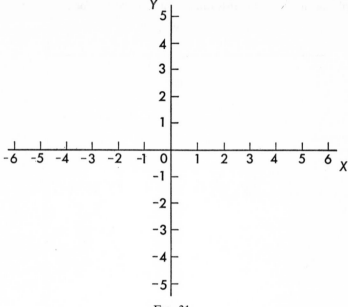

FIG. 31

Our first constraint is that $0 \leqslant x \leqslant 5$. This reduces our range of activity to the unshaded area below.

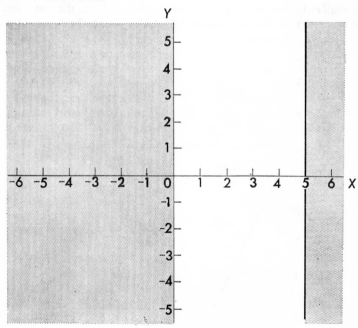

FIG. 32

Applying the second constraint $0 \leqslant y \leqslant 5$, we are further restricted to

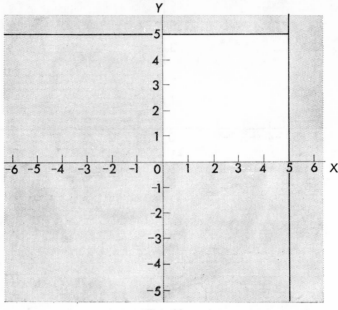

FIG. 33

We shall only draw the top right quadrant in future as the rest is irrelevant.
We now examine a more complex inequality such as $2x+y \geqslant 5$. If we draw
the line $2x+y = 5$ we get

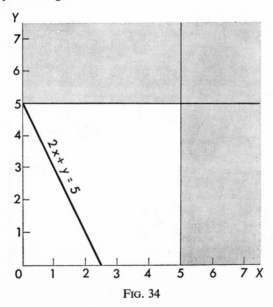

FIG. 34

The line divides the remaining area into two parts. Any point to the left of the line satisfies the inequality $2x+y < 5$ and is therefore out of our consideration. We are interested in the area on or to the right of the line where $2x+y \geqslant 5$. Repeating this argument with the remaining two inequalities, we finally get

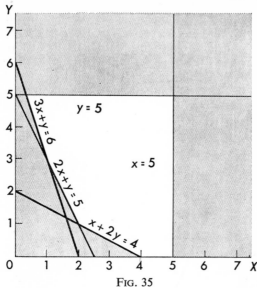

FIG. 35

where the only area of interest to us is that within the curiously shaped polygon bounded by the lines shown.

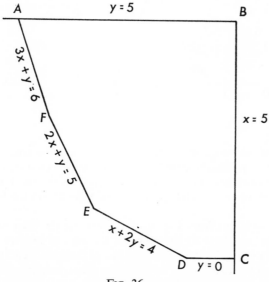

FIG. 36

Examples 7b

Find the areas of interest in Questions 1–5 of Examples 7c (p. 114).

7.3 The Solution

Let us now consider the minimizing of $5x+2y$. In other words, we want a solution to the equation $5x+2y = ?$ where the ? is as small as possible. For the want of a better idea let us make an effort to get $5x+2y$ on the graph somehow by trying $5x+2y = 20$ where 20 is a more or less random number. It is not altogether random as it gives us an easy line to plot which cuts the area of interest but is clear of most of the other complications.

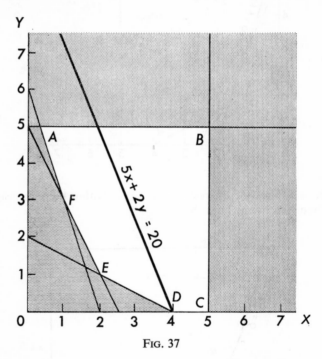

FIG. 37

We note at this stage that a line may either cut the area of interest, miss it altogether or just make contact. If it just makes contact it may either go through just one point of the area of interest as do the lines *PQ*, *RS* and *TU* in Fig. 38 or be parallel to one of the sides as are the lines *VW* or *XY* in Fig. 39.

It will be apparent from Fig. 40 that 20 is not the least value for $5x+2y$ since the line $5x+2y = 20$ has much of the area of interest to the left of it where $5x+2y < 20$. What we need is a line of the form $5x+2y = ?$ which just makes contact with the area of interest after the style of Figs. 38 or 39 and has the area of interest lying to the right of it. This means that we must draw lines

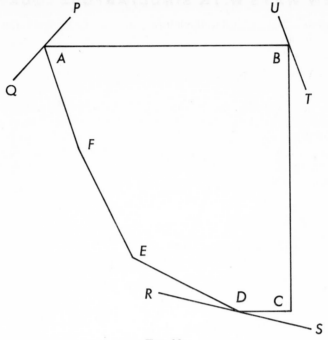

FIG. 38

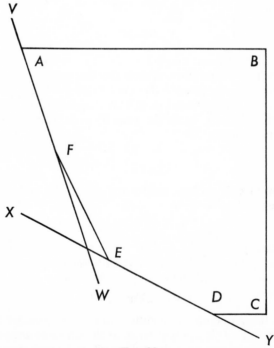

FIG. 39

parallel to $5x+2y = 20$ and to the left of it until we finally reach the position of PQ in Fig. 40.

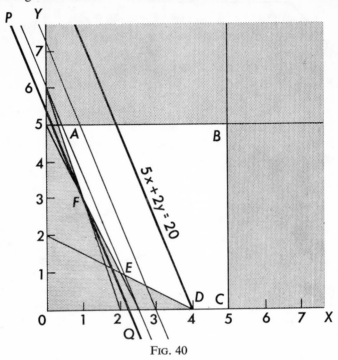

FIG. 40

The line PQ is the last one parallel to $5x+2y = 20$ (i.e. which has the form $5x+2y = ?$), which makes contact with the area of interest. We see from the diagram that it passes through the point F and that there are no points to the left of it within the unshaded area. This therefore is the line we require. Fortunately we can easily locate the point F as the intersection of the two lines whose equations are

$$3x+y = 6$$

and

$$2x+y = 5$$

from Fig. 36.

The solution of these is a simple matter and gives $x = 1$ and $y = 3$. Thus the line we are seeking has the form

$$5x+2y = 5 \times 1+2 \times 3 = 11$$

since it goes through the point F. Translating this back into practical terms we may remember that as far as costs are concerned we are working in units of £100. Thus the costs equation really has the form

$$500x+200y = 1100$$

and £1100 is the minimum expenditure which will produce the required number of tubes of toothpaste per week. If this confuses the reader let him remember that the important point on Fig. 40 is F where $x = 1$ and $y = 3$.

This means that the cheapest way to produce the toothpaste is to run Eastleigh for 1 day and Westleigh for 3 days. Eastleigh costs £500 a day to run and Westleigh £200. The total minimum cost is then

$$£(500 \times 1 + 200 \times 3)$$

which still comes out at £1100. If the reader is worried by the fact that the days each factory is required to work come out to a whole number, we can only leave him once again to reflect upon the lengths to which the author will go to avoid arithmetic.

7.4 A Little Revision

We have been battling with a long and complex problem. We will therefore revise the last part by examining the effects of two of the situations that the industrialist must be well prepared to face—automation and labour costs. It is estimated that proposed automation at Eastleigh will reduce the running costs by as much as £200 a day to a mere £300. On the other hand, vigorous action by the shop stewards at Westleigh may result in the payment of danger money to grade 1 operatives, because of the adverse effects of the products on their teeth. This would result in daily running costs being increased there to £300. How would this affect the running of the two factories?

The basic data concerning factory capacity and customers' requirements remain the same. Only the running costs are altered. Thus the basic graphical work may still be used but the costs matrix is now [3 3] instead of [5 2] and we are interested in the line $3x + 3y = ?$ instead of $5x + 2y = ?$ Choosing a convenient value to fit the line on the graph we try $3x + 3y = 18$ and get

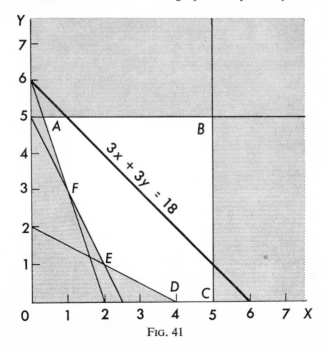

FIG. 41

This time, by drawing our parallels, we find that the costs line leaves the area of interest at the point E. E is the intersection of the two lines

$$2x+y= 5$$

$$x+2y= 4$$

which we solve to give $x = 2$ and $y = 1$. Thus the line representing minimum costs is

$$3x+3y= 3\times 2+3\times 1 = 9$$

which stands for a minimum cost of £900.

We must make it quite clear to the reader that as far as linear programming is concerned we have barely scratched the surface. Let us, for example, consider the effect of a take-over bid which results in the annexing of the Northleigh factory by the Eastleigh–Westleigh combine. Similar problems to the above will result in three unknowns x, y and z which we cannot handle on a two-dimensional graph. The reader may have a sudden urge to lapse into three dimensions and play with pieces of wire and plastic sheeting. We wish him well and merely go on to postulate the construction of a new, streamlined factory at Southleigh which will introduce yet another unknown and leave our reader floundering in the fourth dimension. Such antics obviously require more subtle techniques but the principles are much the same in however many dimensions we care to work. Sooner or later the mathematician is faced with a mass of simultaneous equations to solve and the remainder of this chapter shows various matrix methods which he and his computer may adopt to achieve their aim. These processes will be examined from the computer's point of view and we must remember that he is a simple soul, not too clever at spotting quick methods, but with infinite patience, incredible accuracy and a depressingly fast rate of working. We must therefore take these eccentricities into account when devising techniques for him to follow.

Examples 7c

(The problems need not necessarily give whole-number answers. Use your knowledge of the problem to decide the most suitable whole-number solution where necessary.)

1. Minimize $4x+3y$ subject to the constraints

$$x \geqslant 0, \qquad 4x+y \geqslant 4,$$

$$y \geqslant 0, \qquad x+y \geqslant 2,$$

$$2x+y \geqslant 25.$$

2. Maximize $4x+3y$ subject to the constraints

$$x \geqslant 0, \qquad 4x+y \leqslant 4,$$

$$y \geqslant 0, \qquad x+y \leqslant 2,$$

$$2x+y \leqslant 25.$$

3. Minimize $4x+3y$ subject to the constraints

$$x \geqslant 0, \qquad 4x+y \geqslant 4,$$
$$y \geqslant 0, \qquad x+y \geqslant 2,$$
$$2x+y \geqslant 25,$$
$$x+3y \geqslant 4,$$
$$x+5y \geqslant 6.$$

4. Maximize $4x+3y$ subject to the constraints

$$x \geqslant 0, \qquad 4x+y \leqslant 4,$$
$$y \geqslant 0, \qquad x+y \leqslant 2,$$
$$2x+y \leqslant 25,$$
$$x+3y \leqslant 4,$$
$$x+5y \leqslant 6.$$

5. Minimize $4x+3y$ subject to the constraints

$$x \geqslant 0, \qquad 4x+y \leqslant 4,$$
$$y \geqslant 0, \qquad x+3y \leqslant 4,$$
$$x+5y \leqslant 6.$$

6. In view of the labour troubles at Westleigh to what level must automation at Eastleigh reduce the daily running costs before it becomes economical to close the factory at Westleigh altogether?

7. It is thought that sales of the 'Mammoth' tubes may be increased to 6000 per week by changing the title to the 'Economy' size. What are the implications of this for the two factories at present running costs? Why does your answer seem peculiar and what is the explanation?

8. In order to automate the Eastleigh factory, production there must be reduced to 1000 tubes of each size per day. Running costs have correspondingly been reduced to £300 per day. How does this affect the situation?

9. A firm with factories at Northton and Southton finds that at Northton they can produce 3000 'Large' tubes of toothpaste per day, 5000 'Super' and 2000 'Mammoth'. Southton manages to produce 2000 'Large', 3000 'Super' and 4000 'Mammoth'. Northton costs £800 a day to run and Southton £500. Would they be able to supply the toothpaste ordered in the text more economically than their rivals? (Use the figures of section 7.1 for comparison.)

10. Repairs to machinery temporarily cut the production of 'Mammoth' tubes to 1000 at Southton without reducing running costs. How does this affect the answer to Question 9?

11. Bert and Harry are on holiday. Bert always has 2 eggs for breakfast, 3 rashers of bacon and 2 sausages. Harry always has 1 egg, 4 rashers of bacon and 2 sausages. They have a refrigerator, 30 eggs, 70 rashers of bacon and 50 sausages. They arrange things so as to produce the greatest number of satisfactory breakfasts. What is their solution?

12. Junior and his sister are responsible for washing up. Junior breaks a plate, 2 cups and a saucer at each go. His sister breaks 3 plates, a cup and 2 saucers. Mother has 11 plates and 12 cups and saucers. On this system what is the greatest number of washings up Mother's crockery can stand and how many goes will each child have?

13. Junior and his sister have to visit their three aunties. They do not like this because they are made to eat bread and butter. Junior is always made to eat 5 pieces and his sister 3. Junior likes Aunty Jean best but mother insists that for every visit he makes to her he must make one to each of his other aunties. Sister likes Aunty Joan best but mother says she must visit Aunty Jean just as often and Aunty Jane once for every twice she visits the others. Aunty Jane insists upon being visited at least 10 times during the holiday, Aunty Jean 20 times and Aunty Joan 15 times.

The children decide to minimize the total amount of bread and butter they must consume. What is their decision?

14. A damsel in distress bemoans her fate. 'On the fourth day of Christmas my true love sent to me: 4 calling birds, 3 French hens, 2 turtle doves and a partridge in a pear tree. His rival sent 2 calling birds, 1 French hen, 3 turtle doves and 2 partridges in pear trees. Assuming that I have accommodation for 20 calling birds, 15 French hens, 18 turtle doves and 12 partridges (with pear trees), what is the maximum number of days which must elapse before each of these two gentlemen must be discouraged?'

15. A large industrial combine has two training schools, A and B. At these schools the students are given a year's general training and then categorized according to suitability for office, sales, factory or miscellaneous. Owing to different training techniques, school A finds in general that $\frac{1}{4}$ of its students are suitable for office work, $\frac{1}{5}$ for sales, $\frac{1}{5}$ for factory and $\frac{7}{20}$ for miscellaneous. School B, on the other hand, finds $\frac{1}{5}$ of its pupils suitable for office work, $\frac{3}{10}$ for sales, $\frac{9}{20}$ for factory and $\frac{1}{20}$ for miscellaneous. It is estimated that the combine will need 200 office staff, 180 sales staff, 230 factory staff, and 150 miscellaneous staff. What is the minimum number of recruits that they should take on at each school to meet these requirements?

7.5 The Matrix Approach to Simultaneous Equations

Let us look closely at the pair of simultaneous equations

$$4x + 3y = 11 \qquad \text{(i)}$$

$$5x + 2y = 12 \qquad \text{(ii)}$$

The left-hand side is composed of the coefficients, which we may well write in the form $\begin{bmatrix} 4 & 3 \\ 5 & 2 \end{bmatrix}$, and the unknowns x and y. The unknowns could equally well be represented by p and q, θ and ϕ, or any other pair of symbols we may care to devise. In fact we could quite conveniently do away with them altogether and just represent the left-hand side by the matrix $\begin{bmatrix} 4 & 3 \\ 5 & 2 \end{bmatrix}$. As long as every-body adopted the same convention this could easily be read to mean 'Four times the first variable added to three times the second variable will give us the expression on the left-hand side of the first equation, whilst five times the first variable added to two times the second variable will give us the expression on the left-hand side of the second equation.' The reader need not worry. We are not going to do this. We merely wish to emphasize the importance of the coefficients in our equations, which serve to make them different from any other pair of equations, and minimize the importance of the unknowns which are but random symbols at this stage.

Matrices may be used more happily in this context. Let us take the matrix of coefficients $\begin{bmatrix} 4 & 3 \\ 5 & 2 \end{bmatrix}$ and multiply it on the right by the column matrix $\begin{bmatrix} x \\ y \end{bmatrix}$.

This gives

$$\begin{bmatrix} 4 & 3 \\ 5 & 2 \end{bmatrix} \begin{bmatrix} x \\ y \end{bmatrix} \quad \text{or} \quad \begin{bmatrix} 4x+3y \\ 5x+2y \end{bmatrix}$$

which is the left-hand side of our pair of simultaneous equations wrapped up in a matrix parcel. If we similarly 'matricize' the right-hand side we get

$$\begin{bmatrix} 4x+3y \\ 5x+2y \end{bmatrix} = \begin{bmatrix} 11 \\ 12 \end{bmatrix}.$$

We may say that the two matrices can only be equal if their separate components are equal. Therefore

$$4x+3y = 11$$

and

$$5x+2y = 12$$

Thus the original pair of equations may be legitimately replaced by the matrix equation

$$\begin{bmatrix} 4 & 3 \\ 5 & 2 \end{bmatrix} \begin{bmatrix} x \\ y \end{bmatrix} = \begin{bmatrix} 11 \\ 12 \end{bmatrix}.$$

We may solve an equation such as

$$3x = 6$$

by multiplying both sides by the multiplicative inverse of 3 which is $\frac{1}{3}$.

Thus

$$\frac{1}{3} \times 3x = \frac{1}{3} \times 6$$

or

$$x = 2.$$

Similarly we may solve our matrix equation by multiplying both sides by the inverse of the coefficients matrix $\begin{bmatrix} 4 & 3 \\ 5 & 2 \end{bmatrix}$.

This turns out to be

$$\begin{bmatrix} -\dfrac{2}{7} & \dfrac{3}{7} \\[2mm] \dfrac{5}{7} & -\dfrac{4}{7} \end{bmatrix}$$

(see page 100).

The multiplication gives

$$\begin{bmatrix} -\dfrac{2}{7} & \dfrac{3}{7} \\[2mm] \dfrac{5}{7} & -\dfrac{4}{7} \end{bmatrix} \left\{ \begin{bmatrix} 4 & 3 \\ 5 & 2 \end{bmatrix} \begin{bmatrix} x \\ y \end{bmatrix} \right\} = \begin{bmatrix} -\dfrac{2}{7} & \dfrac{3}{7} \\[2mm] \dfrac{5}{7} & -\dfrac{4}{7} \end{bmatrix} \begin{bmatrix} 11 \\ 12 \end{bmatrix}$$

Although we have only proved the Associative Law for 2×2 matrices, it is in fact true for all finite multipliable matrices so that

$$\left(\begin{bmatrix} -\dfrac{2}{7} & \dfrac{3}{7} \\[2mm] \dfrac{5}{7} & -\dfrac{4}{7} \end{bmatrix} \begin{bmatrix} 4 & 3 \\ 5 & 2 \end{bmatrix} \right) \begin{bmatrix} x \\ y \end{bmatrix} = \begin{bmatrix} -\dfrac{2}{7} & \dfrac{3}{7} \\[2mm] \dfrac{5}{7} & -\dfrac{4}{7} \end{bmatrix} \begin{bmatrix} 11 \\ 12 \end{bmatrix}$$

Our faith in our own ability tells us that the expression inside the curly brackets reduces to $\begin{bmatrix} 1 & 0 \\ 0 & 1 \end{bmatrix}$ so that

$$\begin{bmatrix} 1 & 0 \\ 0 & 1 \end{bmatrix} \begin{bmatrix} x \\ y \end{bmatrix} = \begin{bmatrix} -\dfrac{2}{7} & \dfrac{3}{7} \\[2mm] \dfrac{5}{7} & -\dfrac{4}{7} \end{bmatrix} \begin{bmatrix} 11 \\ 12 \end{bmatrix}$$

$\begin{bmatrix} 1 & 0 \\ 0 & 1 \end{bmatrix}$ behaves as an identity matrix for other matrices it can multiply as well as for the 2×2's on which we have tested it. In any case the reader may easily verify that the left-hand side reduces to just $\begin{bmatrix} x \\ y \end{bmatrix}$. Working out the right-hand side we get, finally,

$$\begin{bmatrix} x \\ y \end{bmatrix} = \begin{bmatrix} 2 \\ 1 \end{bmatrix}$$

In other words, $x = 2$ and $y = 1$ as before. The reader may criticize the method because of its length and complexity but without the explanation it is virtually as quick as the orthodox route. To make our point we give another example without explanation.

Worked example

$$\begin{cases} 3x+y = 4 \\ x-2y = -1 \end{cases}$$

⇓

$$\begin{bmatrix} 3 & 1 \\ 1 & -2 \end{bmatrix} \begin{bmatrix} x \\ y \end{bmatrix} = \begin{bmatrix} 4 \\ -1 \end{bmatrix},$$

⇓

$$\begin{bmatrix} x \\ y \end{bmatrix} = \begin{bmatrix} \dfrac{2}{7} & \dfrac{1}{7} \\ \dfrac{1}{7} & -\dfrac{3}{7} \end{bmatrix} \begin{bmatrix} 4 \\ -1 \end{bmatrix},$$

⇓

$$\begin{bmatrix} x \\ y \end{bmatrix} = \begin{bmatrix} 1 \\ 1 \end{bmatrix},$$

⇓

$$x = 1 \quad \text{and} \quad y = 1.$$

The computer finds this process more satisfactory than the orthodox one. It is purely automatic so that there need be no thought as to which variable we are trying to eliminate. This is a minor problem with two equations and two unknowns but the reader may care to try his skill at a dozen or so of each and see how much native wit is necessary to see him through. If we increase the number of equations and unknowns to several hundreds we then get some idea of the type of problem that the computer is prepared to tackle. The method we have adopted extends quite happily to three or more unknowns.

$$x+2y-z = -2 \tag{i}$$

$$3x+y-2z = -5 \tag{ii}$$

$$2x+2y+3z = 1 \tag{iii}$$

may well be written in the form

$$\begin{bmatrix} 1 & 2 & -1 \\ 3 & 1 & -2 \\ 2 & 2 & 3 \end{bmatrix} \begin{bmatrix} x \\ y \\ z \end{bmatrix} = \begin{bmatrix} -2 \\ -5 \\ 1 \end{bmatrix}$$

and a calculation of the inverse of

$$\begin{bmatrix} 1 & 2 & -1 \\ 3 & 1 & -2 \\ 2 & 2 & 3 \end{bmatrix}$$

would enable us to solve the equations in exactly the same way. We shall not do this as the arithmetic is rather a bore. The reader will find an alternative and more convenient method in the next section.

Another property of the matrix method is that it is extremely efficient in handling series of simultaneous equations where the expressions on the left-hand side remain the same. This may seem a dubious advantage but consider, for example, the toothpaste problem of sections 1–3 of this chapter. Suppose that a projected sales campaign can alter the requirements matrix in various ways. This would alter the shape of the graph considerably but would still require us to solve pairs of simultaneous equations to find important points. If all other factors remained unchanged, the left-hand side of the equations would remain unchanged also but the right-hand side would vary with the requirements. Let us suppose that the running costs of each factory are £300 per day as in section 7.4. Let us also suppose for the sake of simplicity that the management are interested in knowing what would happen if the sale of 'Mammoth' tubes were varied. This would leave Fig. 41 (p. 113) unaltered except for the line ED which would have the same slope but would rise or fall according to circumstances. Thus we may have to consider the situation where the weekly requirement is, say, 3000, 5000, 6000, or 7000 as well as the initial 4000. Even without varying the requirements for the other tubes our task is becoming quite onerous and necessitates the solution of

(i) $2x+y = 5,$ (ii) $2x+y = 5,$ (iii) $2x+y = 5,$

     $x+2y = 3;$ $x+2y = 4;$ $x+2y = 5;$

(iv) $2x+y = 5,$ (v) $2x+y = 5,$

     $x+2y = 6;$ $x+2y = 7.$

Fortunately we easily calculate the inverse of the matrix of coefficients to be

$$\begin{bmatrix} \dfrac{2}{3} & -\dfrac{1}{3} \\[2mm] -\dfrac{1}{3} & \dfrac{2}{3} \end{bmatrix}$$

and write down the solutions as

(i) $\begin{bmatrix} \dfrac{2}{3} & -\dfrac{1}{3} \\[2mm] -\dfrac{1}{3} & \dfrac{2}{3} \end{bmatrix} \begin{bmatrix} 5 \\ 3 \end{bmatrix},$ (ii) $\begin{bmatrix} \dfrac{2}{3} & -\dfrac{1}{3} \\[2mm] -\dfrac{1}{3} & \dfrac{2}{3} \end{bmatrix} \begin{bmatrix} 5 \\ 4 \end{bmatrix},$

(iii) $\begin{bmatrix} \dfrac{2}{3} & -\dfrac{1}{3} \\[2mm] -\dfrac{1}{3} & \dfrac{2}{3} \end{bmatrix} \begin{bmatrix} 5 \\ 5 \end{bmatrix},$ (iv) $\begin{bmatrix} \dfrac{2}{3} & -\dfrac{1}{3} \\[2mm] -\dfrac{1}{3} & \dfrac{2}{3} \end{bmatrix} \begin{bmatrix} 5 \\ 6 \end{bmatrix},$

(v) $\begin{bmatrix} \dfrac{2}{3} & -\dfrac{1}{3} \\[2mm] -\dfrac{1}{3} & \dfrac{2}{3} \end{bmatrix} \begin{bmatrix} 5 \\ 7 \end{bmatrix}.$

A little matrix multiplication soon simplifies these to

$$(\text{i}) \begin{bmatrix} \dfrac{7}{3} \\[2mm] \dfrac{1}{3} \end{bmatrix}, \quad (\text{ii}) \begin{bmatrix} 2 \\ 1 \end{bmatrix}, \quad (\text{iii}) \begin{bmatrix} \dfrac{5}{3} \\[2mm] \dfrac{5}{5} \end{bmatrix}, \quad (\text{iv}) \begin{bmatrix} \dfrac{4}{3} \\[2mm] \dfrac{7}{3} \end{bmatrix}, \quad (\text{v}) \begin{bmatrix} 1 \\ 3 \end{bmatrix}$$

which gives us the number of days that each factory should work in each case. (As before we are assuming that it is economical to work a factory for a third of a day. This may not be true but we cannot have everything in a simplified example.)

Another advantage of this method from the computer point of view is that it is easily checked. The difficult part in more complex cases is the computation of the inverse but, once this is done, it may soon be proved correct by multiplying it with the original matrix and getting the unit matrix of the required size as the result.

The reader may well wonder what happens when the matrix of coefficients has no inverse because the associated determinant is 0. The answer is that we cannot solve the equations. The real reason for this is best shown in an example. Consider

$$x+2y = 3 \tag{i}$$

$$2x+4y = 6 \tag{ii}$$

Here we have only one legitimate equation since the second is twice the first and suspicions are immediately aroused by an examination of the associated determinant which is $\begin{vmatrix} 1 & 2 \\ 2 & 4 \end{vmatrix}$ or 0. Eccentricities of this nature are always shown by the associated determinant and, although it is apparent from the start in this case that all is not well, the situation is not always so straightforward when we have more variables. If we examine the equations

$$x+2y+z = 3 \tag{i}$$

$$4x+3y-2z = 0 \tag{ii}$$

$$x-3y-5z = -9 \tag{iii}$$

we may think that they are a perfectly respectable threesome but unfortunately equation (iii) is merely three times equation (i) subtracted from equation (ii). A difficult thing to spot otherwise but the calculation of the determinant of the coefficients† would give us zero and the secret would be revealed. This technique is of great value when masses of equations are involved and may even be extended to test whether series of equations contradict each other or not. The result is an elegant way of checking the accuracy of a piece of work which produces a large number of simultaneous equations.

† See Bibliography for a source of the relevant techniques.

Examples 7d

Solve by matrix methods the following pairs of equations.

1. $3x+4y = 11,$

 $2x+3y = 8.$

2. $5x+2y = 14,$

 $x+y = 4.$

3. $3x+8y = 30,$

 $x+2y = 8.$

4. $5x-2y = 3,$

 $2x+4y = 6.$

5. $7x-8y = -13,$

 $x-y = -1.$

6. Solve with the minimum effort

 (a) $3x+5y = 8,$ (b) $3x+5y = 13,$ (c) $3x+5y = 11,$ (d) $3x+5y = 16,$

     $x+2y = 3.$ $x+2y = 5.$ $x+2y = 4.$ $x+2y = 6.$

7. Solve with the minimum effort

 (a) $2x+5y = 11,$ (b) $2x+5y = 17,$ (c) $2x+5y = 24,$ (d) $2x+5y = 18,$

     $3x-y = 8.$ $3x-y = 0.$ $3x-y = 2.$ $3x-y = 10.$

7.6 The Gauss–Doolittle or Choleski Method

This is a matrix method of solving simultaneous equations without the inconvenience of calculating the inverse of the matrix of coefficients. The arithmetic still leaves much to be desired but the method does work and it must be remembered that it is again directed towards computers, who are so much better at arithmetic than we are. The whole process rests upon the factorization of the matrix of coefficients which is an idea which we have not considered before.

The principle is simple enough. Suppose that we were lucky enough to have a matrix of coefficients liberally and scientifically bespattered with 0's so that it looked like

$$\begin{bmatrix} 3 & 2 & 1 \\ 0 & 1 & 4 \\ 0 & 0 & 2 \end{bmatrix}$$

The resulting equations would be

$$\begin{bmatrix} 3 & 2 & 1 \\ 0 & 1 & 4 \\ 0 & 0 & 2 \end{bmatrix} \begin{bmatrix} x \\ y \\ z \end{bmatrix} = \begin{bmatrix} 8 \\ 1 \\ 0 \end{bmatrix}, \quad \text{say.}$$

This multiplies out to

$$\begin{bmatrix} 3x+2y+z \\ y+4z \\ 2z \end{bmatrix} = \begin{bmatrix} 8 \\ 1 \\ 0 \end{bmatrix}$$

or

$$3x+2y+z = 8 \qquad \text{(i)}$$

$$y+4z = 1 \qquad \text{(ii)}$$

$$2z = 0 \qquad \text{(iii)}$$

We would not bother to use matrices at all here. Equation (iii) means that $z = 0$ so that equation (ii) gives us $y = 1$. Equation (i) then reduces easily to $x = 2$ and the job is done. A matrix of this fortuitous shape is called an upper triangular matrix since all the numbers below the leading diagonal (N.W.–S.E.) are zeros. We need not be too fussy here. A lower triangular matrix such as

$$\begin{bmatrix} 1 & 0 & 0 \\ 2 & 1 & 0 \\ 3 & 4 & 2 \end{bmatrix}$$

is equally beneficial.

Try

$$\begin{bmatrix} 1 & 0 & 0 \\ 2 & 1 & 0 \\ 3 & 4 & 2 \end{bmatrix} \begin{bmatrix} x \\ y \\ z \end{bmatrix} = \begin{bmatrix} 1 \\ 3 \\ 11 \end{bmatrix},$$

i.e.

$$\begin{bmatrix} x \\ 2x+y \\ 3x+4y+2z \end{bmatrix} = \begin{bmatrix} 1 \\ 3 \\ 11 \end{bmatrix}$$

or

$$x = 1, \qquad \text{(i)}$$

$$2x+y = 3, \qquad \text{(ii)}$$

$$3x+4y+2z = 11. \qquad \text{(iii)}$$

Again old-fashioned algebra is the tool to use. $x = 1$ from equation (i) and therefore $y = 1$ from equation (ii). Substituting in equation (iii) we get $z = 2$.

Thus triangular matrices of either type are very desirable in solving simultaneous equations.

Our next task is therefore to factorize a well-behaved matrix of coefficients into a pair of triangular matrices and do the processes we have just done. An example will make this clearer. The matrix

$$\begin{bmatrix} 1 & 2 & -1 \\ -3 & -4 & 5 \\ 3 & 8 & -2 \end{bmatrix} \text{ factorizes into } \begin{bmatrix} 1 & 0 & 0 \\ -3 & 2 & 0 \\ 3 & 2 & -1 \end{bmatrix} \begin{bmatrix} 1 & 2 & -1 \\ 0 & 1 & 1 \\ 0 & 0 & 1 \end{bmatrix}.$$

(We shall show you how we did this later but you can check now that they multiply correctly.) This means that if we express the equations

$$x+2y-z = 3 \tag{i}$$

$$-3x-4y+5z = -9 \tag{ii}$$

$$3x+8y-2z = 10 \tag{iii}$$

in the form

$$\begin{bmatrix} 1 & 2 & -1 \\ -3 & -4 & 5 \\ 3 & 8 & -2 \end{bmatrix} \begin{bmatrix} x \\ y \\ z \end{bmatrix} = \begin{bmatrix} 3 \\ -9 \\ 10 \end{bmatrix}$$

we may replace the coefficients matrix by the pair of triangular matrices and get

$$\begin{bmatrix} 1 & 0 & 0 \\ -3 & 2 & 0 \\ 3 & 2 & -1 \end{bmatrix} \begin{bmatrix} 1 & 2 & -1 \\ 0 & 1 & 1 \\ 0 & 0 & 1 \end{bmatrix} \begin{bmatrix} x \\ y \\ z \end{bmatrix} = \begin{bmatrix} 3 \\ -9 \\ 10 \end{bmatrix}.$$

This may not look very helpful but we are well on the road to success. Let us name our various matrices so that we may see more easily where we are going. The original equations reduce to

$$AX = C$$

where A is the coefficients matrix, X is the unknowns matrix and C the constants matrix. We have now factorized the coefficients matrix A into a lower triangular matrix which we shall call L and an upper triangular matrix which we shall call U. The equations now read

$$LUX = C.$$

U is a 3×3 matrix and X is a 3×1 matrix. The resulting product is a 3×1 matrix which we shall write as P or $\begin{bmatrix} p \\ q \\ r \end{bmatrix}$ for the moment. The equations now reduce to

$$LP = C$$

or

$$\begin{bmatrix} 1 & 0 & 0 \\ -3 & 2 & 0 \\ 3 & 2 & -1 \end{bmatrix} \begin{bmatrix} p \\ q \\ r \end{bmatrix} = \begin{bmatrix} 3 \\ -9 \\ 10 \end{bmatrix}$$

Writing this in non-matrix form we get

$$p = 3$$

$$-3p+2q = -9$$

$$3p+2q-r = 10$$

which gives $p = 3$, $q = 0$, $r = -1$.

But $\begin{bmatrix} p \\ q \\ r \end{bmatrix}$ is really UX.

$$UX = \begin{bmatrix} 1 & 2 & -1 \\ 0 & 1 & 1 \\ 0 & 0 & 1 \end{bmatrix} \begin{bmatrix} x \\ y \\ z \end{bmatrix} = \begin{bmatrix} x+2y-z \\ y+z \\ z \end{bmatrix}.$$

Therefore

$$\begin{bmatrix} p \\ q \\ r \end{bmatrix} = \begin{bmatrix} x+2y-z \\ y+z \\ z \end{bmatrix}.$$

We have already calculated p, q and r. Therefore the three original equations have reduced to

$$\begin{bmatrix} x+2y-z \\ y+z \\ z \end{bmatrix} = \begin{bmatrix} 3 \\ 0 \\ -1 \end{bmatrix}$$

which means that $z = -1$, $y = 1$ and $x = 0$ and these duly check in the original equations.

We now have to let the reader into the secret of how we factorized the coefficients matrix. We did not. We carefully chose two tidy triangular matrices and multiplied them together to give the original equations so as to make for ease of working. However, we can do it without cheating as we will now demonstrate. We merely write down the result we require and use symbols for numbers we do not know. Thus let

$$\begin{bmatrix} 1 & 2 & -1 \\ -3 & -4 & 5 \\ 3 & 8 & -2 \end{bmatrix} = \begin{bmatrix} a & 0 & 0 \\ b & c & 0 \\ d & e & f \end{bmatrix} \begin{bmatrix} 1 & g & h \\ 0 & 1 & i \\ 0 & 0 & 1 \end{bmatrix}$$

We are lucky in that we can get away with ones along the leading (N.W.–S.E.) diagonal of the second matrix. All that we have to do now is to multiply out the two factors and choose numerical values for a, b, c, d, e, f, g, h and i so as to give the right result. Thus:

$$\begin{bmatrix} 1 & 2 & -1 \\ -3 & -4 & 5 \\ 3 & 8 & -2 \end{bmatrix} = \begin{bmatrix} a & ag & ah \\ b & bg+c & bh+ci \\ d & dg+e & dh+ei+f \end{bmatrix}$$

Comparing numbers this means that $a = 1$; $b = -3$; $d = 3$; $ag = 2$ therefore $g = 2$; $ah = -1$ therefore $h = -1$; $bg+c = -4$ therefore $c = 2$; $bh+ci = 5$ therefore $i = 1$; $dg+e = 8$ therefore $e = 2$; $dh+ei+f = -2$ therefore $f = -1$. Thus the resulting factors are

$$\begin{bmatrix} 1 & 0 & 0 \\ -3 & 2 & 0 \\ 3 & 2 & -1 \end{bmatrix} \begin{bmatrix} 1 & 2 & -1 \\ 0 & 1 & 1 \\ 0 & 0 & 1 \end{bmatrix}$$

as before.

Before we proceed further we will again make the point that this type of process is far easier to do than to explain and we will give as before a worked example with the minimum of explanation.

Worked Example

$$x+2y-z=-2$$
$$3x+y-2z=-5$$
$$2x+2y+3z=1$$

Written in matrix form:

$$\begin{bmatrix} 1 & 2 & -1 \\ 3 & 1 & -2 \\ 2 & 2 & 3 \end{bmatrix} \begin{bmatrix} x \\ y \\ z \end{bmatrix} = \begin{bmatrix} -2 \\ -5 \\ 1 \end{bmatrix}$$

Let

$$\begin{bmatrix} 1 & 2 & -1 \\ 3 & 1 & -2 \\ 2 & 2 & 3 \end{bmatrix} = \begin{bmatrix} a & 0 & 0 \\ b & c & 0 \\ d & e & f \end{bmatrix} \begin{bmatrix} 1 & g & h \\ 0 & 1 & i \\ 0 & 0 & 1 \end{bmatrix} = \begin{bmatrix} a & ag & ah \\ b & bg+c & bh+ci \\ d & dg+e & dh+ei+f \end{bmatrix}$$

Then $a=1$; $b=3$; $d=2$; $ag=2$ therefore $g=2$; $ah=-1$ therefore $h=-1$; $bg+c=1$ therefore $c=-5$; $bh+ci=-2$ therefore $i=-\frac{1}{5}$; $dg+e=2$ therefore $e=-2$; $dh+ei+f=3$ therefore $f=\frac{23}{5}$.

Thus the factors are

$$\begin{bmatrix} 1 & 0 & 0 \\ 3 & -5 & 0 \\ 2 & -2 & \frac{23}{5} \end{bmatrix} \begin{bmatrix} 1 & 2 & -1 \\ 0 & 1 & -\frac{1}{5} \\ 0 & 0 & 1 \end{bmatrix}$$

which we check by multiplying out to

$$\begin{bmatrix} 1 & 2 & -1 \\ 3 & 1 & -2 \\ 2 & 2 & 3 \end{bmatrix}$$

Thus

$$\begin{bmatrix} 1 & 0 & 0 \\ 3 & -5 & 0 \\ 2 & -2 & \frac{23}{5} \end{bmatrix} \begin{bmatrix} 1 & 2 & -1 \\ 0 & 1 & -\frac{1}{5} \\ 0 & 0 & 1 \end{bmatrix} \begin{bmatrix} x \\ y \\ z \end{bmatrix} = \begin{bmatrix} -2 \\ -5 \\ 1 \end{bmatrix}$$

Now

$$\begin{bmatrix} 1 & 0 & 0 \\ 3 & -5 & 0 \\ 2 & -2 & \frac{23}{5} \end{bmatrix} \begin{bmatrix} p \\ q \\ r \end{bmatrix} = \begin{bmatrix} -2 \\ -5 \\ 1 \end{bmatrix}$$

gives

$$p \qquad\qquad = -2$$
$$3p-5q \qquad = -5$$
$$2p-2q+\tfrac{23}{5}r = \ \ 1$$

or

$$p=-2, \qquad q=-\tfrac{1}{5}, \qquad r=1.$$

Thus

$$\begin{bmatrix} 1 & 2 & -1 \\ 0 & 1 & -\frac{1}{5} \\ 0 & 0 & 1 \end{bmatrix} \begin{bmatrix} x \\ y \\ z \end{bmatrix} = \begin{bmatrix} p \\ q \\ r \end{bmatrix} = \begin{bmatrix} -2 \\ -\frac{1}{5} \\ 1 \end{bmatrix}$$

or

$$x + 2y - z = -2,$$

$$y - \tfrac{1}{5}z = -\tfrac{1}{5},$$

$$z = 1,$$

or

$$z = 1, \qquad y = 0, \qquad x = -1.$$

The reader may care to pause and collect his wits before turning his mind to what happens in this process if the three equations have a zero determinant of coefficients and are therefore in fact at the most two genuine equations. We already have an example from section 7.5:

$$x + 2y + z = 3$$

$$4x + 3y - 2z = 0$$

$$x - 3y - 5z = -9$$

In matrix form

$$\begin{bmatrix} 1 & 2 & 1 \\ 4 & 3 & -2 \\ 1 & -3 & -5 \end{bmatrix} \begin{bmatrix} x \\ y \\ z \end{bmatrix} = \begin{bmatrix} 3 \\ 0 \\ -9 \end{bmatrix}.$$

Factorize

$$\begin{bmatrix} 1 & 2 & 1 \\ 4 & 3 & -2 \\ 1 & -3 & -5 \end{bmatrix} = \begin{bmatrix} a & 0 & 0 \\ b & c & 0 \\ d & e & f \end{bmatrix} \begin{bmatrix} 1 & g & h \\ 0 & 1 & i \\ 0 & 0 & 1 \end{bmatrix} = \begin{bmatrix} a & ag & ah \\ b & bg+c & bh+ci \\ d & dg+e & dh+ci+f \end{bmatrix}.$$

$a = 1$; $b = 4$; $d = 1$; $ag = 2$ therefore $g = 2$; $ah = 1$ therefore $h = 1$; $bg+c = 3$ therefore $c = -5$; $bh+ci = -2$ therefore $i = \frac{6}{5}$; $dg+e = -3$ therefore $e = -5$; $dh+ei+f = -5$ therefore $f = 0$.

Thus the factors are

$$\begin{bmatrix} 1 & 0 & 0 \\ 4 & -5 & 0 \\ 1 & -5 & 0 \end{bmatrix} \begin{bmatrix} 1 & 2 & 1 \\ 0 & 1 & \frac{6}{5} \\ 0 & 0 & 1 \end{bmatrix}$$

which multiply correctly to the original.

Therefore

$$\begin{bmatrix} 1 & 0 & 0 \\ 4 & -5 & 0 \\ 1 & -5 & 0 \end{bmatrix} \begin{bmatrix} 1 & 2 & 1 \\ 0 & 1 & \frac{6}{5} \\ 0 & 0 & 1 \end{bmatrix} \begin{bmatrix} x \\ y \\ z \end{bmatrix} = \begin{bmatrix} 3 \\ 0 \\ -9 \end{bmatrix}.$$

As usual

$$\begin{bmatrix} 1 & 0 & 0 \\ 4 & -5 & 0 \\ 1 & -5 & 0 \end{bmatrix} \begin{bmatrix} p \\ q \\ r \end{bmatrix} = \begin{bmatrix} 3 \\ 0 \\ -9 \end{bmatrix}$$

or

$$\begin{bmatrix} p \\ 4p-5q \\ p-5q \end{bmatrix} = \begin{bmatrix} 3 \\ 0 \\ -9 \end{bmatrix}$$

In other words

$$p = 3$$

$$4p - 5q = 0$$

$$p - 5q = -9$$

which gives us that $p = 3$ and $q = \frac{12}{5}$ but is singularly unhelpful as regards r and we are unable to proceed. It is interesting that the factors show us that we only have two genuine equations by merely failing to produce any sign of a third!

Examples 7c

Solve where possible the following equations.

1. $3x + 2y - z = 4,$

 $x + 4y - z = 6,$

 $2x - y - 2z = -1.$

2. $4x - 3y - 2z = -8,$

 $x - 2y + z = 0,$

 $3x + 2y + 4z = 19.$

3. $5x - 7y + z = 1,$

 $x - y + z = 1,$

 $3x - 5y - z = -1.$

4. $4x + y + z = 9,$

 $x + 2y + 2z = 11,$

 $3x - y - z = -2.$

5. $x + 3y - z = -1,$

 $4x + 2y + z = 11,$

 $x - y + 4z = 14.$

7.7 Summary

In this chapter we have expanded our knowledge of the use of matrices. We have dealt in a baby way with some of the problems of industry and examined more sophisticated methods of solving simultaneous equations. The Gauss–Doolittle method in particular may seem clumsy to the reader but it must be remembered that these methods are computer-biased and therefore aim for an automatic line of attack rather than the avoidance of hard labour and a slick technique. Also these methods work just as efficiently for larger numbers of unknowns whereas the more intuitive methods may well get lost. An expert on a hand calculating machine can use a method such as the Gauss-Doolittle to very great effect.

8. PERMUTATIONS

8.1 The General Idea

If three boys, Alan, Brian and Claud, run a race, the result (neglecting ties) must be one of the following.

1st	Alan	Alan	Brian	Brian	Claud	Claud
2nd	Brian	Claud	Alan	Claud	Alan	Brian
3rd	Claud	Brian	Claud	Alan	Brian	Alan

TABLE 32

To be more mathematical we dispense with names and use first letters giving

A	A	B	B	C	C
B	C	A	C	A	B
C	B	C	A	B	A

TABLE 33

which we may describe as the six possible permutations or orders of the three letters (boys) A, B and C.

It is easy to see here that we have listed all possible versions but this is not the case when larger numbers are involved. The reader may care to try five or six boys. We can however calculate in advance the number of different orders we should expect and then we merely look for them systematically.

In the example with the three boys we agree that either Alan, Brian or Claud must come first. Once first place has been filled, either of the other two boys may finish second and the remaining boy must be third. Thus there are three ways of filling the first place, and, once that has been filled, two ways of filling the second. Once first and second place have both been filled, there is only one way of filling the third. In other words, for each of the three ways of filling the first place there are two ways of filling the second, making six ways in all of filling the first two places. Once the first two places are filled, the third is filled in the one possible way. This is expressed more neatly by saying that the three boys could finish in $3 \times 2 \times 1$ different orders.

The idea works equally well with other numbers. Four boys in a race can finish in $4 \times 3 \times 2 \times 1 = 24$ different ways, five boys in $5 \times 4 \times 3 \times 2 \times 1 = 120$ different ways and so on.

Numbers such as $3 \times 2 \times 1$ and $4 \times 3 \times 2 \times 1$ occur frequently in mathematics and are usually abbreviated to 3! or 4! (3 or 4 factorial). Thus six boys could finish in $6! = 6 \times 5 \times 4 \times 3 \times 2 \times 1 = 720$ different ways.

Consider the type of competition which frequently appears in newspapers and magazines where the object is to put, say, twelve fashionable hats or selling points for cars or any other suitable gimmicks in order of merit. The number of possible versions is

$$12! = 12 \times 11 \times 10 \times 9 \times 8 \times 7 \times 6 \times 5 \times 4 \times 3 \times 2 \times 1 = 479{,}001{,}600,$$

so that with one entry your chance of a perfectly correct solution is 1 in 479,001,600 which means that you have probably wasted your *6d*. Even so somebody has to win and we must always allow for our own individual powers of selection!

Perhaps crossword puzzles are more respectable. Faced with an irritating clue such as 'She lamb (anag.) to the singular slaughter' you may have precisely zero idea of what the correct solution should be. Assuming both stupidity and ill luck you may have to try as many as

$$7! = 7 \times 6 \times 5 \times 4 \times 3 \times 2 \times 1 = 5040$$

different versions before spotting it. We deliberately and with great malice fail to give it.

We shall not follow this path further. The surface is too rough and many good men have stubbed their toes badly. Consider, for example, the number of different 'words' which may be constructed from the letters of the word 'cuckoo'. According to the above rule there should be

$$6! = 6 \times 5 \times 4 \times 3 \times 2 \times 1 = 720$$

of them. In fact the number is much reduced because of the repetition of the letters 'c' and 'o'. The references will advise further those readers who like this sort of thing or they may discover the techniques for themselves from the examples.

Examples 8a

1. Write down all possible orders of the letters of the words

(a) he,   (b) she,   (c) they

and make sure that you have the right number.

2. Write down all possible orders of the letters of the words

(a) see,   (b) thee,   (c) teee,   (d) hehe.

3. From your answers to Questions 1 and 2 deduce a rule for finding the number of different orders in which the letters of words may be put when some of the letters are repeated. Test your result on the following words.

(a) scrap,   (b) apple,   (c) poppy,

(d) popop,   (e) ppopp,   (f) popoi.

4. Alan, Brian, Claud and David run a race.
   (a) In how many different orders can they finish?
   (b) How many different possibilities are there for the first three?

5. How are the results of Question 4 affected if Edwin joins in the race? Generalize your results to any number of runners.

6. Many car registration numbers depend on the different number of ways of choosing three letters and three numbers and arranging them in the form 'ABC 123'. In how many different ways may this be done allowing the customary 26 different letters and 10 different numbers, and using each letter or number not more than once. What difference does it make if each symbol may be used more than once? (In practice three-letter words which are liable to cause offence are omitted.)

8.2 Groups Again

We may well use the contents of section 8.1 to tackle more purposefully the simple examples of groups that we met in Chapters 1 and 2. Consider, for example, the rotations of the equilateral triangle (Question 1, Examples 2g,

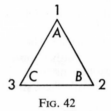

FIG. 42

p. 27). We may give instructions as to which rotation to make, either by referring to the corners of the triangle themselves or to the positions occupied by the corners. Thus 'move 1 place clockwise' is more specifically defined as 'replace corner A by corner C, corner B by corner A and corner C by corner B'. This may be abbreviated to $\begin{pmatrix} ABC \\ CAB \end{pmatrix}$ where the corners in the top row are replaced by those in the bottom row. There is no need for the top row to be kept as ABC. Any other order would do as long as the bottom row is similarly amended. Thus $\begin{pmatrix} CBA \\ BAC \end{pmatrix}$ when written out in full has just the same meaning as $\begin{pmatrix} ABC \\ CAB \end{pmatrix}$ since A is still replaced by C, B by A, and C by B.

On the other hand, we may prefer to convey information by referring to the positions occupied by the corners rather than the corners themselves. In this case 'move one place clockwise' would become 'replace the corner in position 1 by the corner in position 3, replace the corner in position 2 by the corner in position 1 and replace the corner in position 3 by the corner in position 2'. There is no mathematical reason why we cannot abbreviate this similarly to $\begin{pmatrix} 1 & 2 & 3 \\ 3 & 1 & 2 \end{pmatrix}$ but we shall not do so after this as we do not wish to confuse the two methods.

The reader may consider that we are being unnecessarily pedantic about the two lines of attack but there is a real difference between them. Let us suppose, for example, that in the course of manipulation the triangle became turned over so that it looked like

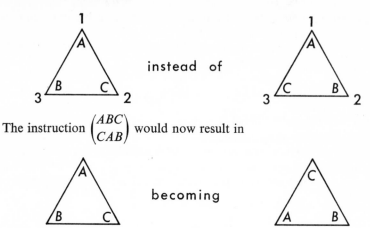

instead of

The instruction $\begin{pmatrix} ABC \\ CAB \end{pmatrix}$ would now result in

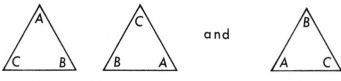

becoming

which in fact is a rotation through one place anti-clockwise. The version based on position however will still rotate the erring triangle one place clockwise. We shall compare these two methods in more detail when we are more fluent at both. For the remainder of this section we shall concentrate on the corner version.

Firmly turning our triangle over again so that it looks like

we see that the results of rotating it clockwise through 0, 1 or 2 places are

and

respectively and that these may be described as

$$\begin{pmatrix} ABC \\ ABC \end{pmatrix}, \quad \begin{pmatrix} ABC \\ CAB \end{pmatrix} \quad \text{and} \quad \begin{pmatrix} ABC \\ BCA \end{pmatrix}.$$

We will label these processes

$$I, \qquad X \qquad \text{and} \qquad Y$$

to conform with the notation of p. 15 under similar circumstances although, as we have already indicated, X and Y can show signs of temperament if the triangle becomes reversed.

There remains only the problem of combining these processes. If we consider X f Y this now means

$$\begin{pmatrix} ABC \\ CAB \end{pmatrix} \quad \text{followed by} \quad \begin{pmatrix} ABC \\ BCA \end{pmatrix}.$$

This means that: A is replaced by C which is replaced by A so that A is
                replaced by A;
             B is replaced by A which is replaced by B so that B is
                replaced by B;
             C is replaced by B which is replaced by C so that C is
                replaced by C.

The result is $\begin{pmatrix} ABC \\ ABC \end{pmatrix}$ which is I.

As usual this is far more difficult to write than to do and processes may be combined very quickly with a little practice. A useful idea for the reader who does find this confusing is to reorganize the second process so that its top row is the same as the bottom row of the first process. Thus we would rewrite Y as $\begin{pmatrix} CAB \\ ABC \end{pmatrix}$. If we now place Y beneath X we get

$$\begin{pmatrix} ABC \\ CAB \end{pmatrix}$$

$$\begin{pmatrix} CAB \\ ABC \end{pmatrix}$$

and a combination of the first and last rows gives us the required result. Any number of processes may be linked together in this way, but it is a little tedious and the reader will soon adapt himself to the first method. The next step is to complete the 'f' table once again and this will provide some of the necessary practice.

Examples 8b

Complete the following table:

f	I	X	Y
I	.	.	.
X	.	.	I
Y	.	.	.

TABLE 34

f	I	X	Y
I	I	X	Y
X	X	Y	I
Y	Y	I	X

TABLE 35

(Compare this with your answer to Question 1, Examples 2g, p. 27.)

The bottom lines of the three processes I, X and Y are three of the permutations on the three letters A, B and C. We may therefore surmise that we have not yet finished with the manipulation of the triangle since there are no less than $3! = 6$ possible permutations for A, B and C, and we are therefore three short. With our superior notation we may even write them down. They are

$$\begin{pmatrix} ABC \\ ACB \end{pmatrix}, \quad \begin{pmatrix} ABC \\ CBA \end{pmatrix} \quad \text{and} \quad \begin{pmatrix} ABC \\ BAC \end{pmatrix},$$

which we shall call

$$P, \qquad Q \qquad \text{and} \qquad R$$

respectively.

Furthermore for completeness we must extend our three-by-three table to a six-by-six table and get

f	I	X	Y	P	Q	R
I	I	X	Y	.	.	.
X	X	Y	I	.	.	.
Y	Y	I	X	.	.	.
P	.	.	.	.	.	.
Q	.	.	.	.	.	.
R	.	.	.	.	.	.

TABLE 36

Examples 8c

Complete the above table.

f	I	X	Y	P	Q	R
I	I	X	Y	P	Q	R
X	X	Y	I	R	P	Q
Y	Y	I	X	Q	R	P
P	P	Q	R	I	X	Y
Q	Q	R	P	Y	I	X
R	R	P	Q	X	Y	I

TABLE 37

We now test for group properties. Closure and uniqueness of result are true enough since each calculation can only produce just one of the six permutations. For once we are in the happy position of being able to prove the Associative Law without too much labour.

We first plan our attack. We know that if we combine two permutations, $X f P$, say, we may do this by reorganizing P so that its top line fits with the bottom line of X thus

$$\begin{pmatrix} ABC \\ CAB \end{pmatrix}$$

$$\begin{pmatrix} CAB \\ BAC \end{pmatrix}$$

and the result is obtained by missing out the middle two rows and leaving $\begin{pmatrix} ABC \\ BAC \end{pmatrix}$ which is R.

To put this in a general form we let small letters a, b, c, d ... represent different orders of the three letters A, B, C. Thus any permutation may be represented in the form $\begin{pmatrix} a \\ b \end{pmatrix}$, where a is one order of ABC and b is another. We have usually kept our first order a as ABC, but, as we have shown above and previously, this is by no means necessary. A further permutation which we wish to combine with $\begin{pmatrix} a \\ b \end{pmatrix}$ may be organized so that its top row is b and we write it as $\begin{pmatrix} b \\ c \end{pmatrix}$. The two may combine as $\begin{pmatrix} a \\ b \end{pmatrix}$

$$\begin{pmatrix} b \\ c \end{pmatrix} \text{ which results in } \begin{pmatrix} a \\ c \end{pmatrix}.$$

We are now ready to tackle the Associative Law. Let us assume that we have three permutations $\begin{pmatrix} a \\ b \end{pmatrix}$, $\begin{pmatrix} b \\ c \end{pmatrix}$ and $\begin{pmatrix} c \\ d \end{pmatrix}$, all arranged so that they fit nicely underneath one another. Then the Associative Law requires that

$$\left. \begin{matrix} \begin{pmatrix} a \\ b \end{pmatrix} \\ \begin{pmatrix} b \\ c \end{pmatrix} \\ \begin{pmatrix} c \\ d \end{pmatrix} \end{matrix} \right\} \text{ gives the same result as } \begin{matrix} \begin{pmatrix} a \\ b \end{pmatrix} \\ \left. \begin{matrix} \begin{pmatrix} b \\ c \end{pmatrix} \\ \begin{pmatrix} c \\ d \end{pmatrix} \end{matrix} \right\} \end{matrix}$$

This is soon proved.

$$\left. \begin{matrix} \begin{pmatrix} a \\ b \end{pmatrix} \\ \begin{pmatrix} b \\ c \end{pmatrix} \\ \begin{pmatrix} c \\ d \end{pmatrix} \end{matrix} \right\} \text{ reduces to } \begin{matrix} \begin{pmatrix} a \\ c \end{pmatrix} \\ \begin{pmatrix} c \\ d \end{pmatrix} \end{matrix} \text{ which reduces to } \begin{pmatrix} a \\ d \end{pmatrix}$$

whilst

$$\begin{Bmatrix} \binom{a}{b} \\ \binom{b}{c} \\ \binom{c}{d} \end{Bmatrix}$$
  reduces to $\begin{matrix} \binom{a}{b} \\ \binom{b}{d} \end{matrix}$ which reduces to $\binom{a}{d}$

as before.

The proof is easy. The only difficulty is finding a way to write it down adequately. If the reader does not like this version we can provide him with an alternative in the next section. Let us continue with the other group axioms.

I is a well-behaved neutral element and occurs just once in each row and column, so that every element has just one inverse. Thus the new 6×6 table forms a group. It is not Abelian since, for example, $X f P = R$ and $P f X = Q$.

But before we finish this section we must connect the three new processes with the original triangle. Consider P which is $\begin{pmatrix} ABC \\ ACB \end{pmatrix}$. This is a process which keeps A fixed and interchanges B and C. In terms of the triangle this can only mean holding it by the corner A and twisting it so that the reverse side comes uppermost and corners B and C duly cross over. Thus

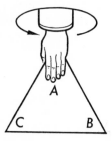 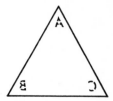

FIG. 43

In the same way Q and R have meaning relative to corners B and C respectively.

In discussing the relative merits of naming processes by corners or positions we made the point that if by some mischance the reverse side of the triangle were to appear uppermost in the corner method, a process such as X would turn it the relevant number of places anti-clockwise instead of clockwise. Unfortunately this happens every time we do P, Q or R so that if we always want our X process to mean a clockwise rotation instead of a specific permutation of corners we will do better to use the alternative method, which we shall examine in the next section.

Examples 8d

1. Label the corners of a square *A*, *B*, *C* and *D* and write down the permutations which result from a rotation clockwise through 0°, 90°, 180° and 270°. Give these the usual names and derive the expected group table.

2. Write down the permutations which may be derived from twisting the square of Question 1 after the style of Junior's fishy tile (page 6). Test whether the four permutations you get form a group. Combine these four permutations with those of Question 1 and form a group of the composite table together with whatever extra permutations you need.

3. Label the corners of a regular hexagon *A*, *B*, *C*, *D*, *E* and *F* and write down the permutations which result from a clockwise rotation through 0°, 60°, 120°, 180°, 240°, 300° and 360°. Derive a group table from the result and compare it with Table 37.

8.3 Matrices Again

The modern mathematician seeks to unify his subject by categorizing the basic principles behind any mathematical situation which may arise. We have already seen this idea in action in Chapter 1 where a single mathematical structure, the Klein Four Group, was seen to be the unifying principle behind the swapping system, Junior and his tile and the four algebraic expressions. In Chapters 3, 4 and 5 we analysed group properties and found in the group structure the unifying idea behind the diverse mathematical situations of Chapters 1 and 2. We also found that normal numbers satisfy the group axioms under certain conditions (p. 75) as do certain sets of matrices under '+' and '×'. Thus the group 'motif' has proved the unifying principle in what we have done so far. In the rest of this book we shall show that matrices themselves are a very strong unifying force. We shall start by showing them in action busily rotating our triangle.

We have seen that rotating the equilateral triangle is virtually the same as permuting the three letters *A*, *B* and *C*. Since we are intending to play with matrices we shall, for the rest of this section, treat the letters as the column matrix $\begin{bmatrix} A \\ B \\ C \end{bmatrix}$. We now 'operate' on $\begin{bmatrix} A \\ B \\ C \end{bmatrix}$ by a judiciously chosen matrix such as

$$\begin{bmatrix} 1 & 0 & 0 \\ 0 & 0 & 1 \\ 0 & 1 & 0 \end{bmatrix}$$

The result of this is

$$\begin{bmatrix} 1 & 0 & 0 \\ 0 & 0 & 1 \\ 0 & 1 & 0 \end{bmatrix} \begin{bmatrix} A \\ B \\ C \end{bmatrix} = \begin{bmatrix} A \\ C \\ B \end{bmatrix}$$

which means that we have interchanged the letters in the last two places. This has the same effect in this case as $\begin{pmatrix} ABC \\ ACB \end{pmatrix}$ which means interchanging B and C but, as we have stated previously, the two processes are not identical.

$$\begin{bmatrix} 1 & 0 & 0 \\ 0 & 0 & 1 \\ 0 & 1 & 0 \end{bmatrix}$$

swaps over the letters in the last two places whatever they may be, $\begin{pmatrix} ABC \\ ACB \end{pmatrix}$ swaps over the letters B and C wherever they may be.

The matrix

$$\begin{bmatrix} 1 & 0 & 0 \\ 0 & 0 & 1 \\ 0 & 1 & 0 \end{bmatrix}$$

and others of similar disposition are called permutation matrices and may be constructed as required. Let us note first of all that each row and column of the permutation matrix has just one 1 in it. The location of these governs the permutation produced and we may already notice that there are three places in which we can put the 1 in the first row, which leaves two places for the 1 in the second row and only one place for the remaining 1 in the third row. This makes a total of $3! = 3 \times 2 \times 1 = 6$ possible ways in which we can construct a 3×3 permutation matrix, which ties up neatly with the six possible ways of permuting the three letters A, B and C.

In the product

$$\begin{bmatrix} 1 & 0 & 0 \\ 0 & 0 & 1 \\ 0 & 1 & 0 \end{bmatrix} \begin{bmatrix} A \\ B \\ C \end{bmatrix}$$

we know that what appears in the first row of the answer is the result of

$$\begin{bmatrix} 1 & 0 & 0 \end{bmatrix} \begin{bmatrix} A \\ B \\ C \end{bmatrix}$$

This is A, the first letter of $\begin{bmatrix} A \\ B \\ C \end{bmatrix}$, since the 1 is situated in the first place in $\begin{bmatrix} 1 & 0 & 0 \end{bmatrix}$. Similarly, the second row of the answer will be filled by C since the relevant part of the permutation matrix is $\begin{bmatrix} 0 & 0 & 1 \end{bmatrix}$ which has the 1 in the third place. The last letter of the result must, of course, be B since it is the only one left but this fits in well with [0 1 0] being the third row of the permutation matrix. We may use this analysis to construct any permutation matrix we require.

Let us suppose that we seek the permutation matrix that will change

$$\begin{bmatrix} A \\ B \\ C \end{bmatrix} \text{ to } \begin{bmatrix} C \\ A \\ B \end{bmatrix}$$

In other words, we wish to fill in the 1's and 0's to satisfy the equation

$$\begin{bmatrix} ? & ? & ? \\ ? & ? & ? \\ ? & ? & ? \end{bmatrix} \begin{bmatrix} A \\ B \\ C \end{bmatrix} = \begin{bmatrix} C \\ A \\ B \end{bmatrix}$$

We require C in the top row of the answer so that the 1 in the top row must go in the third place since C is in third place in $\begin{bmatrix} A \\ B \\ C \end{bmatrix}$. The 1 in the second row must go in first place to pick up A and the 1 in the third row must go in second place to pick up B. The result is

$$\begin{bmatrix} 0 & 0 & 1 \\ 1 & 0 & 0 \\ 0 & 1 & 0 \end{bmatrix}$$

and we may check this by seeing that

$$\begin{bmatrix} 0 & 0 & 1 \\ 1 & 0 & 0 \\ 0 & 1 & 0 \end{bmatrix} \begin{bmatrix} A \\ B \\ C \end{bmatrix} = \begin{bmatrix} C \\ A \\ B \end{bmatrix}$$

as required.

Examples 8e

Construct the permutation matrices which will convert

$$\begin{bmatrix} A \\ B \\ C \end{bmatrix} \text{ into } \begin{bmatrix} A \\ B \\ C \end{bmatrix}, \begin{bmatrix} B \\ C \\ A \end{bmatrix}, \begin{bmatrix} C \\ B \\ A \end{bmatrix} \text{ and } \begin{bmatrix} B \\ A \\ C \end{bmatrix}$$

Below is a complete list of 3×3 permutation matrices together with the symbols by which we shall refer to them in the rest of this section. The letters refer back to section 8.2 and, for example, the matrix X' has the same effect

on $\begin{bmatrix} A \\ B \\ C \end{bmatrix}$ as the permutation X has on ABC although their paths may deviate

in other circumstances.

$$\begin{bmatrix} 1 & 0 & 0 \\ 0 & 1 & 0 \\ 0 & 0 & 1 \end{bmatrix}, \quad \begin{bmatrix} 0 & 0 & 1 \\ 1 & 0 & 0 \\ 0 & 1 & 0 \end{bmatrix}, \quad \begin{bmatrix} 0 & 1 & 0 \\ 0 & 0 & 1 \\ 1 & 0 & 0 \end{bmatrix},$$
$$\qquad I' \qquad\qquad\quad X' \qquad\qquad\quad Y'$$

$$\begin{bmatrix} 1 & 0 & 0 \\ 0 & 0 & 1 \\ 0 & 1 & 0 \end{bmatrix}, \quad \begin{bmatrix} 0 & 0 & 1 \\ 0 & 1 & 0 \\ 1 & 0 & 0 \end{bmatrix}, \quad \begin{bmatrix} 0 & 1 & 0 \\ 1 & 0 & 0 \\ 0 & 0 & 1 \end{bmatrix}.$$
$$\qquad P' \qquad\qquad\quad Q' \qquad\qquad\quad R'$$

The great joy with the $\left(\begin{smallmatrix} ABC \\ ACB \end{smallmatrix} \right)$ version was the ease with which the various permutations could be combined. Matrices are equally well behaved in this direction and the combining operation is matrix multiplication. Consider, for example, the effect of P' and then X' on $\begin{bmatrix} A \\ B \\ C \end{bmatrix}$. P', being

$$\begin{bmatrix} 1 & 0 & 0 \\ 0 & 0 & 1 \\ 0 & 1 & 0 \end{bmatrix}$$

changes over the letters in the last two places to give $\begin{bmatrix} A \\ C \\ B \end{bmatrix}$. If we now operate on this by X' or

$$\begin{bmatrix} 0 & 0 & 1 \\ 1 & 0 & 0 \\ 0 & 1 & 0 \end{bmatrix}$$

which moves the bottom letter to the top and pushes the rest down a place, we get $\begin{bmatrix} B \\ C \\ A \end{bmatrix}$. Writing this more formally we get

$$\begin{bmatrix} 1 & 0 & 0 \\ 0 & 0 & 1 \\ 0 & 1 & 0 \end{bmatrix} \begin{bmatrix} A \\ B \\ C \end{bmatrix} = \begin{bmatrix} A \\ C \\ B \end{bmatrix}$$

and

$$\begin{bmatrix} 0 & 0 & 1 \\ 1 & 0 & 0 \\ 0 & 1 & 0 \end{bmatrix} \begin{bmatrix} A \\ C \\ B \end{bmatrix} = \begin{bmatrix} B \\ A \\ C \end{bmatrix}$$

The two processes written together give

$$\begin{bmatrix} 0 & 0 & 1 \\ 1 & 0 & 0 \\ 0 & 1 & 0 \end{bmatrix} \left\{ \begin{bmatrix} 1 & 0 & 0 \\ 0 & 0 & 1 \\ 0 & 1 & 0 \end{bmatrix} \begin{bmatrix} A \\ B \\ C \end{bmatrix} \right\}$$

Applying the Associative Law we get

$$\left\{ \begin{bmatrix} 0 & 0 & 1 \\ 1 & 0 & 0 \\ 0 & 1 & 0 \end{bmatrix} \begin{bmatrix} 1 & 0 & 0 \\ 0 & 0 & 1 \\ 0 & 1 & 0 \end{bmatrix} \right\} \begin{bmatrix} A \\ B \\ C \end{bmatrix} = \begin{bmatrix} 0 & 1 & 0 \\ 1 & 0 & 0 \\ 0 & 0 & 1 \end{bmatrix} \begin{bmatrix} A \\ B \\ C \end{bmatrix}$$

Thus we may say that P' followed by X' has the same permuting effect as

$$\begin{bmatrix} 0 & 1 & 0 \\ 1 & 0 & 0 \\ 0 & 0 & 1 \end{bmatrix}$$

or R'. We must be careful however. If we want P' to act on $\begin{bmatrix} A \\ B \\ C \end{bmatrix}$ first, we

write it as

$$\begin{bmatrix} 1 & 0 & 0 \\ 0 & 0 & 1 \\ 0 & 1 & 0 \end{bmatrix} \begin{bmatrix} A \\ B \\ C \end{bmatrix}.$$

If we now follow this by X', we write X' to the left of P' giving

$$\begin{bmatrix} 0 & 0 & 1 \\ 1 & 0 & 0 \\ 0 & 1 & 0 \end{bmatrix} \begin{bmatrix} 1 & 0 & 0 \\ 0 & 0 & 1 \\ 0 & 1 & 0 \end{bmatrix} \begin{bmatrix} A \\ B \\ C \end{bmatrix}$$

Thus the result of acting on $\begin{bmatrix} A \\ B \\ C \end{bmatrix}$ by P' and then X' is the same as the result of

acting on $\begin{bmatrix} A \\ B \\ C \end{bmatrix}$ by $X'P'$ and not $P'X'$, which would be the normal way of

writing it.

If we try it the wrong way round we get

$$P'X' = \begin{bmatrix} 1 & 0 & 0 \\ 0 & 0 & 1 \\ 0 & 1 & 0 \end{bmatrix} \begin{bmatrix} 0 & 0 & 1 \\ 1 & 0 & 0 \\ 0 & 1 & 0 \end{bmatrix} = \begin{bmatrix} 0 & 0 & 1 \\ 0 & 1 & 0 \\ 1 & 0 & 0 \end{bmatrix}$$

which is Q' instead of R'. We would not expect the Commutative Law to
work in this case since it did not work in the parallel structure of section 8.2.

Examples 8f

Complete the following table.

second matrix
(the left-hand one)

×	I'	X'	Y'	P'	Q'	R'
I'	·	·	·	·	·	·
X'	·	·	·	Q'	·	·
Y'	·	·	·	·	·	·
P'	·	R'	·	·	·	·
Q'	·	·	·	·	·	·
R'	·	·	·	·	·	·

(first matrix (the right-hand one) labels the rows)

second matrix
(the left-hand one)

×	I'	X'	Y'	P'	Q'	R'
I'	I'	X'	Y'	P'	Q'	R'
X'	X'	Y'	I'	Q'	R'	P'
Y'	Y'	I'	X'	R'	P'	Q'
P'	P'	R'	Q'	I'	Y'	X'
Q'	Q'	P'	R'	X'	I'	Y'
R'	R'	Q'	P'	Y'	X'	I'

(first matrix (the right-hand one))

Matrix version
TABLE 38

second permutation

f	I	X	Y	P	Q	R
I	I	X	Y	P	Q	R
X	X	Y	I	R	P	Q
Y	Y	I	X	Q	R	P
P	P	Q	R	I	X	Y
Q	Q	R	P	Y	I	X
R	R	P	Q	X	Y	I

(first permutation)

Permutation version
TABLE 37 (repeated)

It is apparent that the two tables are not identical. The X' row for example is $X'\ Y'\ I'\ Q'\ R'\ P'$ which does not match the X row which is $X\ Y\ I\ R\ P\ Q$. We should be suspicious however if the two rows did match in view of the two different lines of attack. On the other hand, both techniques in their own way provide the complete set of six permutations on three letters, so that we do have grounds for thinking that the same basic structure must inhere in both. It will pay us to investigate further. A judicious altering around of the rows and columns in one of the tables may result in a more happy pairing between matrices and permutations which will allow the same basic pattern to emerge in each case. We may gain a clue from the fact that the P's, Q's and R's at the end of the first three rows of the permutations table are in the same positions as the P's, Q's and R's at the end of the first three rows of the matrix table except that the X and Y rows seem to have changed places. The same argument applies to the columns. This indicates that we might do well to interchange the X and Y rows and columns and see what happens. It will certainly straighten out the P's, Q's and R's but may well upset the I's, X's and Y's which are reasonably well behaved at the moment. We can only try and see.

second permutation

f	I	Y	X	P	Q	R
I	I	Y	X	P	Q	R
Y	Y	X	I	Q	R	P
X	X	I	Y	R	P	Q
P	P	R	Q	I	X	Y
Q	Q	R	P	Y	I	X
R	R	Q	P	X	Y	I

first permutation (rows I, Y, X, P, Q, R)

TABLE 39

This has certainly tidied up the P's, Q's and R's but we cannot expect to get a corresponding pattern with X and Y the wrong way round in the table. We can alter this quite simply by redefining X as $\begin{pmatrix} ABC \\ BCA \end{pmatrix}$ and Y as $\begin{pmatrix} ABC \\ CAB \end{pmatrix}$ instead of the other way round. This has the effect of replacing X by Y and Y by X in the table to give a final amended version of

second permutation

f	I	X	Y	P	Q	R
I	I	X	Y	P	Q	R
X	X	Y	I	Q	R	P
Y	Y	I	X	R	P	Q
P	P	R	Q	I	Y	X
Q	Q	P	R	X	I	Y
R	R	Q	P	Y	X	I

first permutation (rows I, X, Y, P, Q, R)

TABLE 40

which corresponds exactly to the matrix version. This shows that the two systems have the same basic structure although the obvious correspondence between the elements was not the correct one and had to be amended. (See Question 6, Examples 1d, p. 13 and section 5.5.)

The immediate value to us of the common table between the permutation and the matrix versions is that we do not have to bother to prove that the set of permutation matrices forms a group. Since it behaves in exactly the same way as the permutation version, given the correct correspondence, and since the permutation version forms a group, the matrix version must also form a group. However, we said in the last section that we would indicate an alternative proof for the Associative Law.

We must therefore work our argument in reverse, prove the Associative Law for the 3×3 matrices and hence deduce that it must also work for the permutation version. We have already proved it for 2×2 matrices (see p. 98). The 3×3 version follows exactly the same route but is more tedious although equally valid.

Examples 8g

Repeat Examples 8d using permutation matrices instead of permutations.

8.4. The Dancers Again

If the reader has assiduously fought his way through Examples 8d and 8g (p. 138 and above) he will by now have inadvertently converted the dancers' movements in the circling, swapping and combined tables to both the permutation and the permutation matrix versions and learnt the merits and defects of each. In this section we produce yet a third version based on 2×2 matrices. We do this partly as a check on previous results but also because we are already more familiar with 2×2's than 4×4's and will become even more so in the next few chapters. We shall give the 2×2 matrices names which link them with the corresponding dance movements but will give no justification for the correspondence at this stage. This also will come in the next few chapters. For the moment we shall merely accept it and be thankful.

$$\begin{bmatrix} 1 & 0 \\ 0 & 1 \end{bmatrix}, \quad \begin{bmatrix} -1 & 0 \\ 0 & 1 \end{bmatrix}, \quad \begin{bmatrix} 1 & 0 \\ 0 & -1 \end{bmatrix}, \quad \begin{bmatrix} -1 & 0 \\ 0 & -1 \end{bmatrix},$$
$$\quad I' \qquad\qquad A' \qquad\qquad B' \qquad\qquad C'$$

$$\begin{bmatrix} 0 & 1 \\ -1 & 0 \end{bmatrix}, \quad \begin{bmatrix} 0 & -1 \\ 1 & 0 \end{bmatrix}, \quad \begin{bmatrix} 0 & 1 \\ 1 & 0 \end{bmatrix}, \quad \begin{bmatrix} 0 & -1 \\ -1 & 0 \end{bmatrix},$$
$$\quad X' \qquad\qquad Z' \qquad\qquad P' \qquad\qquad Q'$$

		second matrix (on left)						
×	I'	A'	B'	C'	X'	Z'	P'	Q'
I'	I'	A'	B'	C'	X'	Z'	P'	Q'
A'	A'	I'	C'	B'	P'	Q'	X'	Z'
B'	B'	C'	I'	A'	Q'	P'	Z'	X'
C'	C'	B'	A'	I'	Z'	X'	Q'	P'
X'	X'	Q'	P'	Z'	C'	I'	A'	B'
Z'	Z'	P'	Q'	X'	I'	C'	B'	A'
P'	P'	Z'	X'	Q'	B'	A'	I'	C'
Q'	Q'	X'	Z'	P'	A'	B'	C'	I'

first matrix

(on right)

TABLE 41

This table, as one would expect if the correspondences are right, turns out to have the same pattern as the one produced by the dancers themselves (Table 22, p. 49). Therefore it is not necessary for us to go through the procedure of proving that it forms a group. The other table has a group structure and therefore this version has as well. However, we have frequently promised that we would eventually produce a simple proof for the Associative Law in cases like this (see p. 34, and elsewhere). We have in fact already done it. The Associative Law was proved to be true for 2×2 matrices in general on p. 98 and therefore certainly applies in this particular case.

As we have seen previously (p. 50 and Examples 4e) the 8×8 table will handle a large number of dances primarily based on two couples as long as they keep to a more or less square formation. This is, of course, because the dances are usually made up of the movements we have listed. However, there are irregular versions and we know that there are in fact $4! = 24$ different possible ways of arranging our four dancers. The implications are painful but obvious. For complete certainty in handling dances of the type listed we need a 24×24 table. We shall not produce it as it is a wearisome procedure. We shall therefore extend our Scottish dancing research no more but concentrate in detail on the more common movements we have more nearly under control.

8.5 The Value of Permutation Groups

The reader may well wonder why we have spent so much time on permutation groups which shrink to insignificance when compared with the machinations of the toothpaste tycoon of Chapter 7. We may defend ourselves on historical grounds since much of the early work on group theory was done on permutations before its vital position in mathematics was fully appreciated. However, our main reason for dwelling on permutations is that every finite group can in fact be shown to be a permutation group in disguise. This theorem, stated more precisely, is due to the English mathematician Cayley (1821–95) and will be proved when the necessary mathematical tools have been forged in the next chapter. We merely show it in action here to make our point. We try it on the swapping system which seems sweetly simple after the labours of the past few pages (especially if the reader tackled the 24×24 table).

f	I	A	B	C
I	I	A	B	C
A	A	I	C	B
B	B	C	I	A
C	C	B	A	I

TABLE 1 (repeated)

We may observe this versatile table in yet another light. We may say that I acts on the four elements $(I\ A\ B\ C)$ and leaves them as $(I\ A\ B\ C)$. A, on the other hand, turns them into $(A\,I\,C\,B)$ whilst B and C turn them into $(B\,C\,I\,A)$ and $(C\,B\,A\,I)$ respectively. Thus we may divorce our processes from their dancing origin and redefine them as the four permutations

$$\underset{I}{\begin{pmatrix} I\,A\,B\,C \\ I\,A\,B\,C \end{pmatrix}}, \quad \underset{A}{\begin{pmatrix} I\,A\,B\,C \\ A\,I\,C\,B \end{pmatrix}}, \quad \underset{B}{\begin{pmatrix} I\,A\,B\,C \\ B\,C\,I\,A \end{pmatrix}} \quad \text{and} \quad \underset{C}{\begin{pmatrix} I\,A\,B\,C \\ C\,B\,A\,I \end{pmatrix}}.$$

If we now form a table of I, A, B and C treating them as permutations instead of dancing movements we get

f	I	A	B	C
I	I	A	B	C
A	A	I	C	B
B	B	C	I	A
C	C	B	A	I

TABLE 1 (repeated)

which brings us back to where we started. As we said before, this procedure may be followed for any finite group so that any theorem that we may prove for permutation groups will in fact be true for any other finite group as well.

Examples 8h

1. Write down a set of permutations which will generate the arithmetic mod 3 addition table and check that you are correct.

2. Write down a set of permutations which will generate the dancers' circling table and check that you are correct.

3. Write down an alternative set of permutations to the one given in the text for Table 37 (p. 135) and find a geometrical interpretation for them.

9. ASSORTED ISOMORPHISMS

9.1 The General Idea

If, subject to differences in symbols, two groups give rise to the same table we may say that they are isomorphic or that there is an isomorphism between them. We have used the idea frequently already. In Chapter 1 the three situations: dancers swapping places, Junior and his tile and the algebraic expressions all give rise to a table of the form

*	e	a	b	c
e	e	a	b	c
a	a	e	c	b
b	b	c	e	a
c	c	b	a	e

TABLE 4 (repeated)

Similarly in Chapter 2 the dancers moving in a circle, the four-hour clock arithmetic and the cyclic rotations of a square all give rise to

*	e	a	b	c
e	e	a	b	c
a	a	b	c	e
b	b	c	e	a
c	c	e	a	b

TABLE 7 (repeated)

This simple approach did however cause us a little local difficulty in Chapter 5 when we were deducing that, for example,

*	e	a	b	c
e	e	a	b	c
a	a	b	c	e
b	b	c	e	a
c	c	e	a	b

TABLE 7 (repeated)

and

*	e	a	b	c
e	e	a	b	c
a	a	c	e	b
b	b	e	c	a
c	c	b	a	e

TABLE 29 (repeated)

were basically the same table. By interchanging the b and c rows and columns in the second of these we obtained

*	e	a	c	b
e	e	a	c	b
a	a	c	b	e
c	c	b	e	a
b	b	e	a	c

TABLE 30 (repeated)

which has exactly the same pattern as the first version although b and c are doing each other's jobs. The tables are the same, subject to differences in symbolism, and therefore the two are isomorphic, although this is not at first sight apparent.

In Chapter 8 we again had to juggle with the two versions of the six possible rotations of the equilateral triangle in order to demonstrate that the matrix version was isomorphic with the permutations version (p. 143) and we may feel most relieved that the two versions of the 8×8 tables of dancers' movements (pp. 49 and 145) both adopted the same pattern at the first attempt.

There is a moral to be drawn from our experiences. With the six group and even with the lowly four group we had to think quite deeply about the reorganization of tables. With larger groups the writing down of the whole table is tedious. With infinite groups it is impossible. The juggling of rows and columns is more so in each case. We shall therefore in the next section devise an alternative strategy, which will have basically the same effect as comparing tables, but which will be more useful to us.

9.2 An Alternative Definition

Let us assume that two groups G_1 and G_2 with combining operations $*$ and $\circ$ are isomorphic. In other words, they give rise to what is basically the same table. An alternative way of stating this property is to say that if we do a calculation involving certain elements from G_1 and then do the same calculation with corresponding elements from G_2, we shall get an answer in G_2 which corresponds to the answer we got in G_1. The importance of the last sentence greatly exceeds its clarity. We hope that an example will do better. We know already from Chapter 2 that the table of dancers circling and the table of the four-hour clock are isomorphic, both being different representations of a cyclic four group (p. 20).

f	I	X	Y	Z
I	I	X	Y	Z
X	X	Y	Z	I
Y	Y	Z	I	X
Z	Z	I	X	Y

Dancers circling

TABLE 6 (repeated)

+	4	1	2	3
4	4	1	2	3
1	1	2	3	4
2	2	3	4	1
3	3	4	1	2

4-hour clock

TABLE 10 (repeated)

The two tables above have been organized so that they have the same pattern and the corresponding elements are therefore

$$\begin{array}{cccc} I & X & Y & Z \\ \updownarrow & \updownarrow & \updownarrow & \updownarrow \\ 4 & 1 & 2 & 3 \end{array}$$

If we now do any calculation in the dancing table we should get a corresponding result by doing a corresponding calculation in the four-hour clock system. Let us try.

$$X f Z = I.$$

X corresponds to 1 and Z to 3. $1+3 = 4$ and 4 corresponds to I. Thus in this particular case the corresponding calculation does give the corresponding result. If we did this in every possible case it would take some time. We would eventually decide that the easiest way to show that corresponding calculations give corresponding results is to show that the two groups give rise to tables with the same basic pattern!

We can however use the new idea more profitably. We may argue in this case, for example, that the dancers may be considered to be starting at the four corners of a multiplication sign thus:

FIG. 44

If we situate them at the corners of an addition sign instead, it will not affect their group table and will make our argument clearer.

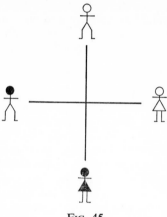

FIG. 45

As our dancers rotate we will assume that the '+' rotates with them. If we now examine the behaviour of the arm of the '+' pointing to ⚲ we will find that it acts in a similar way to the hour hand of the four-hour clock.

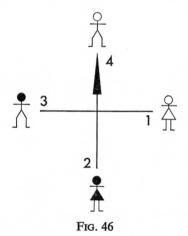

FIG. 46

As the dancers move through 0, 1, 2 or 3 places (i.e. do movements I, X, Y or Z) the hour hand moves through 0(4), 1, 2 or 3 hours on the clock. A succession of dance movements means an addition of hours and we may therefore decide that the two tables will have the same pattern or that corresponding calculations will give corresponding results.

11

Arguments such as the above can be both interesting and instructive, although they are not always as precise as we should like. They enable us to discover connecting links between systems which, although giving rise to tables of the same pattern, do not otherwise seem to be connected. Here the connecting link between the dancers' steps and the four-hour-clock arithmetic is the movement of one arm of the '+'—a geometrical process. We shall examine the root causes between many such isomorphisms in the next few chapters.

We shall use another and more precise form of our 'corresponding calculations give corresponding results' argument in the next section but before we get there we had better summarize the ideas of this section. If we take 'corresponding calculations give corresponding results' as our motto we first note that for the calculations to correspond, the elements which make up the calculations must correspond. Thus every member of the first group must have just one partner somewhere in the second group and similarly every member of the second group must have just one partner somewhere in the first. In other words, there must be 1–1 (one-to-one) correspondence between the elements of the two groups. However, any 1–1 correspondence will not do and the organizing of the correct one is not always easy. The reader may have noticed that we have made a point of starting our tables with *I* or *e,* or whatever the relevant identity element may be, so that at least the identities will be in corresponding positions. This was why we started the clock arithmetic table with 4 instead of 1. Once the correct 1–1 correspondence has been organized we must show that any and every calculation done in the first group gives an answer that corresponds to the equivalent calculation done in the second group. A diagram is useful here.

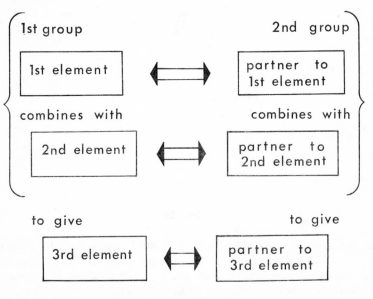

FIG. 47

If we can argue by some means or other that, having organized the correct 1–1 correspondence, the conditions of the above diagram are satisfied in every case, then we can say that the two groups are isomorphic or that there is an isomorphism between them.

Examples 9a

1. We may now look at Fig. 25 (p. 28) in a different light. All systems which give rise to the same abstract table are, in fact, isomorphic. Draw an expanded version of Fig. 25 and include as many different groups as you can. Leave plenty of room for future candidates.

2. Justify the isomorphism between the dancers swapping places and the gyrations of Junior's fish tile by similar means to those illustrated at the beginning of this section.

3. Repeat Question 2 for the dancers swapping places and the situation of Question 8, Examples 1d (p. 12).

4. The combined dancing table can equally well be generated by twisting a square after the manner of Junior's fish tile and rotating it after the style of section 2.5 (p. 25). Show that this is so and expand your technique of Question 2 to demonstrate the isomorphism.

9.3   Isomorphisms between Infinite Groups

The only infinite groups we have met so far are based on orthodox arithmetic (p. 74 *et seq.*) or matrices (pp. 83 and 97). Nevertheless a consideration of some of the isomorphisms between them can be instructive. It will show us matrices in action again as a unifying principle in mathematics and will also provide us with further justification for using ' + ' and ' × ' as the combining operation for both numbers and matrices. The first task in the search for isomorphisms is to locate likely looking 1–1 correspondences. In other words, we must find a convenient and fruitful way of pairing off numbers and, for example, 2×2 matrices.

Now a 2×2 matrix such as $\begin{bmatrix} a & b \\ c & d \end{bmatrix}$ depends in general on four different numbers a, b, c and d so that we cannot obviously pair it off with one particular number. If however we restrict ourselves to versions where b, c and d are all zero we spot an immediate 1–1 correspondence between $\left\{ \begin{bmatrix} a & 0 \\ 0 & 0 \end{bmatrix} \right\}$ and $\{a\}$, where a is a real number.

We must now consider combining operations. Both ' + ' and ' × ' are candidates in each case and we consider each in turn. We may remember (p. 76) that the set of all real numbers under ' + ' forms a group. Two typical numbers are x and y which add to $(x+y)$. The corresponding matrices from

$$\left\{ \begin{bmatrix} a & 0 \\ 0 & 0 \end{bmatrix} \right\} \quad \text{are} \quad \begin{bmatrix} x & 0 \\ 0 & 0 \end{bmatrix} \quad \text{and} \quad \begin{bmatrix} y & 0 \\ 0 & 0 \end{bmatrix}$$

By the rules for addition of matrices from Chapter 6 (p. 80) these add to

$$\begin{bmatrix} x+y & 0 \\ 0 & 0 \end{bmatrix}$$

which is the partner of $(x+y)$. Thus we have proved that corresponding calculations give corresponding results. We may therefore say that $\left\{ \begin{bmatrix} a & 0 \\ 0 & 0 \end{bmatrix} \right\}$ under '+' is isomorphic to $\{a\}$ under '+' where a is any real number. We have not yet proved that $\left\{ \begin{bmatrix} a & 0 \\ 0 & 0 \end{bmatrix} \right\}$ under '+' forms a group but since it behaves in exactly the same way as $\{a\}$ under '+' we know that it must do so. This is one of the beauties of isomorphisms.

Now we turn our attention to multiplication. We may remember (p. 76) that the set of all real numbers excluding 0 forms a group under '×'. Two typical numbers, x and y, multiply to xy. Their partners in

$$\left\{ \begin{bmatrix} a & 0 \\ 0 & 0 \end{bmatrix} \right\} \quad \text{are} \quad \begin{bmatrix} x & 0 \\ 0 & 0 \end{bmatrix} \quad \text{and} \quad \begin{bmatrix} y & 0 \\ 0 & 0 \end{bmatrix}$$

These multiply to $\begin{bmatrix} xy & 0 \\ 0 & 0 \end{bmatrix}$ which is the partner of xy and again there is an isomorphism between the two sets under multiplication. Again we may deduce that $\left\{ \begin{bmatrix} a & 0 \\ 0 & 0 \end{bmatrix} ; \quad a \neq 0 \right\}$ forms a group under '×'.

There are several pitfalls that the reader must avoid. First of all the establishing of a 1–1 correspondence between two sets does not of itself lead to an isomorphism. There is, for example, an obvious and immediate 1–1 correspondence between $\left\{ \begin{bmatrix} a \\ b \end{bmatrix} \right\}$ and $\left\{ \frac{a}{b} \right\}$ where a and b are positive integers. Members of both sets may be combined by '+' but

$$\begin{bmatrix} p \\ q \end{bmatrix} + \begin{bmatrix} r \\ s \end{bmatrix} = \begin{bmatrix} p+r \\ q+s \end{bmatrix}$$

whilst

$$\frac{p}{q} + \frac{r}{s} = \frac{ps+rq}{qs}.$$

The two answers do not correspond and therefore there is no isomorphism.

A further pitfall is to assume that because two sets are isomorphic for one combining operation they are also isomorphic for another. Thus we could have carried out the initial argument of this section using

$$\left\{ \begin{bmatrix} 0 & a \\ 0 & 0 \end{bmatrix} \right\} \quad \text{instead of} \quad \left\{ \begin{bmatrix} a & 0 \\ 0 & 0 \end{bmatrix} \right\}$$

The 1–1 correspondence would still hold as would the isomorphism under '+' but

$$\begin{bmatrix} 0 & x \\ 0 & 0 \end{bmatrix}\begin{bmatrix} 0 & y \\ 0 & 0 \end{bmatrix} = \begin{bmatrix} 0 & 0 \\ 0 & 0 \end{bmatrix}$$

which certainly does not correspond to xy.

Once again we may take our arguments a stage further. Because $\left\{\begin{bmatrix} a & 0 \\ 0 & 0 \end{bmatrix}\right\}$ and $\{a\}$, where a is a real number, behave exactly the same way under '+' and '×' (and hence by inverse properties under '−' and '÷') this does not necessarily mean that they have the same effect elsewhere. For example, we find it useful to define multiplication between a number and a matrix as multiplying every member of the matrix by that number.

Thus

$$3\begin{bmatrix} a & b \\ c & d \end{bmatrix} = \begin{bmatrix} 3a & 3b \\ 3c & 3d \end{bmatrix}$$

Unfortunately this does not correspond with

$$\begin{bmatrix} 3 & 0 \\ 0 & 0 \end{bmatrix}\begin{bmatrix} a & b \\ c & d \end{bmatrix} = \begin{bmatrix} 3a & 3b \\ 0 & 0 \end{bmatrix}$$

We could make this fit by altering our definition of multiplication between number and matrix but this would be both artificial and inconvenient.

For the above reason it is more useful to consider the isomorphism between

$$\left\{\begin{bmatrix} a & 0 \\ 0 & a \end{bmatrix}\right\} \quad \text{and} \quad \{a\}$$

where a is any real number. The reader should check that the same isomorphisms occur as between

$$\left\{\begin{bmatrix} a & 0 \\ 0 & 0 \end{bmatrix}\right\} \quad \text{and} \quad \{a\}$$

and hence of course between any two of the three sets

$$\left\{\begin{bmatrix} a & 0 \\ 0 & 0 \end{bmatrix}\right\}, \quad \left\{\begin{bmatrix} a & 0 \\ 0 & a \end{bmatrix}\right\} \quad \text{and} \quad \{a\}.$$

We stated above that

$$3\begin{bmatrix} a & b \\ c & d \end{bmatrix} = \begin{bmatrix} 3a & 3b \\ 3c & 3d \end{bmatrix}.$$

If we now consider

$$\begin{bmatrix} 3 & 0 \\ 0 & 3 \end{bmatrix}\begin{bmatrix} a & b \\ c & d \end{bmatrix} \quad \text{we get} \quad \begin{bmatrix} 3a & 3b \\ 3c & 3d \end{bmatrix}$$

which corresponds exactly. This is much better and we shall use the $\begin{bmatrix} a & 0 \\ 0 & a \end{bmatrix}$

form frequently in future. Even so the situation is not completely under control.

$$3\begin{bmatrix} a & b & c \\ d & e & f \\ g & h & i \end{bmatrix} = \begin{bmatrix} 3a & 3b & 3c \\ 3d & 3e & 3f \\ 3g & 3h & 3i \end{bmatrix}$$

whereas

$$\begin{bmatrix} 3 & 0 \\ 0 & 3 \end{bmatrix} \begin{bmatrix} a & b & c \\ d & e & f \\ g & h & i \end{bmatrix}$$

is not defined. We may notice that a matrix such as $\begin{bmatrix} 3 & 0 \\ 0 & 3 \end{bmatrix}$ factorizes into $3\begin{bmatrix} 1 & 0 \\ 0 & 1 \end{bmatrix}$ so that multiplication by $\begin{bmatrix} 3 & 0 \\ 0 & 3 \end{bmatrix}$ when this is possible is equivalent to multiplying by $\begin{bmatrix} 1 & 0 \\ 0 & 1 \end{bmatrix}$, which has no effect, and then by 3.

Examples 9b

Decide which of the following sets of 2×2 matrices are isomorphic with
    (a) the group of all real numbers under '+',
    (b) the group of all integers under '+',
    (c) the group of all real numbers, excluding 0, under '×',
    (d) the group of all positive rationals under '×'.
Also, where possible, when there is no isomorphism, amend the sets from which the numbers in the matrices are chosen so as to establish one.

1. $\left\{ \begin{bmatrix} a & 0 \\ 0 & a \end{bmatrix} \right\}$ where a is a positive integer under '+',

2. $\left\{ \begin{bmatrix} 0 & 0 \\ 0 & a \end{bmatrix} \right\}$ where a is a rational number under '×',

3. $\left\{ \begin{bmatrix} 0 & a \\ a & 0 \end{bmatrix} \right\}$ where a is a real number under '+',

4. $\left\{ \begin{bmatrix} 0 & a \\ a & 0 \end{bmatrix} \right\}$ where a is a negative integer under '×',

5. $\left\{ \begin{bmatrix} 0 & a \\ b & 0 \end{bmatrix} \right\}$ where a and b are real numbers under '+',

6. $\left\{ \begin{bmatrix} 0 & a \\ 1 & 0 \end{bmatrix} \right\}$ where a is an integer under '×'.

9.4 More Isomorphisms

This section follows closely the arguments of the last one but in less detail.

If we take any set of matrices of the same size and shape and dependent on just one number in corresponding positions then these, under '+', form a group isomorphic with the set of real numbers under '+'.

Consider, for example,

$$\left\{ \begin{bmatrix} a & 0 \\ 0 & a \\ a & 0 \end{bmatrix} \right\}$$

where a is any real number. The shape of the matrix has no significance. We need only notice that it depends upon a alone. If we now follow the customary route for '+':

$$\begin{bmatrix} x & 0 \\ 0 & x \\ x & 0 \end{bmatrix} + \begin{bmatrix} y & 0 \\ 0 & y \\ y & 0 \end{bmatrix} = \begin{bmatrix} x+y & 0 \\ 0 & x+y \\ x+y & 0 \end{bmatrix}$$

which corresponds to $(x+y)$, the sum of x and y. Therefore there is the usual isomorphism between

$$\left\{ \begin{bmatrix} a & 0 \\ 0 & a \\ a & 0 \end{bmatrix} \right\} \quad \text{and} \quad \{a\}$$

where the mutual combining operation is '+'.

We shall not be equally lucky with '×'.

$$\left\{ \begin{bmatrix} a & 0 \\ 0 & a \\ a & 0 \end{bmatrix} \right\}$$

is no longer a candidate since we cannot multiply two 3×2's together. In fact, we find ourselves restricted to square matrices where we can multiply any two either way round.

$$\left\{ \begin{bmatrix} a & 0 & 0 \\ 0 & 0 & 0 \\ 0 & 0 & 0 \end{bmatrix} \right\},$$

for example, turns out to be as well behaved as its little brother $\left\{ \begin{bmatrix} a & 0 \\ 0 & 0 \end{bmatrix} \right\}$ and as before

$$\left\{ \begin{bmatrix} a & 0 & 0 \\ 0 & a & 0 \\ 0 & 0 & a \end{bmatrix}; \ a \neq 0 \right\}$$

is more useful. Thus $x \times y = xy$,

$$\begin{bmatrix} x & 0 & 0 \\ 0 & x & 0 \\ 0 & 0 & x \end{bmatrix} \begin{bmatrix} y & 0 & 0 \\ 0 & y & 0 \\ 0 & 0 & y \end{bmatrix} = \begin{bmatrix} xy & 0 & 0 \\ 0 & xy & 0 \\ 0 & 0 & xy \end{bmatrix}$$

and the two answers correspond. This establishes the isomorphism between

$$\left\{ \begin{bmatrix} a & 0 & 0 \\ 0 & a & 0 \\ 0 & 0 & a \end{bmatrix} \right\}$$

under '×' and $\{a\}$ under '×', where a is any real number except 0.

As with 2×2 matrices, multiplying by

$$\begin{bmatrix} x & 0 & 0 \\ 0 & x & 0 \\ 0 & 0 & x \end{bmatrix}$$

when this is possible, has the same effect as multiplying by

$$x\begin{bmatrix} 1 & 0 & 0 \\ 0 & 1 & 0 \\ 0 & 0 & 1 \end{bmatrix}$$

or just x.

The above argument may be repeated for any size of square matrix.

Examples 9c

Repeat Examples 9b for

1. $\{[a \quad 0 \quad 0]\}$ where a is a positive integer under '+',

2. $\left\{\begin{bmatrix} a \\ a \\ a \end{bmatrix}\right\}$ where a is a rational number under '$\times$',

3. $\left\{\begin{bmatrix} a & a & 0 \\ 0 & 0 & a \end{bmatrix}\right\}$ where a is a real number under '+',

4. $\left\{\begin{bmatrix} a & 0 & 0 & 0 \\ 0 & a & 0 & 0 \\ 0 & 0 & a & 0 \\ 0 & 0 & 0 & a \end{bmatrix}\right\}$ where a is a negative integer under '$\times$'.

9.5   Numbers as Matrices and vice versa

We have already established that $\{a\}$ and $\left\{\begin{bmatrix} a & 0 \\ 0 & a \end{bmatrix}\right\}$ behave in exactly the same way under '+' and '$\times$'. Hence, by group inverse properties, they also behave in the same way under '$-$' and '$\div$'. We may therefore do any calculation involving real numbers by the relevant 2×2 matrices instead. For example, we could, if we so desired, ask for a $\begin{bmatrix} 3 & 0 \\ 0 & 3 \end{bmatrix} d.$ bus ticket to High Street and still get the right change from $\begin{bmatrix} 6 & 0 \\ 0 & 6 \end{bmatrix} d.$ if the conductor was of a similar disposition. We do not recommend this.

Certain 2×2 matrices therefore behave amongst themselves in exactly the same way as real numbers and as far as results are concerned it is not possible to distinguish between them. We may therefore from many points of view look upon $\left\{\begin{bmatrix} a & 0 \\ 0 & a \end{bmatrix}\right\}$ and $\{a\}$ as being two different ways of writing the same thing. On these grounds we may look upon 2×2 matrices as extending our normal arithmetic or, more mathematically, our normal arithmetic as but a part of the more complete arithmetic of 2×2 matrices. It is by reasoning such as the above that we justify using the signs '+' and '×' as the combining operations for both real numbers and 2×2 matrices.

The arguments of the preceding paragraph have their flaws. As we showed on p. 156

$$3\begin{bmatrix} a & b & c \\ d & e & f \\ g & h & i \end{bmatrix} \text{ is defined whereas } \begin{bmatrix} 3 & 0 \\ 0 & 3 \end{bmatrix}\begin{bmatrix} a & b & c \\ d & e & f \\ g & h & i \end{bmatrix}$$

is not. Also

$$\begin{bmatrix} 3 & 0 \\ 0 & 3 \end{bmatrix} + \begin{bmatrix} a & b \\ c & d \end{bmatrix} \text{ is defined whereas } 3 + \begin{bmatrix} a & b \\ c & d \end{bmatrix}$$

is not. 2×2 matrices and real numbers are not the same and never will be. However, the above point of view does have its merits, and the extensions to normal arithmetic do have their practical applications (see p. 161).

We end this section by emphasizing the 'unifying properties' of group theory and matrices. We used the idea of group isomorphisms to establish the fact that we may look upon numbers themselves as special types of matrices. We now ask the reader to look back at Chapter 8 where we reduced the combined table of dancers' movements to an 8×8 table of 2×2 matrices (p. 145). All of these must belong to the extended arithmetic. Two of them,

$$\begin{bmatrix} 1 & 0 \\ 0 & 1 \end{bmatrix} \text{ and } \begin{bmatrix} -1 & 0 \\ 0 & -1 \end{bmatrix}$$

are the alternative representations of 1 and -1 and behave similarly. We shall meet the rest in the next few chapters and provide some justification for the apparent coincidence in symbolism.

9.6 Eccentricities of the Extended Arithmetic

The reader may remember solving equations such as

$$x^2 - 3x + 2 = 0$$

which conveniently breaks down into

$$(x - 2)(x - 1) = 0$$

and provides solutions

$$x = 2 \quad \text{and} \quad x = 1.$$

He may also remember having to use

$$x = \frac{-b \pm \sqrt{(b^2 - 4ac)}}{2a}$$

to solve equations such as $x^2 + 4x + 1 = 0$ which refused to factorize.

The last horror that could be produced was of the style $x^2 + x + 1 = 0$ where

$$x = \frac{-1 \pm \sqrt{(1^2 - 4 \times 1 \times 1)}}{2} = \frac{-1 \pm \sqrt{-3}}{2}$$

and we met the square root of a negative number. We would then dutifully write 'no real roots' and sit back relieved that we did not have to work it out. We would be unlucky in the extended arithmetic. The equation $x^2 + x + 1 = 0$ certainly has a solution if 2×2 matrices are allowed.

Let x be $\begin{bmatrix} -\dfrac{1}{2} & \dfrac{\sqrt{3}}{2} \\[2ex] -\dfrac{\sqrt{3}}{2} & -\dfrac{1}{2} \end{bmatrix}$.

Then $x^2 = \begin{bmatrix} -\dfrac{1}{2} & \dfrac{\sqrt{3}}{2} \\[2ex] -\dfrac{\sqrt{3}}{2} & -\dfrac{1}{2} \end{bmatrix} \begin{bmatrix} -\dfrac{1}{2} & \dfrac{\sqrt{3}}{2} \\[2ex] -\dfrac{\sqrt{3}}{2} & -\dfrac{1}{2} \end{bmatrix} = \begin{bmatrix} -\dfrac{1}{2} & -\dfrac{\sqrt{3}}{2} \\[2ex] \dfrac{\sqrt{3}}{2} & -\dfrac{1}{2} \end{bmatrix}$.

Thus $x^2 + x + 1 = \begin{bmatrix} -\dfrac{1}{2} & -\dfrac{\sqrt{3}}{2} \\[2ex] \dfrac{\sqrt{3}}{2} & -\dfrac{1}{2} \end{bmatrix} + \begin{bmatrix} -\dfrac{1}{2} & \dfrac{\sqrt{3}}{2} \\[2ex] -\dfrac{\sqrt{3}}{2} & -\dfrac{1}{2} \end{bmatrix} + \begin{bmatrix} 1 & 0 \\ 0 & 1 \end{bmatrix}$

$= \begin{bmatrix} 0 & 0 \\ 0 & 0 \end{bmatrix}$ or 0.

Therefore

$$\begin{bmatrix} -\dfrac{1}{2} & \dfrac{\sqrt{3}}{2} \\[2ex] -\dfrac{\sqrt{3}}{2} & -\dfrac{1}{2} \end{bmatrix}$$

is certainly a solution. The reader may care to check that

$$\begin{bmatrix} -\dfrac{1}{2} & -\dfrac{\sqrt{3}}{2} \\[2ex] \dfrac{\sqrt{3}}{2} & -\dfrac{1}{2} \end{bmatrix}$$

is also a solution. We are now in a predicament.

Once again a rule which we thought inviolate has failed us. A quadratic that should have no roots turns out to have two. Can a quadratic in this system have more than two? if so, how do we find them—or the original two for that matter? Furthermore is there any practical value in following this line of reasoning or is this just another form of mental circuit training?

The last question is best answered first. As a result of all this we shall reach a compromise whereby we shall evolve an in-between arithmetic which will enable us to solve all quadratics and to find two roots for each but no more. This did evolve originally as a mathematician's plaything which does in fact have many useful applications in pure mathematics. Later the physicists and electrical engineers took over and it has turned out to be a most powerful tool in alternating current theory.

Let us return to the idea of a quadratic having more than two roots. Consider again

$$x^2 - 3x + 2 = 0$$

which we solved previously to give

$$x = 1 \quad \text{and} \quad 2, \quad \text{or} \quad \begin{bmatrix} 1 & 0 \\ 0 & 1 \end{bmatrix} \quad \text{and} \quad \begin{bmatrix} 2 & 0 \\ 0 & 2 \end{bmatrix} \quad \text{in matrix notation.}$$

Now let us try $\begin{bmatrix} 2 & 0 \\ 3 & 1 \end{bmatrix}$ as a solution.

$$x^2 = \begin{bmatrix} 2 & 0 \\ 3 & 1 \end{bmatrix} \begin{bmatrix} 2 & 0 \\ 3 & 1 \end{bmatrix} = \begin{bmatrix} 4 & 0 \\ 9 & 1 \end{bmatrix}$$

$$-3x = -3 \begin{bmatrix} 2 & 0 \\ 3 & 1 \end{bmatrix} = \begin{bmatrix} -6 & 0 \\ -9 & -3 \end{bmatrix}$$

$$2 = \begin{bmatrix} 2 & 0 \\ 0 & 2 \end{bmatrix}$$

Therefore

$$x = \begin{bmatrix} 2 & 0 \\ 3 & 1 \end{bmatrix} \Rightarrow x^2 - 3x + 2 = \begin{bmatrix} 4 & 0 \\ 9 & 1 \end{bmatrix} + \begin{bmatrix} -6 & 0 \\ -9 & -3 \end{bmatrix} + \begin{bmatrix} 2 & 0 \\ 0 & 2 \end{bmatrix}$$

$$= \begin{bmatrix} 0 & 0 \\ 0 & 0 \end{bmatrix} \quad \text{or} \quad 0.$$

Thus $x^2 - 3x + 2 = 0$ has at least three solutions in the extended system, i.e.

$$\begin{bmatrix} 1 & 0 \\ 0 & 1 \end{bmatrix}, \quad \begin{bmatrix} 2 & 0 \\ 0 & 2 \end{bmatrix}, \quad \text{and} \quad \begin{bmatrix} 2 & 0 \\ 3 & 1 \end{bmatrix}.$$

We must now see how to get these extra roots. To do this we first of all consider how we found the ordinary variety.

Once again

$$x^2 - 3x + 2 = 0,$$
$$\Downarrow$$
$$(x - 2)(x - 1) = 0.$$

We now state that if two expressions multiply to 0 then one of them must be 0. This is certainly true for normal numbers but it is not true for 2×2 matrices. For example,

$$\begin{bmatrix} 3 & 0 \\ 0 & 0 \end{bmatrix} \begin{bmatrix} 0 & 0 \\ 2 & 3 \end{bmatrix} = \begin{bmatrix} 0 & 0 \\ 0 & 0 \end{bmatrix}$$

We must therefore argue more carefully.

$$(x-2)(x-1) = 0.$$

Either $(x-2)$ has a multiplicative inverse or it has not. If it has, we may multiply through by it and eliminate $(x-2)$. Thus

$$(x-2)^{-1}\{(x-2)(x-1)\} = 0$$
$$\Downarrow$$
$$\{(x-2)^{-1}(x-2)\}(x-1) = 0$$
$$\Downarrow$$
$$(x-1) = 0.$$

This gives us one of the orthodox results $x = 1$.

Similarly, $x-1$ either has an inverse or it has not. If it has, we proceed as before and get $x = 2$ as a solution. We are left with the cases where $x = 2$ has no inverse and $x = 1$ has no inverse.

Assume that $x-2$ has no inverse.

Rewrite x as $\begin{bmatrix} a & b \\ c & d \end{bmatrix}$ and -2 as $\begin{bmatrix} -2 & 0 \\ 0 & -2 \end{bmatrix}$.

Then

$$x-2 = \begin{bmatrix} a & b \\ c & d \end{bmatrix} + \begin{bmatrix} -2 & 0 \\ 0 & -2 \end{bmatrix} = \begin{bmatrix} a-2 & b \\ c & d-2 \end{bmatrix}.$$

This has no inverse and therefore its determinant is zero (see page 101). Therefore,

$$(a-2)(d-2) = bc.$$

This means that if we choose any four numbers to satisfy

$$(a-2)(d-2) = bc$$

we shall get a matrix for $x-2$ which has no inverse. Similarly, if we write down the condition that $x-1$ has no inverse we get

$$(a-1)(d-1) = bc.$$

In order to get more solutions than the original two we must assume that neither $x-1$ nor $x-2$ has an inverse since the existence of an inverse for one immediately implies that the other is 0. On this assumption therefore both $(a-2)(d-2) = bc$ and $(a-1)(d-1) = bc$ must be true. From this $(a-1)(d-1) = (a-2)(d-2)$. One set of circumstances where this happens is when both sides are 0, i.e. when $a = 1$ and $d = 2$ or $a = 2$ and $d = 1$. In this case $bc = 0$ which means (since b and c are real numbers) $b = 0$ or $c = 0$. We are therefore faced with the following series of solutions for

$$x^2 - 3x + 2 = 0,$$

$$\begin{bmatrix} 1 & 0 \\ 0 & 1 \end{bmatrix}, \begin{bmatrix} 2 & 0 \\ 0 & 2 \end{bmatrix} \quad \text{(the orthodox ones),}$$

and

$$\begin{bmatrix} 1 & 0 \\ c & 2 \end{bmatrix}, \begin{bmatrix} 1 & b \\ 0 & 2 \end{bmatrix}, \begin{bmatrix} 2 & 0 \\ c & 1 \end{bmatrix} \text{ and } \begin{bmatrix} 2 & b \\ 0 & 1 \end{bmatrix}$$

where the b's and c's can be any real number.

We had better check this. Try $\begin{bmatrix} 1 & b \\ 0 & 2 \end{bmatrix}$ as a solution.

$$x^2 = \begin{bmatrix} 1 & b \\ 0 & 2 \end{bmatrix} \begin{bmatrix} 1 & b \\ 0 & 2 \end{bmatrix} = \begin{bmatrix} 1 & 3b \\ 0 & 4 \end{bmatrix},$$

$$-3x = -3 \begin{bmatrix} 1 & b \\ 0 & 2 \end{bmatrix} = \begin{bmatrix} -3 & -3b \\ 0 & -6 \end{bmatrix},$$

$$2 = \begin{bmatrix} 2 & 0 \\ 0 & 2 \end{bmatrix}.$$

$$x^2 - 3x + 2 = \begin{bmatrix} 1 & 3b \\ 0 & 4 \end{bmatrix} + \begin{bmatrix} -3 & -3b \\ 0 & -6 \end{bmatrix} + \begin{bmatrix} 2 & 0 \\ 0 & 2 \end{bmatrix} = \begin{bmatrix} 0 & 0 \\ 0 & 0 \end{bmatrix} \quad \text{or} \quad 0.$$

We have now found an infinite number of solutions to what was always considered to be a most reputable quadratic. This stretches our morale too far. We shall therefore cut out all matrices that have no multiplicative inverse, except $\begin{bmatrix} 0 & 0 \\ 0 & 0 \end{bmatrix}$ which is a necessity as the neutral element for '+'. We still however have to satisfy the group axioms for both '+' and '×' as well as contain the real numbers as part of the system. The best way is to consider only matrices of the form $\begin{bmatrix} a & -b \\ b & a \end{bmatrix}$. These can only have no inverse if $a^2 + b^2 = 0$ which means that both a and b are 0. This gives us $\begin{bmatrix} 0 & 0 \\ 0 & 0 \end{bmatrix}$ which we have allowed. An examination of this system is the topic for the next section.

Examples 9d

Find as many roots as possible in the extended arithmetic for the following quadratics.

1. $x^2 = 0$,

2. $x^2 - 1 = 0$,

3. $x^2 + 1 = 0$,

4. $x^2 - 2x + 1 = 0$,

5. $x^2 - 5x + 4 = 0$,

6. $x^2 - x + 3 = 0$.

9.7 Complex Numbers

By now the reader should be in a position to prove that matrices of the form $\begin{bmatrix} a & -b \\ b & a \end{bmatrix}$, where a and b are real numbers, form a group under '+' and, if $\begin{bmatrix} 0 & 0 \\ 0 & 0 \end{bmatrix}$ is omitted, that they also form a group under '$\times$'. Let us examine our new toys more closely.

$$\begin{bmatrix} a & -b \\ b & a \end{bmatrix} = \begin{bmatrix} a & 0 \\ 0 & a \end{bmatrix} + \begin{bmatrix} 0 & -b \\ b & 0 \end{bmatrix}$$

which we may consider as being effectively a real number added to $\begin{bmatrix} 0 & -b \\ b & 0 \end{bmatrix}$. This in turn may be further broken down into $b\begin{bmatrix} 0 & -1 \\ 1 & 0 \end{bmatrix}$. Thus we may deduce that any matrix in the new family may be written as the sum of a real number and the product of another real number and $\begin{bmatrix} 0 & -1 \\ 1 & 0 \end{bmatrix}$. $\begin{bmatrix} 0 & -1 \\ 1 & 0 \end{bmatrix}$ is usually written as i and so our new system has reduced to $a+bi$ where a and b are real numbers.

$a+bi$ is called a complex number. a is called its real part and bi its imaginary part. The terminology is unfortunate and conjures up dreadful difficulties. It was thought up before the nature of the things was fully appreciated and, in spite of persuasion, has just stuck. There is nothing complex or imaginary about these numbers. The reader has doubtless noted that we have even managed to keep the number of new symbols down to one—a relative triumph.

Let us consider the nature of i.

i is $\begin{bmatrix} 0 & -1 \\ 1 & 0 \end{bmatrix}$. i^2 is therefore

$$\begin{bmatrix} 0 & -1 \\ 1 & 0 \end{bmatrix}\begin{bmatrix} 0 & -1 \\ 1 & 0 \end{bmatrix} = \begin{bmatrix} -1 & 0 \\ 0 & -1 \end{bmatrix}$$

which is effectively -1.

Therefore

$$i^2 = -1$$

or

$$i = \pm\sqrt{-1}.$$

Let us go further

$$i^3 = i \times i^2 = i \times (-1) = -i,$$

$$i^4 = i^2 \times i^2 = (-1) \times (-1) = 1.$$

Thus we may note that i has a curious little arithmetic of its own which we may express as

×	1	i	-1	$-i$
1	1	i	-1	$-i$
i	i	-1	$-i$	1
-1	-1	$-i$	1	i
$-i$	$-i$	1	i	-1

TABLE 42

which is a group isomorphic to the cyclic four group. We will justify the isomorphism geometrically in the next chapter.

We may note that the introduction of i gives negative numbers a measure of respectability previously only enjoyed by their positive colleagues in that they now all have square roots. Thus we may write the square root of -4 as $\pm\sqrt{(4i)^2} = \pm 2i$. This leads us back to the start of this discussion two sections ago with the solution of quadratic equations. We failed with

$$x^2 + x + 1 = 0$$

because we ended with

$$x = \frac{-1 \pm \sqrt{-3}}{2}.$$

However we may now progress a stage further with

$$x = -\frac{1}{2} + i\frac{\sqrt{3}}{2} \quad \text{or} \quad x = -\frac{1}{2} - i\frac{\sqrt{3}}{2}$$

which, in matrix form, is

$$\begin{bmatrix} -\dfrac{1}{2} & -\dfrac{\sqrt{3}}{2} \\ \dfrac{\sqrt{3}}{2} & -\dfrac{1}{2} \end{bmatrix} \quad \text{or} \quad \begin{bmatrix} -\dfrac{1}{2} & \dfrac{\sqrt{3}}{2} \\ -\dfrac{\sqrt{3}}{2} & -\dfrac{1}{2} \end{bmatrix}$$

which we have already checked on p. 160. We may therefore state that this quadratic, or any other that involves the square root of a negative number, may be shown to have two solutions as do those involving the square root of a positive number.

The reader may have some qualms about accepting solutions involving i in as much as they may not consider it to be a 'proper' number. The difficulty here is one of familiarity and the propriety of a number probably depends upon its practicability rather than anything else. '2' is perfectly respectable as is '$\frac{1}{2}$'. '-2' is more tricky, but we can cover ourselves by talking airily about 'owing' and thermometer scales. We can accept $\sqrt{2}$—just—because of the passion for

Pythagoras, as the length of the hypotenuse of an isosceles right-angled triangle whose other two sides are of length 1. However, we see little virtue in '0·2020020002...' and consider that i is at least as respectable. As we mentioned at the end of the previous section, i can be used to solve problems both purely mathematical and highly practical, and is therefore, as we see it, perfectly acceptable.

It is not our task here to give a detailed account of complex numbers. The bibliography will guide the interested reader. We shall meet them again geometrically in the next chapter.

Examples 9e

Solve the equations of Examples 9d in the set of complex numbers, making sure that you get just two roots to each equation.

9.8 Proof of Cayley's Theorem

The reader may recall that we introduced this theorem at the end of Chapter 8 but left its proof until the reader was more familiar with iso-morphisms. The theorem states that, given any finite group, we may find a permutation group isomorphic to it. It is very simple to prove, but, as we found before with permutations, it is quite difficult to write down. We will dabble a little with notation before tackling the proof proper.

Let us assume that we have a group G with combining operation $*$ as usual and let us put the elements of G into some particular order. A natural one to choose would be the one across the top of the table. In the swapping system we might therefore choose $\{I, A, B, C\}$. For the moment we will use the symbol G to represent the set of elements of G in this specific order.

We will now operate on G by one of its own elements, x say. This we may write as $G * x$ which gives us the elements of G in a different order. Thus if we decide to operate on $\{I, A, B, C\}$ by A, for example, we would write it as $\{I, A, B, C\} f A$ which means $\{I f A, A f A, B f A, C f A\}$ which simplifies to $\{A, I, C, B\}$.

We may therefore look upon $\left(\dfrac{G}{G * x} \right)$ as a permutation on the elements of G.

In our example this would mean $\left(\dfrac{IABC}{(IABC) f A} \right)$ which reduces to the more

familiar $\left(\dfrac{IABC}{AICB} \right)$.

We have established previously (p. 132) that we may alter the top row of a permutation and still leave its meaning unchanged if we alter the bottom row

to correspond. Thus we may alter $\left(\dfrac{IABC}{AICB} \right)$ to $\left(\dfrac{BCIA}{CBAI} \right)$ with no change of

meaning. This is alternatively expressed as altering $\left(\dfrac{IABC}{(IABC) f A} \right)$ to

$\left(\dfrac{BCIA}{(BCIA) f A} \right)$. But the new version $(BCIA)$ can itself be expressed as

$(IABC)\mathrm{f}\,B$ and therefore, with much confusion, we may write $\left(\dfrac{IABC}{(IABC)\mathrm{f}\,A}\right)$

has the same meaning as $\left(\dfrac{(IABC)\mathrm{f}\,B}{[(IABC)\mathrm{f}\,B]\mathrm{f}\,A}\right)$.

We may usefully apply the Associative Law to the bottom line of the second

permutation to give $\left(\dfrac{(IABC)\mathrm{f}\,B}{(IABC)\mathrm{f}(B\mathrm{f}\,A)}\right)$.

This looks a little tidier and has the advantage of showing that all the extra elements with which we attack $(IABC)$ may be combined first of all.

Although the arguments given above look messy they appear far tidier in

the general case. Our original permutation was $\left(\dfrac{G}{G*x}\right)$. We may alter the top

row by combining each element of G with y, say, where y is a member of G. In order to keep the permutation the same, however, we must do the same

to G in the bottom line before we combine with x. Thus $\left(\dfrac{G}{G*x}\right)$ has the same

meaning as $\left(\dfrac{G*y}{(G*y)*x}\right)$. By applying the Associative Law we alter the bottom

row of the second matrix to $G*(y*x)$ so that $\left(\dfrac{G}{G*x}\right)$ has the same meaning

as $\left(\dfrac{G*y}{G*(y*x)}\right)$.

After all this playing with notation we are now in a position to prove Cayley's theorem easily. We may link each element x of G with the

permutation $\left(\dfrac{G}{G*x}\right)$ thus establishing a 1–1 correspondence between elements

and permutations. To show that the two are isomorphic we merely have to prove that corresponding calculations give corresponding results. Thus we

must establish that if we link x with y and $\left(\dfrac{G}{G*x}\right)$ with $\left(\dfrac{G}{G*y}\right)$ we get

corresponding answers. The result of linking x and y is $x*y$. To link $\left(\dfrac{G}{G*x}\right)$

and $\left(\dfrac{G}{G*y}\right)$ is more difficult. To do this we alter the top row of $\left(\dfrac{G}{G*y}\right)$ to

$G*x$ (see p. 134). As we have shown above, the corresponding version is now

$\left(\dfrac{G*x}{G*(x*y)}\right)$. $\left(\dfrac{G}{G*x}\right)$ and $\left(\dfrac{G*x}{G*(x*y)}\right)$ now link to give $\left(\dfrac{G}{G*(x*y)}\right)$ which

corresponds to $x*y$. Thus the set of elements and the set of their corresponding permutations are isomorphic under their respective combining operations which proves the theorem.

10. GEOMETRY

10.1 A New Approach

It is only fitting that after nine chapters of assorted arithmetics we should turn to geometry for the classification of our ideas. Mercifully we no longer teach our children arithmetic, algebra and geometry as three separate disciplines at the rate of two periods per topic per week and most teachers of mathematics these days would be prepared to illustrate that

$$(a+b)^2 = a^2 + 2ab + b^2$$

by a geometrical aid such as

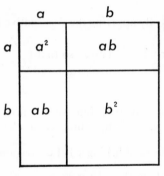

FIG. 48

However, the links between the three disciplines are far more fundamental than this and again we rely on group theory and matrices to expose them for us.

Before we can make progress however we must decide what we mean by geometry. Schoolboy geometry seemed to consist of an endless supply of congruent triangles and although this does the noble Euclid scant justice we will concentrate on this aspect for the moment as it is probably most familiar to the reader.

Avoiding details such as 'two sides and the included angle' and other unnecessary complications, we may say that two triangles are congruent if they may be twisted around and turned about until one fits exactly on top of the other. Working in the world of Euclid instead of Lewis Carroll, we are entitled to assume that our triangles remain unaltered as regards shape and size. Life is more interesting without these restrictions but that will come later. In the next few pages we shall treat congruence according to the definition given above.

10.2 Motion Geometry

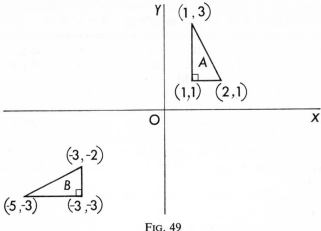

Fig. 49

The two triangles in the above diagram are congruent (two sides and right-angle). We will now assume that the two axes and the triangle B are made of wire and are fixed, whereas triangle A is on a large, flat sheet of cardboard, which may move freely beneath the wire. We now describe the physical processes necessary to move triangle A directly beneath B and thus establish the congruence.

We must first of all rotate the sheet of cardboard so that the sides of A are parallel to those of B. For the sake of simplicity we will assume that we always rotate the sheet of cardboard about the point which is directly below the origin O where the two wires cross. Should we require rotation about any other point on the cardboard we merely slide it until the point lies beneath O and then rotate. The value of this idea will appear when we come to write down these processes more precisely.

The rotation of the plane until the sides of A are parallel to those of B gives us

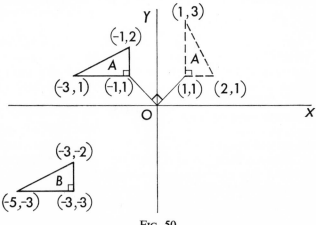

Fig. 50

In this case we may find the new coordinates for the corners of A by common sense. Better techniques for more complex cases will appear later. We may note that each corner of the triangle is still exactly the same distance from O as it was before and that the line joining each corner to O has rotated through 90°. This, of course, is the amount of rotation necessary to align the corresponding sides of the triangles. Remember that whilst all this has been going on, triangle B has stayed where it was.

All that is necessary now to establish congruence is to give our sheet of cardboard a sharp tug to the left and downwards, being careful to avoid further rotation. Such a movement, which keeps the directions of lines unaltered but moves their positions, is technically called a translation. In this case we may describe the translation as 'two squares to the left and four down' and by sliding the cardboard by these amounts the triangles will be made to coincide.

Thus the movements required to fit triangle A exactly beneath triangle B may be summarized as

(i) a rotation anti-clockwise through 90°,

(ii) a translation of two squares to the left and four down.

Other congruence situations may be described by similar means. Unfortunately there is a complication. Euclid would have it that ◿ and ◺ are congruent and no amount of rotating or translating will fit one beneath the other. We will deal with this in the next section.

Examples 10a

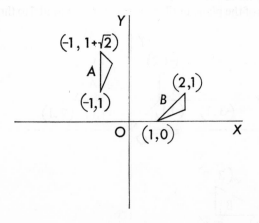

Fig. 51

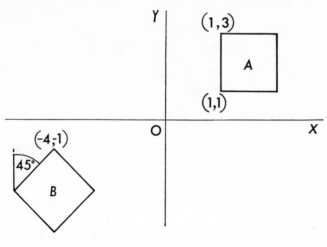

FIG. 52

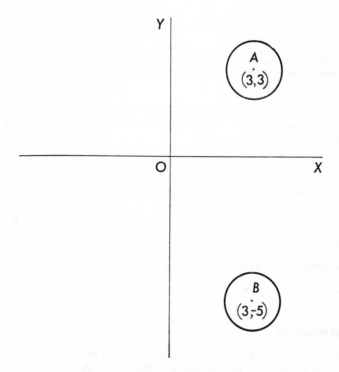

FIG. 53

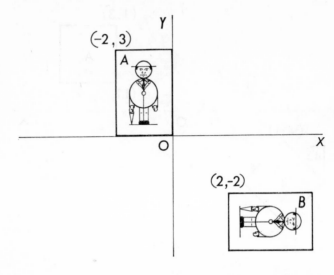

Fig. 54

1. In the above figures describe the rotations and translations necessary to demonstrate the congruences. Sometimes there are several possibilities. Why is this? Find them all.

2. In the text we rotated the triangle first and then translated it. Analyse your answers to Question 1 to see whether we would get the same effect by translating first and then rotating.

3. Congruence may be demonstrated in all the above figures without translation if a centre of rotation is chosen which is not at the origin O. Find, by drawing, the centre of rotation and the angle of rotation in each case and hence evolve a general rule for so doing.

4. Do the set of all rotations of a figure about the origin form a group under the combining operation 'followed by'?

5. Do the set of all translations of a figure form a group under the combining operation 'followed by'?

10.3 Reflection

If we try to repeat the procedure of section 10.2 in the following situation we see that no amount of rotation will align the sides of the two triangles although they are obviously congruent as before.

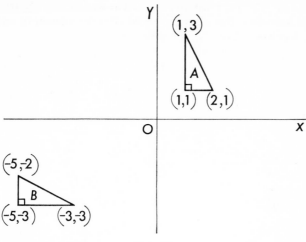

FIG. 55

What is required is that A, and therefore our cardboard plane, should be turned completely over. Unfortunately we could not then see A so that we will replace the cardboard sheet by a Perspex one and proceed as before. Again for simplicity's sake we restrict the turning-over process to a twisting about the line $y = 0$. In other words, we pretend that the horizontal wire acts as an axle about which we can momentarily turn the plane giving us

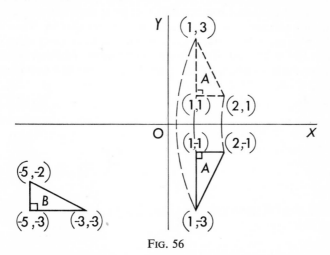

FIG. 56

The new position of A we call the reflection of A in the line $y = 0$—a choice of title whose aptness we shall discuss later in the chapter. As with rotation we could turn the plane about any other line in the plane, but to do this we would first of all rotate and slide the line until it lay under the horizontal wire. This again will make for simplicity when we come to write these movements down. However, our main task in this section was to turn the triangle over and now we have done this we can proceed after the manner of section 10.2.

An anti-clockwise rotation of 90° gives us

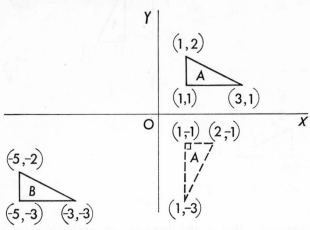

FIG. 57

and a translation of six to the left and four down finishes the process. Thus congruence is demonstrated by a reflection, a rotation and a translation.

The results of this section and the preceding one may be generalized to all plane figures so that we may say that if two plane figures are congruent, one may be moved to fit exactly beneath the other by at most one reflection in the line $y = 0$, one rotation about the origin and one translation. Thus we may reduce the physical demonstration of congruence to at most three distinct types of movement. The rest of this chapter will consist of a closer examination of these after the lines which we have developed in the first nine chapters.

Examples 10b

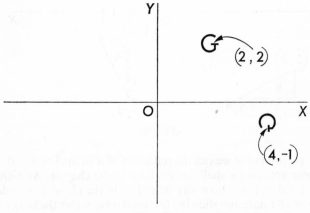

FIG. 58

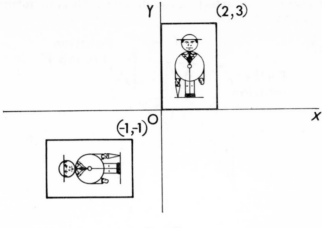

FIG. 59

1. In the above figures describe the reflections, rotations, and translations necessary to demonstrate the congruences.

2. In the text we reflected first, then rotated, and then translated. There are six different orders in which we could have done these processes. Analyse your answers to Question 1 to see which of these orders will have the same effect as the original.

3. We have so far restricted ourselves to reflection about the line $y = 0$. What is the effect of a reflection about a line followed by a reflection about a line parallel to the first and 1 in. away from it?

4. What is the effect of a reflection in a line followed by a reflection in a line which cuts the first at an angle of 30°? What is the result if the angle is increased to 90°?

5. Draw enlargements of Figs. 51, 52, 53, and 54 on graph paper and construct lines about which the figures may be reflected in order to demonstrate the congruences by reflection only.

10.4 Rotations

In our examination of each type of motion we have two main aims. Firstly, we wish to test the relevance of group theory and secondly, where possible, we wish to find a way of expressing these movements in matrix form. This will enable us to establish the relationship, if any, between this work and the work we have done previously.

We first examine the group aspect. Let us suppose that triangle A, and hence the whole plane, is rotated about the origin through an angle P and then through an angle Q. For convenience, we will make a point of always measuring angles in an anti-clockwise direction. The two rotations will result in something like this:

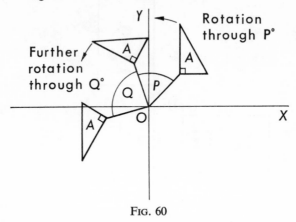

FIG. 60

Such rotations are easy and amusing to draw. If, for example, we wish to demonstrate the effect of a 20° rotation we merely draw straight lines from each corner of the triangle to the origin, rotate each line through 20°, and then join up the ends. Polar graph paper is ideal for this exercise.

We now test for group properties. The set of elements under consideration is the set of rotations of the cardboard plane through various angles. A rotation through $P°$ is one such element, which we will represent by P. Similarly a rotation through $Q°$ we will call Q. As in earlier examples involving rotations we shall never require a rotation greater than 360°.

The combining operation we shall use is the ubiquitous '+'. The effect of a rotation P followed by a rotation Q is a rotation through $(P+Q)°$ which we represent by $P+Q$. This is in itself a rotation whatever P and Q may be and therefore we have closure under '+'. The combination of rotations, as just defined, gives rise to just one result for each pair of rotations, so that both closure and uniqueness hold good for the set of rotations under '+'.

For the Associative Law we require three rotations, P, Q and R. $P+(Q+R)$ means a rotation first of all through $P°$ and then through $(Q+R)°$. The net result is a rotation through $(P+Q+R)°$ whether we work it out this way or as $(P+Q)+R$, so that the Associative Law is true. If this seems unconvincing we shall eventually convert these rotations to 2×2 matrices under '$\times$' for which the Associative Law has already been proved to be true.

A rotation through 0° is an obvious neutral element whilst, since we take P to be a rotation of $P°$ in an anti-clockwise direction, we may accept $-P$ as being a rotation of $P°$ in a clockwise direction. $-P$ now undoes the work of P in that $P+(-P) = (-P)+P = 0$, so that P and $-P$ are inverses. Alternatively, we may look upon a rotation of $(360-P)°$ as being the inverse of P.

We note finally that the combined effect of P and Q is a rotation of $(P+Q)°$ whether we link them as $P+Q$ or $Q+P$, so that the Commutative Law is also true. Thus the set of rotations under '+' forms an Abelian group.

The next step is to convert our rotation to matrices. To do this we examine the effect of a rotation of $P°$ on just one point of the plane.

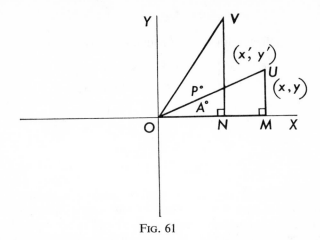

FIG. 61

Let the point be at U with coordinates (x, y) before rotation and let OU make an angle A with the horizontal. After rotation we will assume that the point has moved to V of coordinates (x', y'). We are interested in the relationship between U and V, or, in other words, the connexions between (x, y) and (x', y'). Remember that by the very nature of pure rotation V is the same distance from O as U. Now

$$x' = ON$$
$$= OV \cos(A+P)$$
$$= OU \cos(A+P)$$
$$= OU(\cos A \cos P - \sin A \sin P)$$
$$= OU\left(\frac{OM}{OU} \cos P - \frac{UM}{OU} \sin P\right)$$
$$= OM \cos P - UM \sin P$$
$$= x \cos P - y \sin P.$$

Similarly,
$$y' = VN$$
$$= OV \sin(A+P)$$
$$= OU \sin(A+P)$$
$$= OU(\sin A \cos P + \cos A \sin P)$$
$$= OU\left(\frac{UM}{OU} \cos P + \frac{OM}{OU} \sin P\right)$$
$$= UM \cos P + OM \sin P$$
$$= y \cos P + x \sin P.$$

To summarize:

$$x' = x\cos P - y\sin P,$$

$$y' = x\sin P + y\cos P,$$

which from our efforts with simultaneous equations (p. 117) we may write as

$$\begin{bmatrix} x' \\ y' \end{bmatrix} = \begin{bmatrix} \cos P & -\sin P \\ \sin P & \cos P \end{bmatrix} \begin{bmatrix} x \\ y \end{bmatrix}$$

Thus the 'process' which converts $\begin{bmatrix} x \\ y \end{bmatrix}$ to $\begin{bmatrix} x' \\ y' \end{bmatrix}$ is the 2×2 matrix

$$\begin{bmatrix} \cos P & -\sin P \\ \sin P & \cos P \end{bmatrix}$$

which, logically enough, depends only on the angle of rotation P.

We have now achieved the second of our initial aims and converted rotations to 2×2 matrices. However, we have not as yet evolved an official combining operation, although we may well suspect that it is going to be matrix multiplication. Let us try and see.

A rotation through $P°$ followed by one through $Q°$ is written as

$$\begin{bmatrix} \cos P & -\sin P \\ \sin P & \cos P \end{bmatrix} \text{ followed by } \begin{bmatrix} \cos Q & -\sin Q \\ \sin Q & \cos Q \end{bmatrix}.$$

With matrix multiplication as the combining operation this would be written as

$$\begin{bmatrix} \cos Q & -\sin Q \\ \sin Q & \cos Q \end{bmatrix} \begin{bmatrix} \cos P & -\sin P \\ \sin P & \cos P \end{bmatrix},$$

allowing for the normal matrix habit of working backwards. Matrix multiplication simplifies this to

$$\begin{bmatrix} \cos Q \cos P - \sin Q \sin P & -(\cos Q \sin P + \sin Q \cos P) \\ \sin Q \cos P + \cos Q \sin P & \cos Q \cos P - \sin Q \sin P \end{bmatrix}$$

$$= \begin{bmatrix} \cos(P+Q) & -\sin(P+Q) \\ \sin(P+Q) & \cos(P+Q) \end{bmatrix}$$

which represents a rotation through $(P+Q)°$ as required.

We have thus achieved our aims as far as rotations are concerned. We have shown the relevance of group theory and have also shown that a matrix representation of rotation is perfectly feasible. Many members of

$$\left\{ \begin{bmatrix} \cos P & -\sin P \\ \sin P & \cos P \end{bmatrix} \right\}$$

have appeared previously. We shall trace some of the connecting links in the next section.

Examples 10c

1. Express in the simplest possible matrix form rotation through

(a) 0°,   (d) 60°,   (g) 135°,

(b) 30°,   (e) 90°,   (h) 150°,

(c) 45°,   (f) 120°,   (i) 180°.

We shall use these most frequently and the reader will find it convenient to be able to recognize them.

2. We constructed $\left\{ \begin{bmatrix} \cos P & -\sin P \\ \sin P & \cos P \end{bmatrix} \right\}$ under '×' to be isomorphic to the set of rotations under '+'. To check the validity of our reasoning establish the isomorphism by the normal methods of 'corresponding calculations give corresponding results'.

3. By Question 2, $\left\{ \begin{bmatrix} \cos P & -\sin P \\ \sin P & \cos P \end{bmatrix} \right\}$ forms a group under '×' since the set of rotations forms a group under '+'. Check that this is so by proving that $\left\{ \begin{bmatrix} \cos P & -\sin P \\ \sin P & \cos P \end{bmatrix} \right\}$ under '×' satisfies the group axioms directly.

10.5 Some Deductions from 10.4

Our main object in representing rotations by 2×2 matrices is to enable us to link them with what we have done previously. We may first of all notice that $\left\{ \begin{bmatrix} \cos P & -\sin P \\ \sin P & \cos P \end{bmatrix} \right\}$ is a subset of $\left\{ \begin{bmatrix} a & -b \\ b & a \end{bmatrix} \right\}$ which are the complex numbers of Chapter 9. Thus some complex numbers have the effect of pure rotation. We shall examine later what the others do. The distinguishing feature of the $\begin{bmatrix} \cos P & -\sin P \\ \sin P & \cos P \end{bmatrix}$ type is that its associated determinant is $\cos^2 P + \sin^2 P = 1$ for all values of P and we may use this characteristic to separate them from other complex numbers.

We discover further links if we consider other cases where we have used pure rotation. In the last chapter we were careful to examine the connexions between the four-hour clock arithmetic and the dancers' circling. Each hourly movement means a rotation of 90°, so that the rotations involved for 4, 1, 2 and 3 hours are 0° (−360°), −90°, −180°, and −270° respectively. (− signs are necessary because the rotation is in the clockwise or negative direction.) Writing these in the new matrix form we get

$$\begin{bmatrix} \cos 0° & -\sin 0° \\ \sin 0° & \cos 0° \end{bmatrix}, \quad \begin{bmatrix} \cos(-90°) & -\sin(-90°) \\ \sin(-90°) & \cos(-90)° \end{bmatrix},$$

$$\begin{bmatrix} \cos(-180°) & -\sin(-180°) \\ \sin(-180°) & \cos(-180°) \end{bmatrix} \quad \text{and} \quad \begin{bmatrix} \cos(-270°) & -\sin(-270°) \\ \sin(-270°) & \cos(-270°) \end{bmatrix}$$

which simplify to

$$\begin{bmatrix} 1 & 0 \\ 0 & 1 \end{bmatrix}, \quad \begin{bmatrix} 0 & 1 \\ -1 & 0 \end{bmatrix}, \quad \begin{bmatrix} -1 & 0 \\ 0 & -1 \end{bmatrix} \text{ and } \begin{bmatrix} 0 & -1 \\ 1 & 0 \end{bmatrix}$$

These are the same matrices that we evolved previously (p. 164) and correspond to the complex numbers $1, -i, -1, i$ (p. 165) which provided a cyclic four-group isomorphic to the four-hour clock arithmetic and the dancers' circling. This chain of isomorphisms deserves careful study. We may explain it by the fact that each of the various systems eventually consists of rotation through the four angles $0°, 90°, 180°$ and $270°$ clockwise.

Even yet we have not abstracted all significance from this situation. Let us take any point on our cardboard plane—say $(1, 2)$ for the sake of our arithmetic and write it as $\begin{bmatrix} 1 \\ 2 \end{bmatrix}$ so that the matrices can get to work on it.

$$\begin{bmatrix} 1 & 0 \\ 0 & 1 \end{bmatrix} \begin{bmatrix} 1 \\ 2 \end{bmatrix} = \begin{bmatrix} 1 \\ 2 \end{bmatrix}$$

and has no effect as we would expect.

$$\begin{bmatrix} 0 & 1 \\ -1 & 0 \end{bmatrix} \begin{bmatrix} 1 \\ 2 \end{bmatrix} = \begin{bmatrix} 2 \\ -1 \end{bmatrix}$$

$$\begin{bmatrix} -1 & 0 \\ 0 & -1 \end{bmatrix} \begin{bmatrix} 1 \\ 2 \end{bmatrix} = \begin{bmatrix} -1 \\ -2 \end{bmatrix}$$

and

$$\begin{bmatrix} 0 & -1 \\ 1 & 0 \end{bmatrix} \begin{bmatrix} 1 \\ 2 \end{bmatrix} = \begin{bmatrix} -2 \\ 1 \end{bmatrix}$$

These points appear in the following positions

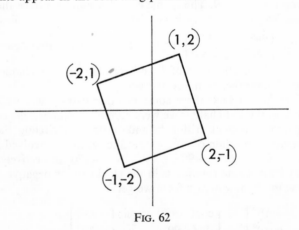

Fig. 62

and form the corners of a square. The square, if rotated about its centre in the usual way, will give rise to a cyclic four-group, which is of course isomorphic to the group of four matrices which generate the four corners. We may note further that if we operate on the four corners by any of the matrices we merely move them round 0, 1, 2 and 3 places according to the matrix chosen. Thus

$$\begin{bmatrix} 0 & 1 \\ -1 & 0 \end{bmatrix} \begin{bmatrix} 1 \\ 2 \end{bmatrix} = \begin{bmatrix} 2 \\ -1 \end{bmatrix}$$

$$\begin{bmatrix} 0 & 1 \\ -1 & 0 \end{bmatrix} \begin{bmatrix} -2 \\ 1 \end{bmatrix} = \begin{bmatrix} 1 \\ 2 \end{bmatrix}$$

$$\begin{bmatrix} 0 & 1 \\ -1 & 0 \end{bmatrix} \begin{bmatrix} -1 \\ -2 \end{bmatrix} = \begin{bmatrix} -2 \\ 1 \end{bmatrix}$$

$$\begin{bmatrix} 0 & 1 \\ -1 & 0 \end{bmatrix} \begin{bmatrix} 2 \\ -1 \end{bmatrix} = \begin{bmatrix} -1 \\ -2 \end{bmatrix}$$

and the points appear in the same cyclic order, but move one place round.

We may adopt similar techniques to the above with any regular polygon and thus convert any structure based on pure rotation in a plane to 2×2 matrices of the form $\begin{bmatrix} \cos P & -\sin P \\ \sin P & \cos P \end{bmatrix}$ and therefore of the type dealt with in this section.

Examples 10d

1. The arguments of this section were based on the various representations of the cyclic four group. Try to follow a similar route for the three-group.
2. Repeat Question 1 with the cyclic six-group.
3. Repeat Question 1 with the two-group.
4. Repeat Question 1 with the Klein four-group.
5. Re-examine your chart of Question 1, Examples 9a, p. 153 in the light of this section and the above examples.

10.6 The Argand Diagram

The matrix $\begin{bmatrix} x \\ y \end{bmatrix}$ depends on two numbers, x and y, as does the point (x, y) and we have therefore been justified in using $\begin{bmatrix} x \\ y \end{bmatrix}$ to represent (x, y) and vice versa. In other words there is a 1–1 correspondence between $\left\{ \begin{bmatrix} x \\ y \end{bmatrix} \right\}$ and $\{(x, y)\}$ where x and y are real numbers. Similarly there is a 1–1 correspondence between $\{(x, y)\}$ and $\left\{ \begin{bmatrix} x & -y \\ y & x \end{bmatrix} \right\}$, the set of complex numbers, so that we are justified in representing these by points on a graph if we so desire. $\begin{bmatrix} x & -y \\ y & x \end{bmatrix}$ is in general more amenable to discipline than $\begin{bmatrix} x \\ y \end{bmatrix}$ in that we can both add and multiply its members. Adding and multiplying points is a dubious hobby at this stage but interpretations on the graph will follow in due course. For the moment we will just accept that complex numbers may be so represented and see what evolves. The correspondence is easier to see in the $x + iy$ form where, for example, $3 + 2i$ is simply plotted as $(3, 2)$. The type of graph on which we are prepared to plot complex numbers as points is called the Argand diagram after the famous Swiss mathematician Dr Argand (1768–1822).

Fortunately, a rotation such as $\begin{bmatrix} \cos P & -\sin P \\ \sin P & \cos P \end{bmatrix}$ has the same effect on

$\begin{bmatrix} x & -y \\ y & x \end{bmatrix}$ as it has on $\begin{bmatrix} x \\ y \end{bmatrix}$ since

$$\begin{bmatrix} \cos P & -\sin P \\ \sin P & \cos P \end{bmatrix} \begin{bmatrix} x \\ y \end{bmatrix} = \begin{bmatrix} x\cos P - y\sin P \\ x\sin P + y\cos P \end{bmatrix}$$

and

$$\begin{bmatrix} \cos P & -\sin P \\ \sin P & \cos P \end{bmatrix} \begin{bmatrix} x & -y \\ y & x \end{bmatrix} = \begin{bmatrix} x\cos P - y\sin P & -(y\cos P + x\sin P) \\ x\sin P + y\cos P & x\cos P - y\sin P \end{bmatrix},$$

both results corresponding to $\{(x\cos P - y\sin P), (x\sin P + y\cos P)\}$. Therefore we may apply all that we have discovered about rotation so far to the Argand

diagram. Also the very rotation $\begin{bmatrix} \cos P & -\sin P \\ \sin P & \cos P \end{bmatrix}$ corresponds to a point

$(\cos P, \sin P)$ on the Argand diagram and we may note that this is the point reached by the point $(1, 0)$ when the plane is rotated through angle $P°$.

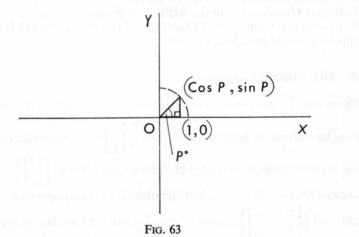

FIG. 63

We now show an amusing alternative to the process of section 10.5 for the rotation of a regular polygon. We will tackle the equilateral triangle and therefore start by solving the equation $Z^3 = 1$, since the triangle has three sides. We would normally be content with the solution $Z = 1$, but our new-found freedom makes us go further.

$$Z^3 = 1$$
$$\Downarrow$$
$$Z^3 - 1 = 0$$
$$\Downarrow$$
$$(Z-1)(Z^2+Z+1) = 0$$
$$\Downarrow$$
$$Z = 1 \quad \text{or} \quad Z^2+Z+1 = 0.$$

We have previously solved

$$Z^2+Z+1 = 0 \qquad \text{(p. 165)}$$

to give

$$Z = -\frac{1}{2}+\frac{\sqrt{3}}{2}i \quad \text{or} \quad -\frac{1}{2}-\frac{\sqrt{3}}{2}i,$$

so that the three solutions to $Z^3 = 1$ are

$$Z = 1, \quad -\frac{1}{2}+\frac{\sqrt{3}}{2}i \quad \text{and} \quad -\frac{1}{2}-\frac{\sqrt{3}}{2}i.$$

These may be plotted on the Argand diagram as the points $(1,0)$, $\left(-\frac{1}{2},\frac{\sqrt{3}}{2}\right)$ and $\left(-\frac{1}{2},-\frac{\sqrt{3}}{2}\right)$,

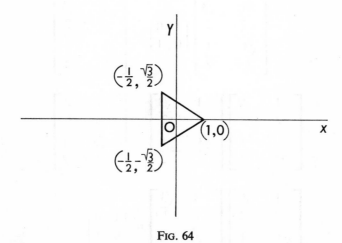

FIG. 64

which gives us our equilateral triangle. For a square we would solve completely $Z^4 = 1$, for a regular pentagon $Z^5 = 1$ and so on. The solution of such

13

equations can be tricky, but we may note that the three corners of our triangle may be expressed in matrix form as

$$\begin{bmatrix} 1 & 0 \\ 0 & 1 \end{bmatrix}, \quad \begin{bmatrix} -\dfrac{1}{2} & -\dfrac{\sqrt{3}}{2} \\[2mm] \dfrac{\sqrt{3}}{2} & -\dfrac{1}{2} \end{bmatrix} \quad \text{and} \quad \begin{bmatrix} -\dfrac{1}{2} & \dfrac{\sqrt{3}}{2} \\[2mm] -\dfrac{\sqrt{3}}{2} & -\dfrac{1}{2} \end{bmatrix}$$

which may be written as

$$\begin{bmatrix} \cos 0° & -\sin 0° \\ \sin 0° & \cos 0° \end{bmatrix}, \quad \begin{bmatrix} \cos 120° & -\sin 120° \\ \sin 120° & \cos 120° \end{bmatrix} \quad \text{and} \quad \begin{bmatrix} \cos 240° & -\sin 240° \\ \sin 240° & \cos 240° \end{bmatrix}$$

and represent rotations of 0°, 120° and 240° respectively. Thus for the equilateral triangle there are three roots that correspond to rotation of multiples of $\dfrac{360°}{3} = 120°$. Similarly for a regular pentagon there are five roots corresponding to rotations of multiples of $\dfrac{360°}{5} = 72°$.

Finally, we may note that the three matrices form a (cyclic) three-group under matrix multiplication isomorphic to the one we originally obtained by rotating the equilateral triangle in the plane (p. 134) and that if, in their capacity as points, we operate on them by one of themselves in its capacity as a rotation we turn the triangle through 0°, 120° or 240° according to choice. Thus

$$\begin{bmatrix} -\dfrac{1}{2} & -\dfrac{\sqrt{3}}{2} \\[2mm] \dfrac{\sqrt{3}}{2} & -\dfrac{1}{2} \end{bmatrix} \begin{bmatrix} 1 & 0 \\ 0 & 1 \end{bmatrix} = \begin{bmatrix} -\dfrac{1}{2} & -\dfrac{\sqrt{3}}{2} \\[2mm] \dfrac{\sqrt{3}}{2} & -\dfrac{1}{2} \end{bmatrix}$$

$$\begin{bmatrix} -\dfrac{1}{2} & -\dfrac{\sqrt{3}}{2} \\[2mm] \dfrac{\sqrt{3}}{2} & -\dfrac{1}{2} \end{bmatrix} \begin{bmatrix} -\dfrac{1}{2} & -\dfrac{\sqrt{3}}{2} \\[2mm] \dfrac{\sqrt{3}}{2} & -\dfrac{1}{2} \end{bmatrix} = \begin{bmatrix} -\dfrac{1}{2} & \dfrac{\sqrt{3}}{2} \\[2mm] -\dfrac{\sqrt{3}}{2} & -\dfrac{1}{2} \end{bmatrix},$$

$$\begin{bmatrix} -\dfrac{1}{2} & -\dfrac{\sqrt{3}}{2} \\[2mm] \dfrac{\sqrt{3}}{2} & -\dfrac{1}{2} \end{bmatrix} \begin{bmatrix} -\dfrac{1}{2} & \dfrac{\sqrt{3}}{2} \\[2mm] -\dfrac{\sqrt{3}}{2} & -\dfrac{1}{2} \end{bmatrix} = \begin{bmatrix} 1 & 0 \\ 0 & 1 \end{bmatrix}$$

and the triangle is rotated anti-clockwise through 120°.

Examples 10e

Repeat the initial stages of Questions 1–4 of Examples 10d by the alternative method.

10.7 Practical Rotations

We must not allow the mathematical treatment of rotations to obscure their practical nature. Rotations appeared as part of the process for physically depositing one triangle on top of another and many of the other examples we have used reflect similar practical situations. The reader should make a habit of noting and classifying such situations as they arise in everyday life. For example, what group structure is inherent in the rotation of a set of spokes in a bicycle wheel, the various positions of a switch on an electric cooker, or the patterns on certain types of wallpaper? The development of one's mathematical 'eye' in this is invaluable, especially of course for teachers or intending teachers, and the ability to discover the pattern behind a complex situation is part of the essence of the true mathematician.

We may well construct rotational situations for ourselves. A circular piece of

paper (e.g. a filter paper) when folded into sixteen gives us

and we can hack a pattern into the edge to give .

At this stage do not make holes away from the folded edges as this introduces nasty side-effects, which we shall handle in the next chapter. The pattern opens out to

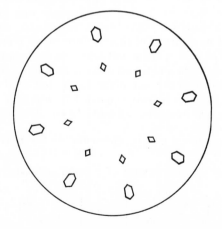

FIG. 65

which is the repetition by rotation of the pattern

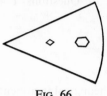

Fig. 66

eight times.

The reader's ingenuity will enable him to expand on this idea.

Examples 10f

1. By judiciously folding and cutting assorted filter papers produce patterns which may be used to generate

(a) a cyclic 4-group,

(b) a cyclic 8-group,

(c) a cyclic 3-group. (This is possible with cunning.)

Try various combinations of these and observe what groups (if any) may be generated by the result. Keep your results.

2. Make a point of examining nature, art and industry for examples of rotational situations. In each case notice the number of times the pattern is repeated, consider why this number was chosen and also the effect of altering the number of repetitions.

10.8 Translations

Broadly speaking we follow the same principles with translations as we did with rotations. We begin by finding an adequate way of describing such motions. We have already used the obvious 'two squares to the left and four down' (p. 170) and now formalize this by agreeing to represent translations by two numbers. The first of these will represent the number of squares the plane is moved to the right and the second the number of squares it is moved upwards. If we wish to move our plane to the left or downwards we use negative numbers. Thus our 'two squares left and four down' would be represented by the two numbers -2 and -4 or, if we like, by the matrix $\begin{bmatrix} -2 \\ -4 \end{bmatrix}$. This is a convenient matrix representation for us as it fits in well with the use of $\begin{bmatrix} x \\ y \end{bmatrix}$ as the coordinates of a point. Alternatively, we may use

$$\begin{bmatrix} -2 & -(-4) \\ -4 & -2 \end{bmatrix} \quad \text{or} \quad \begin{bmatrix} -2 & 4 \\ -4 & -2 \end{bmatrix}$$

when we are playing with the Argand diagram.

Let us now consider the effects of two translations in succession. $\begin{bmatrix} 1 \\ 2 \end{bmatrix}$

followed by $\begin{bmatrix} 3 \\ 4 \end{bmatrix}$ means that

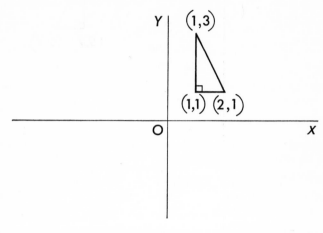

FIG. 67

turns into

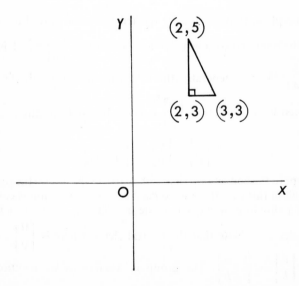

FIG. 68

which turns into

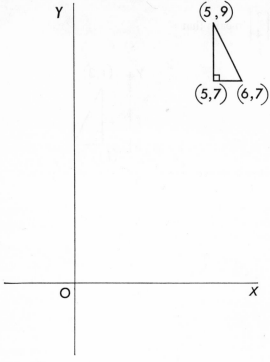

FIG. 69

The whole plane (represented by the triangle) has moved a total of four squares to the right and six upwards—a translation of $\begin{bmatrix} 4 \\ 6 \end{bmatrix}$ which is the sum of $\begin{bmatrix} 1 \\ 2 \end{bmatrix}$ and $\begin{bmatrix} 3 \\ 4 \end{bmatrix}$. We may generalize this by saying that the result of a translation $\begin{bmatrix} a \\ b \end{bmatrix}$ followed by a translation $\begin{bmatrix} c \\ d \end{bmatrix}$ is given by the translation

$$\begin{bmatrix} c \\ d \end{bmatrix} + \begin{bmatrix} a \\ b \end{bmatrix} = \begin{bmatrix} c+a \\ d+b \end{bmatrix}.$$

We have kept to the convention that with matrices the one on the right happens first although in this case there is no need as matrix addition is commutative.

The reader should now check that the translations, or 2×1 matrices, form a group under '+'. Note that the neutral element here is $\begin{bmatrix} 0 \\ 0 \end{bmatrix}$ and that the inverse of $\begin{bmatrix} a \\ b \end{bmatrix}$ is $\begin{bmatrix} -a \\ -b \end{bmatrix}$. The group is Abelian as we mentioned in the previous paragraph.

We may now usefully express translations as a pair of equations. The result of a translation $\begin{bmatrix} a \\ b \end{bmatrix}$ is that each x coordinate in the plane is increased by a and each y coordinate is increased by b. Then if x' and y' are the new coordinates of the point previously at (x, y) we get

$$\begin{aligned} x' &= x+a \\ y' &= y+b \end{aligned} \quad \text{or} \quad \begin{bmatrix} x' \\ y' \end{bmatrix} = \begin{bmatrix} x \\ y \end{bmatrix} + \begin{bmatrix} a \\ b \end{bmatrix}$$

in matrix form.

Unfortunately, the representation of translations in the $\begin{bmatrix} a \\ b \end{bmatrix}$ form precludes their comparison with the other group systems, which we have so carefully converted to 2×2 matrices. We may therefore find the $\begin{bmatrix} a & -b \\ b & a \end{bmatrix}$ form more fruitful.

The reader should check that the work we have done so far in this section is relevant in the new form. The combining operation for translations is still '+' and the new version of the above equation is

$$\begin{bmatrix} x' & -y' \\ y' & x' \end{bmatrix} = \begin{bmatrix} x & -y \\ y & x \end{bmatrix} + \begin{bmatrix} a & -b \\ b & a \end{bmatrix}$$

The $\begin{bmatrix} a & -b \\ b & a \end{bmatrix}$ type of matrix appears with considerable frequency on the Argand diagram. We have already used it to represent a point and, in the $\begin{bmatrix} \cos P & -\sin P \\ \sin P & \cos P \end{bmatrix}$ variety, to represent a rotation by multiplication. We now see that it represents a translation by addition. Such economy of notation is the sign of a tidy piece of mathematics and is both pleasing and rare.

As with rotation we end this section by emphasizing the practical side of translations. To do this we refer the reader once again to the wall of the bathroom so adequately mutilated by Junior in Chapter 1.

Let us suppose that part of the wall looks like this:

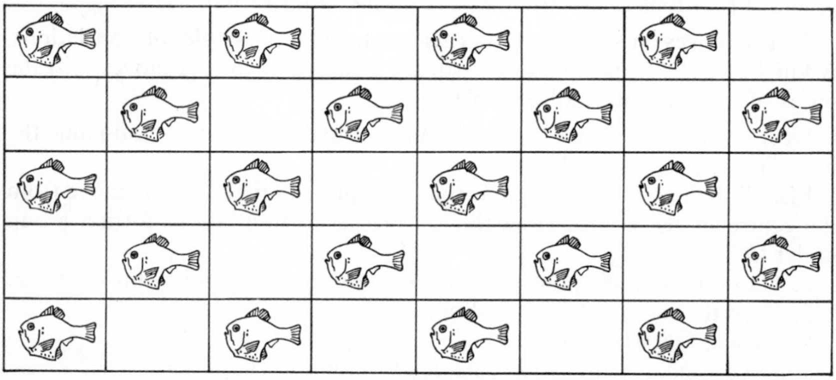

FIG. 70

We may if we wish consider this wall as a series of translations of the pattern

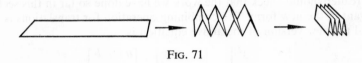. Considering the point O as origin and the fish in the bottom left

square as the initial fish we may adequately describe the pattern as the series
of the translations

$$\begin{bmatrix} 0 \\ 0 \end{bmatrix}, \begin{bmatrix} 2 \\ 0 \end{bmatrix}, \begin{bmatrix} 4 \\ 0 \end{bmatrix}, \begin{bmatrix} 6 \\ 0 \end{bmatrix}; \begin{bmatrix} 1 \\ 1 \end{bmatrix}, \begin{bmatrix} 3 \\ 1 \end{bmatrix}, \begin{bmatrix} 5 \\ 1 \end{bmatrix}, \begin{bmatrix} 7 \\ 1 \end{bmatrix}; \begin{bmatrix} 0 \\ 2 \end{bmatrix}, \&c.$$

In other words, the series of all translations where coordinates add to an even
number subject to the limitations of the size of wall.

Examples 10g

1. Fold a long strip of paper concertina-wise.

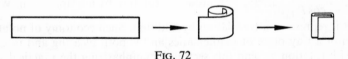

FIG. 71

Cut a pattern in the edge and open out to show the relevant series of
translations.

If the paper is folded round itself instead, as in Fig. 72, would this alter
the result?

FIG. 72

Try to see and justify logically what happens. Keep your results.

2. Search for practical translations in the same way that you searched for
practical rotations in Question 2 of Examples 10f (p. 186).

3. The moves on a chessboard provide interesting examples of translations.
A knight travels from square A to square B in Fig. 73 in four moves. List the
series of translations in all possible cases.

Devise your own routes for the knight to travel from A to B and name the
list of translations in each case.

List all the possible translations that a knight can make in one move from
the centre of the board. Does this set of special translations form a group
under 'followed by'?

4. Choosing suitable points on a chessboard repeat Question 3 for a pawn.

5. Repeat Question 4 for a bishop.

6. Repeat Question 4 for a king.

7. Do a similar analysis for a game of draughts.

8. Do a similar analysis for a game of snakes and ladders.

FIG. 73

10.9 Reflection again

We restricted ourselves here by only allowing reflections in the line $y = 0$ (p. 173). This means at this stage that either our plane (now Perspex) is twisted over or it is not. Thus we are limited to two processes: T, which means twist the plane about $y = 0$, and D, which means do not. We congratulate ourselves on this after the infinite number of processes which have appeared in the past few sections and rapidly construct a group table before we change our minds. We use the old standby 'f' meaning 'followed by' as a combining operation.

f	D	T
D	D	T
T	T	D

TABLE 43

The reader should be able to handle this kind of thing with aplomb by now. The only difficulty is perhaps $TfT = D$, which simply means that if we turn our Perspex plane over twice about the line $y = 0$ we are just as we were apart from a mild dizziness.

Let us now see what happens to the coordinates.

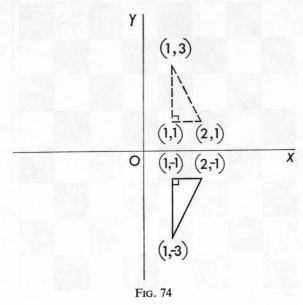

Since we have twisted the plane about $y = 0$ the x coordinates are unaltered. As we can see from the diagram however the corners of the triangle are all as much below the x-axis as they were previously above it. In other words, if we replace y by $-y$ and leave x alone for all parts of the plane we get the required result. Formally this gives us

$$x' = x, \qquad y' = -y$$

as the new position of the point which was previously at (x, y). In 2×2 matrices this gives us

$$\begin{bmatrix} x' \\ y' \end{bmatrix} = \begin{bmatrix} 1 & 0 \\ 0 & -1 \end{bmatrix} \begin{bmatrix} x \\ y \end{bmatrix}$$

and if we call $\begin{bmatrix} 1 & 0 \\ 0 & -1 \end{bmatrix}$ T (twist) and $\begin{bmatrix} 1 & 0 \\ 0 & 1 \end{bmatrix}$ D (do not) we find that matrix multiplication gives us the group table of the beginning of this section.

There are disadvantages in our approach to reflections although it does fit in nicely with the other motions of the plane. When we normally speak of reflections we think in terms of mirrors or other polished surfaces and it is true that if we look at △ in a mirror we can get ◁ (subject to judicious placing of self and mirror, of course). But the ◁ we get by the reflection is the front of △ whereas the ◁ we get by twisting the plane is the back of it. In other words, if △ is painted white on the front and red on the back, the reflected  is white and the twisted  is red. We could virtually ignore this problem on a flat plane, but unfortunately three dimensions upset things a little.

Let us assume that the reader is a little fat man with a bowler hat and an umbrella.

FIG. 75

The silhouette of his profile would look like

FIG. 76

which would reflect in a mirror perpendicular to the page as

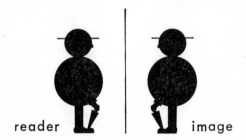

reader   image

FIG. 77

As far as silhouettes are concerned, i.e. in two dimensions, the reader could be turned into his image or vice versa by rotating the page about the line representing the mirror. If, on the other hand, we consider the whole figure we find that the umbrella has mysteriously changed hands and that no amount of rotation will change it back again.

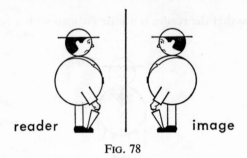

reader   image

Fig. 78

We will consider this point in more detail in the next section.

Examples 10h

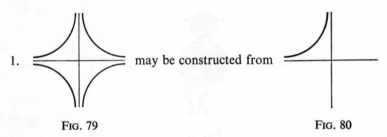

1.   may be constructed from

Fig. 79   Fig. 80

by a series of reflections, a series of rotations or a mixture of both. Analyse the various ways in which this is possible. Keep your answers.

2. Repeat Question 1 with

and

Fig. 81   Fig. 82

and explain carefully the ways in which this situation differs from the previous one. Keep your answers.

3. This section and section 10.10 are most usefully followed through practically. A small mirror may be wedged in wood or plasticine to keep it

vertical. Multiple reflections may be obtained by placing two such mirrors at various angles.

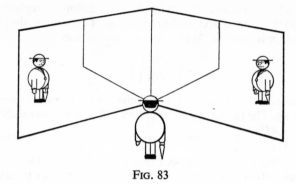

FIG. 83

Examine the reflections of two-dimensional and three-dimensional objects and especially of the figures which we have used to generate the various groups.

4. Spill a little ink on to a piece of paper and fold with caution. When you have gained confidence, try with a mixture of colours.

5. Analyse your paper patterns from Question 1, Examples 10f and Question 1, Examples 10g for reflections.

6. Search for practical reflections in the same way that you searched for practical rotations and translations in Question 2 of Examples 10f and Question 2 of Examples 10g.

10.10 The Tetrahedron

No amount of rotation will turn

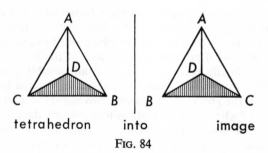

tetrahedron   into   image

FIG. 84

Try it. We may note the position of the tetrahedron by listing its corners in some recognized order such as (top, back, right, left). The tetrahedron may therefore be denoted by $(ADBC)$ and its image by $(ADCB)$. We have calculated that the total number of possible orders of the four letters is $4! = 4 \times 3 \times 2 \times 1 = 24$ (p. 130). Twelve of these orders belong to the original tetrahedron and twelve to the mirror image. The twelve belonging to the original tetrahedron may be obtained by rotating it so that it stands on a different face, and the rotations may be described in the same way that we described permutations earlier in the book (p. 132). Thus $\begin{pmatrix} ADBC \\ CDAB \end{pmatrix}$ is the process whereby the point D is kept fixed, B is slid along to replace C, and the whole tetrahedron tipped over to the right. Thus A ends up on the ground and C takes its place in mid-air. Meanwhile the image does

$$\begin{pmatrix} ADCB \\ CDBA \end{pmatrix}.$$

A closer examination of either set of twelve rotations would show that they formed a group. The reader would be unlucky if, in trying to establish this, he came across $\begin{pmatrix} ADBC \\ ADCB \end{pmatrix}$. This process tries to 'rotate' the tetrahedron into its mirror image. We have already seen that this is not possible under normal circumstances but we can manage it if we allow ourselves to take hold of corner C, say, and pull it through the middle of the triangle ABD.

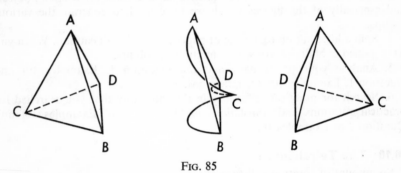

FIG. 85

We have now effectively constructed the mirror image and can physically derive all possible permutations of the four corners from the original tetrahedron. The twenty-four motions involved will form yet another group which is the group of all possible permutations of the four letters $(ABCD)$. But this we met briefly when we examined all possible positions of our dancers (p. 49), so that once again we find an unexpected isomorphism— this time between the group of all possible movements of a tetrahedron into itself (allowing reflections) and our ubiquitous country dancers.

It is interesting to note that many chemical substances are looked upon as having a molecular structure that is in the form of a tetrahedron. This means that we are able to find two different forms of these substances made up of the same components and having the same chemical properties, but being quite distinct from each other in that they are built to form either a 'left-handed' or a 'right-handed' tetrahedron. Apparently in chemistry it is not considered respectable to push molecules through the middle of each other! However, chemists do have a jolly time shooting polarized light at them and seeing which way it bounces. The most common of these substances is glucose, which consists of the two distinct forms: dextrose and laevulose. Tartaric and lactic acids behave similarly.

Examples 10i

1. Construct a cardboard and Sellotape tetrahedron and paint the corners so as to be able to distinguish them. Use this and the vertical mirror of Question 3, Examples 10h (p. 194) to follow through this section.

2. Can a tetrahedron be used to generate a twelve-group isomorphic to that obtained by rotating a threepenny-bit in its plane?

10.11 Summary

We began this chapter by examining the traditional topic of congruence from a new point of view and managed to reduce the motions necessary to place one congruent figure directly beneath another to a maximum of three—one reflection, one rotation and one translation. In succeeding sections we examined these three types of motion in more detail and as a result managed to rediscover by isomorphism many of the group structures of the earlier chapters. In the next chapter we link the three processes together again so that we may demonstrate congruences by just one process, and then go on to consider more exotic geometries where figures change both shape and size as we move them relative to our fixed axes.

11. MORE GEOMETRY

11.1 Reflections and 90° Rotations

In the previous chapter we only permitted reflections in the line $y = 0$. In this section and the next we extend the idea to reflections about any line through the origin. As we indicated previously (p. 173) the technique here is to rotate the plane until the reflecting line coincides with $y = 0$, reflect and then rotate back again. For the moment we will concentrate on reflections in the line $x = 0$. This necessitates a rotation of 90° anti-clockwise, a reflection and a rotation of 90° clockwise. The triangle will again show us what happens.

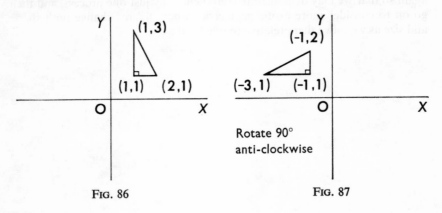

FIG. 86   FIG. 87

Turn about $y = 0$

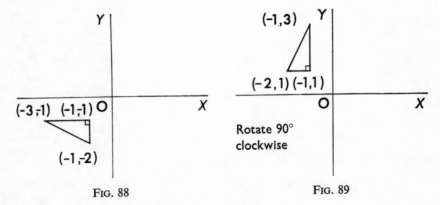

FIG. 88   FIG. 89

and the triangle is duly reflected in $x = 0$.

The matrices which will do these jobs for us are

$$\begin{bmatrix} \cos 90° & -\sin 90° \\ \sin 90° & \cos 90° \end{bmatrix}, \quad \begin{bmatrix} 1 & 0 \\ 0 & -1 \end{bmatrix} \quad \text{and} \quad \begin{bmatrix} \cos(-90°) & -\sin(-90°) \\ \sin(-90°) & \cos(-90°) \end{bmatrix}$$

(rotate through 90°   (reflect in   (rotate through 90°
anti-clockwise) $y = 0$)   clockwise)

which simplify to

$$\begin{bmatrix} 0 & -1 \\ 1 & 0 \end{bmatrix}, \quad \begin{bmatrix} 1 & 0 \\ 0 & -1 \end{bmatrix} \quad \text{and} \quad \begin{bmatrix} 0 & 1 \\ -1 & 0 \end{bmatrix}$$

respectively.

If we apply these to any point (x, y) in the plane, we get (using the usual matrix reverse order idea),

$$\begin{bmatrix} 0 & 1 \\ -1 & 0 \end{bmatrix} \begin{bmatrix} 1 & 0 \\ 0 & -1 \end{bmatrix} \begin{bmatrix} 0 & -1 \\ 1 & 0 \end{bmatrix} \begin{bmatrix} x \\ y \end{bmatrix}$$

$$= \begin{bmatrix} 0 & -1 \\ -1 & 0 \end{bmatrix} \begin{bmatrix} 0 & -1 \\ 1 & 0 \end{bmatrix} \begin{bmatrix} x \\ y \end{bmatrix}$$

$$= \begin{bmatrix} -1 & 0 \\ 0 & 1 \end{bmatrix} \begin{bmatrix} x \\ y \end{bmatrix}$$

$$= \begin{bmatrix} -x \\ y \end{bmatrix}$$

which means that we change the sign of the x value but leave the y values alone. This can be easily seen from the diagram and is perfectly obvious anyway but it is nice to have one's methods vindicated.

If we had forgotten to reverse the order of our matrices in applying them to $\begin{bmatrix} x \\ y \end{bmatrix}$ and written them as $\begin{bmatrix} 0 & -1 \\ 1 & 0 \end{bmatrix} \begin{bmatrix} 1 & 0 \\ 0 & -1 \end{bmatrix} \begin{bmatrix} 0 & 1 \\ -1 & 0 \end{bmatrix}$ we should have still reached $\begin{bmatrix} -1 & 0 \\ 0 & 1 \end{bmatrix}$. This is not usual. In this case however the reflecting line would be moved to coincide with $y = 0$ whether we rotated the plane through 90° clockwise or anti-clockwise so that we reach the same result either way. We now have two reflecting matrices: $\begin{bmatrix} 1 & 0 \\ 0 & -1 \end{bmatrix}$ which reflects in $y = 0$ and $\begin{bmatrix} -1 & 0 \\ 0 & 1 \end{bmatrix}$ which reflects in $x = 0$. These are the first matrices that we have come across so far in geometry which do not conform to the complex number pattern of $\begin{bmatrix} a & -b \\ b & a \end{bmatrix}$. Complex numbers essentially

14

restrict themselves to rotations, translations and alterations in magnitude (which we shall deal with later in the chapter). Reflection, which in two dimensions may be looked upon either as pulling a plane through itself or twisting a plane out of itself, is a different type of process and therefore requires a different form of matrix.

$\begin{bmatrix} 1 & 0 \\ 0 & -1 \end{bmatrix}$ and $\begin{bmatrix} -1 & 0 \\ 0 & 1 \end{bmatrix}$ have other amusing eccentricities. Each is its own inverse and the two multiply to $\begin{bmatrix} -1 & 0 \\ 0 & -1 \end{bmatrix}$, which suggests that the effect of two reflections in succession in lines at right-angles to each other is the same as rotating the plane through 180°.

$$\left(\begin{bmatrix} -1 & 0 \\ 0 & -1 \end{bmatrix} \text{ is } \begin{bmatrix} \cos P & -\sin P \\ \sin P & \cos P \end{bmatrix} \text{ where } P = 180°. \right)$$

This again is easily demonstrated with the triangle.

The three above matrices together with the unit matrix $\begin{bmatrix} 1 & 0 \\ 0 & 1 \end{bmatrix}$ form a Klein 4 group as we have previously shown in Question 2, Examples 6f, p. 102. This involves isomorphisms with the group of gyrations of Junior's bathroom tile (p. 5), which consisted of a twisting about a horizontal and a vertical axis, a 180°-rotation, and a leaving alone; and also with the Scottish dancers' swapping system. This last we may well justify from a different point of view.

Assume that our four dancers are standing at points $(-1, 1)$, $(1, 1)$, $(1, -1)$ and $(-1, -1)$ respectively.

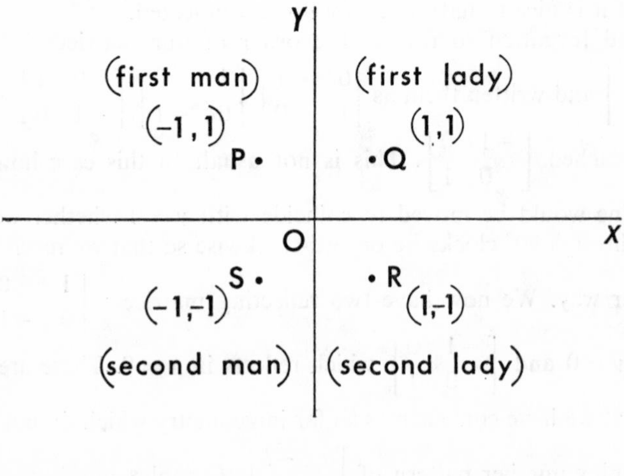

FIG. 90

Then $\begin{bmatrix} -1 & 0 \\ 0 & 1 \end{bmatrix}$ implies 'change place crossways' for

$$\begin{bmatrix} -1 & 0 \\ 0 & 1 \end{bmatrix} \begin{bmatrix} -1 \\ 1 \end{bmatrix} = \begin{bmatrix} 1 \\ 1 \end{bmatrix}$$

and P goes to Q.

Similarly

$$\begin{bmatrix} -1 & 0 \\ 0 & 1 \end{bmatrix} \begin{bmatrix} 1 \\ 1 \end{bmatrix} = \begin{bmatrix} -1 \\ 1 \end{bmatrix}$$

and Q goes to P. The same thing works for S and R and the reader will find that the other matrices adequately describe the other movements of our four dancers. Incidentally this procedure may be followed by all the 2×2 matrices of p. 145.

11.2 Reflections in General

The line $y = x \tan P$ goes through the origin and makes an angle $P°$ with the x-axis. If we were to reflect the plane in this line we would rotate the plane clockwise through $P°$ (or anti-clockwise through $(180-P)°$ to make it coincide with the x-axis and then reflect and rotate back again. This means that we first of all do

$$\begin{bmatrix} \cos(-P) & -\sin(-P) \\ \sin(-P) & \cos(-P) \end{bmatrix} = \begin{bmatrix} \cos P & \sin P \\ -\sin P & \cos P \end{bmatrix}$$

then $\begin{bmatrix} 1 & 0 \\ 0 & -1 \end{bmatrix}$ and then $\begin{bmatrix} \cos P & -\sin P \\ \sin P & \cos P \end{bmatrix}$. These combine to form the grand process

$$\begin{bmatrix} \cos P & -\sin P \\ \sin P & \cos P \end{bmatrix} \begin{bmatrix} 1 & 0 \\ 0 & -1 \end{bmatrix} \begin{bmatrix} \cos P & \sin P \\ -\sin P & \cos P \end{bmatrix}$$

(notice the reverse order) which simplifies to

$$\begin{bmatrix} \cos P & \sin P \\ \sin P & -\cos P \end{bmatrix} \begin{bmatrix} \cos P & \sin P \\ -\sin P & \cos P \end{bmatrix} = \begin{bmatrix} \cos 2P & \sin 2P \\ \sin 2P & -\cos 2P \end{bmatrix}.$$

Arithmetic can be tiresome in examples but let us try a reflection in the line $y = x$ which means that $\tan P = 1$ or $P = 45°$.

$\begin{bmatrix} \cos 2P & \sin 2P \\ \sin 2P & -\cos 2P \end{bmatrix}$ becomes $\begin{bmatrix} 0 & 1 \\ 1 & 0 \end{bmatrix}$. Our long-suffering triangle has

corners $\begin{bmatrix} 1 \\ 1 \end{bmatrix}$, $\begin{bmatrix} 1 \\ 3 \end{bmatrix}$ and $\begin{bmatrix} 2 \\ 1 \end{bmatrix}$, which are converted to

$$\begin{bmatrix} 0 & 1 \\ 1 & 0 \end{bmatrix} \begin{bmatrix} 1 \\ 1 \end{bmatrix}, \quad \begin{bmatrix} 0 & 1 \\ 1 & 0 \end{bmatrix} \begin{bmatrix} 1 \\ 3 \end{bmatrix} \quad \text{and} \quad \begin{bmatrix} 0 & 1 \\ 1 & 0 \end{bmatrix} \begin{bmatrix} 2 \\ 1 \end{bmatrix}$$

which simplify to $\begin{bmatrix} 1 \\ 1 \end{bmatrix}$, $\begin{bmatrix} 3 \\ 1 \end{bmatrix}$ and $\begin{bmatrix} 1 \\ 2 \end{bmatrix}$ respectively. The net result is that

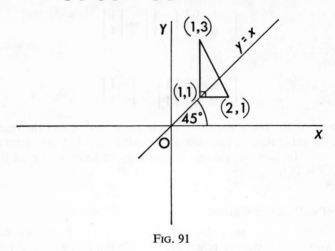

FIG. 91

becomes

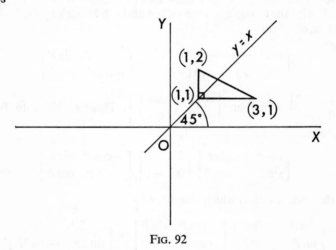

FIG. 92

which again looks right.

We are now in a position to consider the possibility that the set of all rotations and reflections forms a group. Since a reflection about any line through the origin may be broken down into two rotations and a reflection in the line $y = 0$ we have simplified our task considerably. Consider the results of a typical rotation $\begin{bmatrix} \cos P & -\sin P \\ \sin P & \cos P \end{bmatrix}$ followed by the reflection $\begin{bmatrix} 1 & 0 \\ 0 & -1 \end{bmatrix}$.

This gives $\begin{bmatrix} 1 & 0 \\ 0 & -1 \end{bmatrix} \begin{bmatrix} \cos P & -\sin P \\ \sin P & \cos P \end{bmatrix}$ or $\begin{bmatrix} \cos P & -\sin P \\ -\sin P & -\cos P \end{bmatrix}$. Note that if we reflect first and then rotate we get

$$\begin{bmatrix} \cos P & -\sin P \\ \sin P & \cos P \end{bmatrix} \begin{bmatrix} 1 & 0 \\ 0 & -1 \end{bmatrix} = \begin{bmatrix} \cos P & \sin P \\ \sin P & -\cos P \end{bmatrix}$$

which is not at all the same thing so that the Commutative Law is certainly not true in this case. If we write the second answer as

$$\begin{bmatrix} \cos(-P) & -\sin(-P) \\ -\sin(-P) & -\cos(-P) \end{bmatrix}$$

the two are in strictly comparable form and we see that the first involves an anti-clockwise or positive angle and the second a clockwise or negative angle. An analysis of the physical movements involved will show the justice of this.

We now have two distinct types of elements: rotations, which we have already proved to form a group (p. 176) and which have the general form $\begin{bmatrix} \cos P & -\sin P \\ \sin P & \cos P \end{bmatrix}$; and rotations and reflections (or vice versa) which have the general form $\begin{bmatrix} \cos P & -\sin P \\ -\sin P & -\cos P \end{bmatrix}$. The two types are identical except for the sign of the bottom row and we may therefore write both in the form

$$\begin{bmatrix} \cos P & -\sin P \\ e\sin P & e\cos P \end{bmatrix}$$

where $e = \pm 1$ or $e^2 = 1$. Thus our problem reduces to proving whether or not matrices of the type $\begin{bmatrix} \cos P & -\sin P \\ e\sin P & e\cos P \end{bmatrix}$ form a group under matrix multiplication.

If we can win the closure battle the rest is relatively simple. Consider

$$\begin{bmatrix} \cos P & -\sin P \\ e_1\sin P & e_1\cos P \end{bmatrix} \begin{bmatrix} \cos Q & -\sin Q \\ e_2\sin Q & e_2\cos Q \end{bmatrix}$$

where $e_1^2 = e_2^2 = 1$. This gives

$$\begin{bmatrix} \cos P\cos Q - e_2\sin P\sin Q & -(\cos P\sin Q + e_2\sin P\cos Q) \\ e_1(\sin P\cos Q + e_2\cos P\sin Q) & e_1(-\sin P\sin Q + e_2\cos P\cos Q) \end{bmatrix}$$

If $e_2 = +1$ we get

$$\begin{bmatrix} \cos P\cos Q - \sin P\sin Q & -(\cos P\sin Q + \sin P\cos Q) \\ e_1(\sin P\cos Q + \cos P\sin Q) & e_1(-\sin P\sin Q + \cos P\cos Q) \end{bmatrix}$$

$$= \begin{bmatrix} \cos(P+Q) & -\sin(P+Q) \\ e_1\sin(P+Q) & e_1\cos(P+Q) \end{bmatrix}$$

which is of the required form and is a rotation or a reflection/rotation according to whether e_1 is $+1$ or -1.

If, on the other hand, $e_2 = -1$ we get

$$\begin{bmatrix} \cos P \cos Q + \sin P \sin Q & -(\cos P \sin Q - \sin P \cos Q) \\ e_1(\sin P \cos Q - \cos P \sin Q) & e_1(-\sin P \sin Q - \cos P \cos Q) \end{bmatrix}$$

$$= \begin{bmatrix} \cos(P-Q) & \sin(P-Q) \\ e_1 \sin(P-Q) & -e_1 \cos(P-Q) \end{bmatrix}$$

$$= \begin{bmatrix} \cos(Q-P) & -\sin(Q-P) \\ (-e_1)\sin(Q-P) & (-e_1)\cos(Q-P) \end{bmatrix}$$

which is a reflection/rotation or a rotation according to whether $e_1 = +1$ or -1.

This means that the product of any two matrices of our set is a matrix which is also a member of the set. Thus closure holds good and the normal properties of 2×2 matrices tell us that uniqueness of result and the Associative Law are also true.

$\begin{bmatrix} 1 & 0 \\ 0 & 1 \end{bmatrix}$ is the unit matrix as usual and we have already shown that the pure rotation matrices have inverses (p. 179). This leaves us with the task of finding inverses for matrices of the type $\begin{bmatrix} \cos P & -\sin P \\ -\sin P & -\cos P \end{bmatrix}$. This is easy. Each is its own inverse, since

$$\begin{bmatrix} \cos P & -\sin P \\ -\sin P & -\cos P \end{bmatrix} \begin{bmatrix} \cos P & -\sin P \\ -\sin P & -\cos P \end{bmatrix}$$

$$= \begin{bmatrix} \cos^2 P + \sin^2 P & -\sin P \cos P + \sin P \cos P \\ -\sin P \cos P + \sin P \cos P & \sin^2 P + \cos^2 P \end{bmatrix}$$

$$= \begin{bmatrix} 1 & 0 \\ 0 & 1 \end{bmatrix}$$

so that the matrix version of assorted rotations and reflections forms a group under matrix multiplication.

A combination of rotations and our one reflection process has enabled us to reflect about any line in the plane by the rotation–reflection–rotation sequence. It has also enabled us to link various applications of the Klein 4-group with the general geometrical pattern we are evolving. There are plenty more applications of this idea as we may see from the examples.

Examples 11a

1. Describe the various methods which you adopted in Questions 1 and 2 of Examples 10h (p. 194) using matrix notation.

2. Verify that Fig. 90 (p. 200) and the associated matrices adequately describe the movements of the dancers' swapping system.

3. Apply the principles of reflection and rotation to an equilateral triangle to produce a set of 2×2 matrices which are isomorphic to the group of Table 37, p. 135, under multiplication.

4. From Question 4 of examples 10b (p. 174) we may have surmised that a reflection about each of two intersecting lines was equivalent to a rotation. Justify this using matrices where the angle between the lines is

(a) 90°,　　　　(b) 45°,　　　　(c) 30°,

and prove your result in the general case.

5. By applying the relevant rotating and reflecting matrices to the following figure repeat analytically Question 1 of Examples 10f (p. 186).

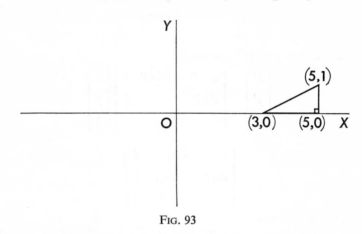

FIG. 93

Will the sets of matrices which generate the various patterns form groups under matrix multiplication? If so, name the groups and consider and justify the various isomorphisms. If not make sure you know exactly why not.

11.3 Reflections, Rotations and Translations

By this time the reader has probably forgotten why we started this. By the end of section 10.3 we had established that the congruence of two triangles could be shown by at most one reflection, one rotation and one translation. The object of this section is to combine all three into one magnificent matrix and then to show, inevitably, that the set of all such matrices forms a group under a suitable combining operation.

In the previous section we combined reflection and rotation to some effect, but unfortunately translations use matrix addition instead of multiplication as the combining operation (p. 188) so that some juggling is necessary. We will first of all concentrate on rotations and translations since reflections may be brought in later by a judicious sprinkling of e's.

A typical rotation would give

$$\begin{bmatrix} x' \\ y' \end{bmatrix} = \begin{bmatrix} \cos P & -\sin P \\ \sin P & \cos P \end{bmatrix} \begin{bmatrix} x \\ y \end{bmatrix},$$

or

$$\begin{bmatrix} x' \\ y' \end{bmatrix} = \begin{bmatrix} x\cos P & -y\sin P \\ x\sin P & +y\cos P \end{bmatrix}$$

A translation $\begin{bmatrix} h \\ k \end{bmatrix}$ on top of this would give

$$x' = x\cos P - y\sin P + h,$$
$$y' = x\sin P + y\cos P + k.$$

This will not go directly into matrix form as it stands but we may delicately write underneath $1 = 1$ and get

$$x' = x\cos P - y\sin P + h,$$
$$y' = x\sin P + y\cos P + k,$$
$$1 = 1.$$

This now goes into matrix form nicely as

$$\begin{bmatrix} x' \\ y' \\ 1 \end{bmatrix} = \begin{bmatrix} \cos P & -\sin P & h \\ \sin P & \cos P & k \\ 0 & 0 & 1 \end{bmatrix} \begin{bmatrix} x \\ y \\ 1 \end{bmatrix}$$

with

$$\begin{bmatrix} \cos P & -\sin P & h \\ \sin P & \cos P & k \\ 0 & 0 & 1 \end{bmatrix}$$

as the operating matrix.

Let us now check that it does its job. The congruence of section 10.2 required a rotation through $90°$ and a translation $\begin{bmatrix} -2 \\ -4 \end{bmatrix}$. In matrix terms this is

$$\begin{bmatrix} 0 & -1 & -2 \\ 1 & 0 & -4 \\ 0 & 0 & 1 \end{bmatrix}$$

If we now apply this in turn to the three corners of the triangle we find the destination of $(1, 3)$ by evaluating

$$\begin{bmatrix} 0 & -1 & -2 \\ 1 & 0 & -4 \\ 0 & 0 & 1 \end{bmatrix} \begin{bmatrix} 1 \\ 3 \\ 1 \end{bmatrix} = \begin{bmatrix} -5 \\ -3 \\ 1 \end{bmatrix}$$

so that $(1, 3)$ goes to $(-5, -3)$.

Similarly

$$\begin{bmatrix} 0 & -1 & -2 \\ 1 & 0 & -4 \\ 0 & 0 & 1 \end{bmatrix} \begin{bmatrix} 2 \\ 1 \\ 1 \end{bmatrix} = \begin{bmatrix} -3 \\ -2 \\ 1 \end{bmatrix}$$

so that $(2, 1)$ goes to $(-3, -1)$, and

$$\begin{bmatrix} 0 & -1 & -2 \\ 1 & 0 & -4 \\ 0 & 0 & 1 \end{bmatrix} \begin{bmatrix} 1 \\ 1 \\ 1 \end{bmatrix} = \begin{bmatrix} -3 \\ -3 \\ 1 \end{bmatrix}$$

so that $(1, 1)$ goes to $(-3, -3)$, and the matrix does what it is supposed to do.

To calculate the correct matrix for the congruence of section 10.3 requires a little more skill. The steps were: reflection in the y-axis $\left(\begin{bmatrix} 1 & 0 \\ 0 & -1 \end{bmatrix}\right)$, rotation through $90°$ $\left(\begin{bmatrix} 0 & -1 \\ 1 & 0 \end{bmatrix}\right)$ and translation $\left(\begin{bmatrix} -6 \\ -4 \end{bmatrix}\right)$. The product of the first two in the reverse order gives us the relevant numbers for the rotation/ reflection part and we then fit in the translation as before. Thus

$$\begin{bmatrix} 0 & -1 \\ 1 & 0 \end{bmatrix}\begin{bmatrix} 1 & 0 \\ 0 & -1 \end{bmatrix} = \begin{bmatrix} 0 & 1 \\ 1 & 0 \end{bmatrix}$$

and the required matrix is

$$\begin{bmatrix} 0 & 1 & -6 \\ 1 & 0 & -4 \\ 0 & 0 & 1 \end{bmatrix}.$$

The reader should check that it does in fact establish the relevant congruence.

Our method could if we liked be used to prove congruence directly. Suppose that we wished to test if the triangle whose corners were $(0,0)$, $(1,1)$, and $(2,1)$ was congruent to the triangle whose corners were $(-4,-5)$, $\left(\dfrac{\sqrt{3}-7}{2}, -\dfrac{\sqrt{3}-9}{2}\right)$, $\left(\sqrt{3}-\dfrac{7}{2}, -4-\dfrac{\sqrt{3}}{2}\right)$. (Do not worry! With numbers like this they must be congruent and as usual we have cut down the arithmetic to the minimum.) The technique is to consider what matrix (if any) of the form

$$\begin{bmatrix} \cos P & -\sin P & h \\ e\sin P & e\cos P & k \\ 0 & 0 & 1 \end{bmatrix}$$

where $e^2 = 1$ will act on the three corners of the first triangle to give the second. We could tackle each corner separately but it looks more professional to do them all at the same time. Thus we want to find e, P, h and k such that

$$
\begin{array}{ccc}
& \text{1st} \quad \text{2nd} \quad \text{3rd} \\
& \text{corner corner corner}
\end{array}
$$

$$\begin{bmatrix} \cos P & -\sin P & h \\ e\sin P & e\cos P & k \\ 0 & 0 & 1 \end{bmatrix}\begin{bmatrix} 0 & 1 & 2 \\ 0 & 1 & 1 \\ 1 & 1 & 1 \end{bmatrix}$$

$$= \begin{bmatrix} -4 & \dfrac{\sqrt{3}-7}{2} & \sqrt{3}-\dfrac{7}{2} \\ -5 & -\dfrac{\sqrt{3}-9}{2} & -4-\dfrac{\sqrt{3}}{2} \\ 1 & 1 & 1 \end{bmatrix}$$

This tells us that

$$\begin{bmatrix} h & \cos P - \sin P + h & 2\cos P - \sin P + h \\[2mm] k & e\sin P + e\cos P + k & 2e\sin P + e\cos P + k \\[2mm] 1 & 1 & 1 \end{bmatrix}$$

$$= \begin{bmatrix} -4 & \dfrac{\sqrt{3}-7}{2} & \sqrt{3}-\dfrac{7}{2} \\[3mm] -5 & -\dfrac{\sqrt{3}+9}{2} & -4-\dfrac{\sqrt{3}}{2} \\[3mm] 1 & 1 & 1 \end{bmatrix}$$

In other words, $h = -4$, $k = -5$. Therefore

$$\begin{cases} \cos P - \sin P - 4 = \dfrac{\sqrt{3}-7}{2} \\[3mm] 2\cos P - \sin P - 4 = \sqrt{3} - \dfrac{7}{2} \end{cases}$$

$$\Downarrow$$

$$\begin{cases} \cos P - \sin P = \dfrac{\sqrt{3}}{2} + \dfrac{1}{2} \\[3mm] 2\cos P - \sin P = \sqrt{3} + \dfrac{1}{2} \end{cases}$$

$$\Downarrow$$

$$\cos P = \frac{\sqrt{3}}{2}, \quad \sin P = -\frac{1}{2}$$

$$\Downarrow$$

$$P = 330°.$$

Also

$$e(\sin P + \cos P) + k = -\frac{\sqrt{3}+9}{2}$$

$$\Downarrow$$

$$e\left(-\frac{1}{2} + \frac{\sqrt{3}}{2}\right) = -\frac{\sqrt{3}}{2} + \frac{1}{2}$$

$$\Downarrow$$

$$e = -1.$$

We must verify these results by seeing that

$$2e\sin P + e\cos P + k = -2\left(-\frac{1}{2}\right) - \frac{\sqrt{3}}{2} - 5$$

$$= -4 - \frac{\sqrt{3}}{2}.$$

as required. Thus we may find a matrix of the required form which will transform the one triangle into the other and the two are therefore congruent.

If we wish to examine the exact process by which the congruence may be physically demonstrated we see that there must be a reflection since $e = -1$. The rotation/reflection part is

$$\begin{bmatrix} \dfrac{\sqrt{3}}{2} & \dfrac{1}{2} \\ \dfrac{1}{2} & -\dfrac{\sqrt{3}}{2} \end{bmatrix}$$

which we can split up into

$$\begin{bmatrix} \dfrac{\sqrt{3}}{2} & -\dfrac{1}{2} \\ \dfrac{1}{2} & \dfrac{\sqrt{3}}{2} \end{bmatrix} \begin{bmatrix} 1 & 0 \\ 0 & -1 \end{bmatrix} \quad \text{or} \quad \begin{bmatrix} \cos 30° & -\sin 30° \\ \sin 30° & \cos 30° \end{bmatrix} \begin{bmatrix} 1 & 0 \\ 0 & -1 \end{bmatrix}$$

which signifies reflection in the x-axis followed by rotation through 30°. We then do the translation $\begin{bmatrix} -4 \\ -5 \end{bmatrix}$ to complete the movement. Notice that without reflection the angle P indicates the amount of rotation. With reflection the amount of rotation is $360° - P$. Trace back through section 11.2 to see why.

We shall only give an outline proof that the set of matrices of the form

$$\begin{bmatrix} \cos P & -\sin P & h \\ e \sin P & e \cos P & k \\ 0 & 0 & 1 \end{bmatrix}$$

and the motions they represent form a group under their respective combining operations. Let us place the triangle inscribed on our perspex plane beneath its wire doppleganger. We may now move it away in the same plane by as many reflections, rotations and translations as we like, but we know by the evidence of p. 174 that we can make it return by a maximum of one reflection, one rotation, and one translation. Thus a series of such threesomes, as represented by matrices of the above form, can always be expressed as a single matrix or threesome. This establishes closure. Uniqueness of result and the Associative Law are properties of matrix multiplication.

$$\begin{bmatrix} 1 & 0 & 0 \\ 0 & 1 & 0 \\ 0 & 0 & 1 \end{bmatrix}$$

is the neutral element as we would expect. Inverses present little difficulty. If we can move our triangle from A to B we must be able to move it back again from B to A and, as we have already shown (p. 174), such a movement may be reduced to one reflection, one rotation and one translation, which means that it may be represented by a matrix of the relevant form.

This indicates the proof of the group axioms for both the matrices and the movements they represent. The reader may check that the Commutative Law is not true. The group is of sufficient importance to merit the title of the group of Euclidean transformations since, under the motions considered, Euclidean properties of size and shape are invariant or unchanged. We again have to thank Klein, of four group fame, for this approach to geometry, although it would not of course be fair to blame him for everything in this chapter.

Examples 11b

1. Examine the effect on the triangle of corners $(1,2)$, $(3,1)$, and $(1,1)$ of

(a)
$$\begin{bmatrix} 0 & -1 & 1 \\ 1 & 0 & 1 \\ 0 & 0 & 1 \end{bmatrix}$$

(b)
$$\begin{bmatrix} 0 & -1 & 1 \\ -1 & 0 & 1 \\ 0 & 0 & 1 \end{bmatrix}$$

(c)
$$\begin{bmatrix} 0 & -2 & 2 \\ -2 & 0 & 2 \\ 0 & 0 & 1 \end{bmatrix}$$

and break up each matrix into its separate components.

2. Find the matrices which will demonstrate the congruences of Figs. 51 and 52 (p. 170). Where there is more than one possibility find them all.

3. Prove by matrices that we cannot find a Euclidean transformation which will carry $(1,1)$, $(1,2)$, $(2,1)$, $(2,2)$ into $(0,0)$, $(1,0)$, $(1,-1)$, $(2,-1)$.

4. Use matrices to discover the effect of reflection in
   (a) $y = 0$ followed by $y = 1$,
   (b) $y = 2$ followed by $y = 1$,
   (c) $y = a$ followed by $y = b$.

5. Express in the form of a single matrix a reflection in the line $y = 0$, a rotation of $-45°$, and a translation of two to the left and three down. Try your result on the triangle of corners $(1,2)$, $(3,1)$, and $(1,1)$. There are six different orders in which the transformation could be carried out. Try each of these physically with diagrams or a cardboard triangle, find the relevant matrix in each case and break it down into their separate components of reflection, rotation and translation in that order.

11.4 Symmetry

The reader will probably agree that △ is symmetrical. He may think that △ is more symmetrical and that ◣ is not at all. He may be a bit dubious about ▱ and give it the benefit of the doubt but probably thinks that ▢ is more symmetrical than any of them and that ◯ is still more so. In all these assumptions he would be quite correct but it is dubious whether even after all that he could actually say what 'symmetrical' means. In view of previous work however we may adequately define it as follows: a figure is symmetrical if, when acted upon by a Euclidean transformation which is not the identity, it is apparently unmoved. This is a working definition in that it not only tells us what symmetry is but also how to locate it. It also gives us a measure of symmetry. The more transformations that leave the figure apparently unmoved the more symmetrical it is! With these points in mind we may now look for transformations which will demonstrate the symmetry of the figures at the beginning of the paragraph.

△ may be reflected in △ and still look the same so that it is symmetrical.

There is no point about which we can rotate △ without it showing and there is no reason to translate it anywhere, so that there is just reflective symmetry about the perpendicular bisector of the base.

△ is much more symmetrical in that we can reflect it in ⊿ , △

and △. Also we can rotate it about the intersection of these three through 0°, 120° and 240° and get two rotational symmetries. But, of course, we are quite familiar with these processes already (p. 132). ◿ is not symmetrical.

▱ presents more difficulty. There is no line about which we can reflect it once to show symmetry but two reflections will do the trick. Thus

Alternatively, we may rotate the parallelogram through 180° about the intersection of its diagonals which has precisely the same effect. (Remember

$$\begin{bmatrix} 1 & 0 \\ 0 & -1 \end{bmatrix} \begin{bmatrix} -1 & 0 \\ 0 & 1 \end{bmatrix} = \begin{bmatrix} -1 & 0 \\ 0 & -1 \end{bmatrix}$$

or two reflections in perpendicular lines have the same effect as a 180° rotation (p. 200).)

We rightly decided that ▢ is the most symmetrical so far.

are suitable mirror lines, whilst a rotation about the intersection of the diagonals through 0°, 90°, 180° and 270° will also preserve the appearance of the figure.

Finally, ◯ has an infinite number of symmetries in that any line through the centre will serve as an adequate mirror line and any rotation about the centre will leave the circle apparently unchanged.

We have not yet met any symmetries based on translations in this section. Let us refer once again to the bathroom wall, whose tiles are alternately plain or fishy (Fig. 70). If we imagine a wall of infinite dimensions covered in this way we may see that a translation such as '2 tiles to the right and 4 up' will leave the situation apparently unaltered. Of course such considerations are of no practical value but if we have a large expanse of wall patterned in this way we do loosely call it symmetrical even though a translation might move it several inches off the ground or a foot or two into the adjoining bedroom!

Although we have essentially restricted ourselves to two dimensions, the same principles carry over quite happily into three. We shall do no more now, but the reader has already played with the symmetries of a regular tetrahedron (p. 195) and may pursue this line in the examples.

Examples 11c

1. How many symmetries have the following figures? (Include the identity symmetry for the sake of completeness.)

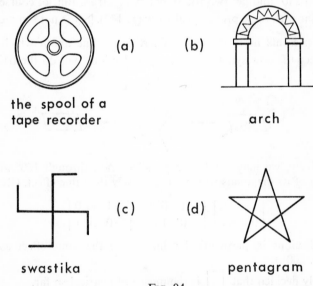

(a)   (b)

the spool of a
tape recorder   arch

(c)   (d)

swastika   pentagram

FIG. 94

Use the figures to generate groups of the same order as the number of symmetries.

2. Count the symmetries of the examples in Fig. 23 (p. 27).

3. Count the symmetries of
    (a) a regular tetrahedron,   (b) a cube,   (c) a cuboid.

4. Examine for symmetry your collections of reflections, rotations and translations from everyday life (see pp. 186, 190 and 195).

11.5 Variations in Size

In the next few sections we shall gradually loosen the restrictions of Euclidean geometry and see what happens. The first thing that we allow to vary is size. By doubling the size of our triangle we shall mean doubling the length of each side, which multiplies the area by four. The simplest way of doing this is just to double the coordinates of the corners so that

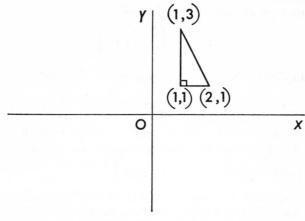

FIG. 67 (repeated)

becomes

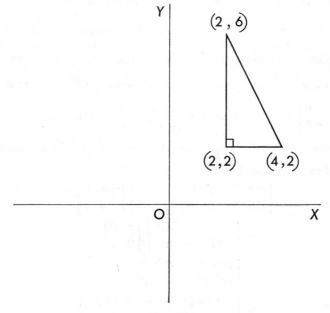

FIG. 95

This we may write as $\qquad x' = 2x$

$$y' = 2y$$

and note that each point on the plane is now twice as far from the origin as it was before. We will assume for the rest of this section that our plane is now made of rubber and that four good men and true are stationed one at each corner and are pulling hard, stretching the sheet evenly, but leaving the origin exactly where it was.

The matrix form of the equation gives us

$$\begin{bmatrix} x' \\ y' \end{bmatrix} = \begin{bmatrix} 2 & 0 \\ 0 & 2 \end{bmatrix} \begin{bmatrix} x \\ y \end{bmatrix}$$

so that multiplication by $\begin{bmatrix} 2 & 0 \\ 0 & 2 \end{bmatrix}$ corresponds to multiplying by 2 which is

what we would expect. Similarly multiplication by $\begin{bmatrix} r & 0 \\ 0 & r \end{bmatrix}$ has the same effect

as multiplication by r and results in a magnification or shrinkage according to whether r is greater or less than 1. Negative r's may be ignored since $\begin{bmatrix} -3 & 0 \\ 0 & -3 \end{bmatrix}$, for example, will split up into $\begin{bmatrix} 3 & 0 \\ 0 & 3 \end{bmatrix} \begin{bmatrix} -1 & 0 \\ 0 & -1 \end{bmatrix}$ which is a rotation through 180° followed by multiplication by 3. Nevertheless, this means that we now have a place for all real numbers except 0 in geometry. They represent either magnification or shrinkages according to size with or without a 180° rotation according to whether they are negative or positive. For convenience we refer to magnifications such as -3 or $\frac{1}{2}$ when we mean magnification three times with 180° rotation or shrinkage to half-size respectively.

With the addition of magnification to our repertoire we may treat similar figures in much the same way as we treated congruent ones. Thus we may demonstrate the similarity of any two figures by at most one magnification, one reflection, one rotation and one translation. The grand matrix which combines these four processes consists of the product of $\begin{bmatrix} r & 0 \\ 0 & r \end{bmatrix}$ for magnifica-

tion, $\begin{bmatrix} 1 & 0 \\ 0 & -1 \end{bmatrix}$ for reflection and $\begin{bmatrix} \cos P & -\sin P \\ \sin P & \cos P \end{bmatrix}$ for rotation together

with the translation effect $\begin{bmatrix} h \\ k \end{bmatrix}$ spread round the outside as before. The product of the first three is

$$\begin{bmatrix} \cos P & -\sin P \\ \sin P & \cos P \end{bmatrix} \begin{bmatrix} 1 & 0 \\ 0 & -1 \end{bmatrix} \begin{bmatrix} r & 0 \\ 0 & r \end{bmatrix}$$

$$= \begin{bmatrix} \cos P & \sin P \\ \sin P & -\cos P \end{bmatrix} \begin{bmatrix} r & 0 \\ 0 & r \end{bmatrix}$$

$$= \begin{bmatrix} r\cos P & r\sin P \\ r\sin P & -r\cos P \end{bmatrix}$$

$$= \begin{bmatrix} r\cos(-P) & -r\sin(-P) \\ -r\sin(-P) & -r\cos(-P) \end{bmatrix}$$

Combining this with the translation $\begin{bmatrix} h \\ k \end{bmatrix}$ we get

$$\begin{bmatrix} r\cos(-P) & -r\sin(-P) & h \\ -r\sin(-P) & -r\cos(-P) & k \\ 0 & 0 & 1 \end{bmatrix}$$

This looks most cumbersome and we therefore write it more simply and in its completely general form as

$$\begin{bmatrix} a & -b & h \\ eb & ea & k \\ 0 & 0 & 1 \end{bmatrix}$$

where $e = +1$ or -1 according to the absence or presence of a reflection, $a = r\cos Q$ (tidier than $-P$), $b = r\sin Q$, and r, Q, h and k are four numbers which specify the particular transformation involved. We could now go chasing group properties but the argument is so similar to that of the previous section but one that we leave it to the reader. The group is called the group of similitudes.

When no reflection is involved, the 2×2 matrix in the top left corner is $\begin{bmatrix} a & -b \\ b & a \end{bmatrix}$ which is the matrix form for complex numbers. We have previously met $\begin{bmatrix} a & -b \\ b & a \end{bmatrix}$ with '+' as the combining operation when dealing with translations on the Argand diagram (p. 186). We are also used to the special form $\begin{bmatrix} \cos P & -\sin P \\ \sin P & \cos P \end{bmatrix}$ with '$\times$' as the combining operation representing an anti-clockwise rotation through $P°$. Now we complete the meaning of complex numbers in this context since $\begin{bmatrix} a & -b \\ b & a \end{bmatrix}$ is short for

$$\begin{bmatrix} r\cos Q & -r\sin Q \\ r\sin Q & r\cos Q \end{bmatrix} = \begin{bmatrix} r & 0 \\ 0 & r \end{bmatrix} \begin{bmatrix} \cos Q & -\sin Q \\ \sin Q & \cos Q \end{bmatrix}$$

which means a rotation through $Q°$ anti-clockwise followed by a multiplication by r.

Finally, let us make sure that we can calculate the size of the magnification and rotation. The important part is $\begin{bmatrix} a & -b \\ eb & ea \end{bmatrix}$. If e is -1 there is a reflection. Separate it out into $\begin{bmatrix} a & -b \\ b & a \end{bmatrix} \begin{bmatrix} 1 & 0 \\ 0 & -1 \end{bmatrix}$. In either case we only want $\begin{bmatrix} a & -b \\ b & a \end{bmatrix}$. The associated determinant (p. 100) is $a^2 + b^2$. The matrix may

15

also be expressed as $\begin{bmatrix} r\cos Q & -r\sin Q \\ r\sin Q & r\cos Q \end{bmatrix}$. The associated determinant here is

$$r^2\cos^2 Q + r^2\sin^2 Q = r^2$$

where r is the magnifier. Thus $r^2 = a^2+b^2$ or $r = \sqrt{(a^2+b^2)}$.

$$\begin{bmatrix} r\cos Q & -r\sin Q \\ r\sin Q & r\cos Q \end{bmatrix}$$

further breaks down into

$$\begin{bmatrix} r & 0 \\ 0 & r \end{bmatrix} \begin{bmatrix} \cos Q & -\sin Q \\ \sin Q & \cos Q \end{bmatrix}$$

and once we have found r it is a relatively simple matter to find Q.

An example may help. If

$$\begin{bmatrix} 2\sqrt{3} & 2 & 3 \\ 2 & -2\sqrt{3} & 2 \\ 0 & 0 & 1 \end{bmatrix}$$

is the transformation, the translation is $\begin{bmatrix} 3 \\ 2 \end{bmatrix}$ and the rest of the information

is contained in $\begin{bmatrix} 2\sqrt{3} & 2 \\ 2 & -2\sqrt{3} \end{bmatrix}$. This is not in complex number form, but

breaks down into

$$\begin{bmatrix} 2\sqrt{3} & -2 \\ 2 & 2\sqrt{3} \end{bmatrix} \begin{bmatrix} 1 & 0 \\ 0 & -1 \end{bmatrix}$$

where $\begin{bmatrix} 2\sqrt{3} & -2 \\ 2 & 2\sqrt{3} \end{bmatrix}$ is in the required form. $\begin{bmatrix} 2\sqrt{3} & -2 \\ 2 & 2\sqrt{3} \end{bmatrix}$ has associated

determinant $(2\sqrt{3})^2 + 2^2 = 16$. Thus $r^2 = 16$ and $r = 4$. Thus we can break

$\begin{bmatrix} 2\sqrt{3} & -2 \\ 2 & 2\sqrt{3} \end{bmatrix}$ down further into

$$\begin{bmatrix} 4 & 0 \\ 0 & 4 \end{bmatrix} \begin{bmatrix} \dfrac{\sqrt{3}}{2} & -\dfrac{1}{2} \\ \dfrac{1}{2} & \dfrac{\sqrt{3}}{2} \end{bmatrix}$$

This implies that $\cos Q = \dfrac{\sqrt{3}}{2}$ and $\sin Q = \dfrac{1}{2}$ so that $Q = 30°$. The original

matrix therefore represents a multiplication by 4, a reflection in $y = 0$, a rotation of 30° anti-clockwise and a translation of 3 across and 2 up.

Examples 11d

1. The complete breakdown of the non-translation part of the matrix in the text is

$$\begin{bmatrix} 4 & 0 \\ 0 & 4 \end{bmatrix} \begin{bmatrix} \dfrac{\sqrt{3}}{2} & -\dfrac{1}{2} \\ \dfrac{1}{2} & \dfrac{\sqrt{3}}{2} \end{bmatrix} \begin{bmatrix} 1 & 0 \\ 0 & -1 \end{bmatrix}$$

This we referred to as a multiplication by 4, a reflection in $y = 0$ and a rotation of 30° anti-clockwise, thus altering the order of events. Were we justified in so doing? What alterations in order would we be justified in making?

2. Prove that the set of all similitudes in two dimensions forms a group.

3. Prove by matrix methods that the two shapes in Fig. 96 are similar.

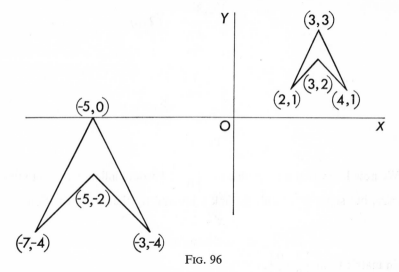

Fig. 96

4. Similar figures may be easily constructed by a judicious use of similar triangles. Thus a quadrilateral may be doubled in size by taking a point, drawing lines from it to the corners of the quadrilateral, doubling the length of the lines and joining up the resulting four points as in Fig. 97.

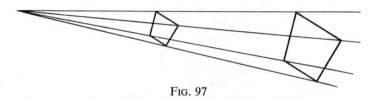

Fig. 97

Enlarge an irregular polygon of your own choosing to three times its size on a piece of graph paper and prove that the two figures are similar by matrix methods. (Choose and place your first polygon judiciously to avoid arithmetic.)

Also use this method and your ingenuity to produce figures enlarged by $\frac{1}{2}$ and -2.

5. Search for examples of similar figures in everyday life—particularly in the grocer's shop.

11.6 Variations in Shape

This is a do-it-yourself section and readers will learn more from the examples than from the text, which will only give a brief outline of procedure and a few technical terms. We now throw caution to the winds and vary size, shape and direction as the mood takes us. To do this we need your help in your bowler-hatted, umbrella-ed form.

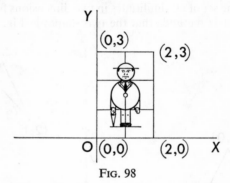

FIG. 98

We now know that a magnification $\begin{bmatrix} 2 & 0 \\ 0 & 2 \end{bmatrix}$ would inflate our ego to twice its size, but suppose we only do half a job and try the transformation

$$x' = 2x,$$
$$y' = y$$

or in matrix form $\begin{bmatrix} 2 & 0 \\ 0 & 1 \end{bmatrix}$.

This would give us

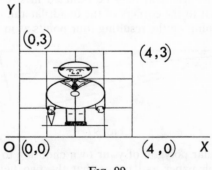

FIG. 99

which is hardly flattering to an already over-effusive waistline. The alternative $\begin{bmatrix} 1 & 0 \\ 0 & 2 \end{bmatrix}$ suits us better. Here

$$x' = x,$$

$$y' = 2y.$$

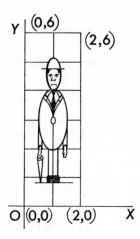

FIG. 100

Both such transformations are called stretchings of the plane and, as with magnification, the origin remains fixed and it is all relevant distances from the origin which are doubled. We may visualize our rubber plane as having an equally strong man at each end of the x- or y-axis as the case may be. As they pull, the origin stays where it is and the plane is stretched evenly. The general form of these distortions is $\begin{bmatrix} r & 0 \\ 0 & 1 \end{bmatrix}$ or $\begin{bmatrix} 1 & 0 \\ 0 & r \end{bmatrix}$ where r is positive. We may decide to stretch both ways at once but more one way than the other. This is equivalent to a combined magnification and stretching such as

$$\begin{bmatrix} 2 & 0 \\ 0 & 2 \end{bmatrix} \begin{bmatrix} 3 & 0 \\ 0 & 1 \end{bmatrix} = \begin{bmatrix} 6 & 0 \\ 0 & 2 \end{bmatrix}.$$

The results of a heavy evening may well be represented by

$$x' = x+y,$$

$$y' = y$$

or $\begin{bmatrix} 1 & 1 \\ 0 & 1 \end{bmatrix}.$

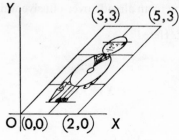

FIG. 101

This is called a shearing of the plane and has the general form $\begin{bmatrix} 1 & k \\ 0 & 1 \end{bmatrix}$. An upward shearing would have the form $\begin{bmatrix} 1 & 0 \\ k & 1 \end{bmatrix}$. The plane may be sheared if the two strong men each pull harder with their right hands.

The stretchings and shearings we have dealt with so far have been parallel to the two axes. This is by no means a necessary limitation and stretchings and shearings in other directions may be arranged by the usual technique of rotating, stretching or shearing as the case may be and rotating back again.

By this time we will assume that the reader's stomach is turning over $\left(\begin{bmatrix} 1 & 0 \\ 0 & -1 \end{bmatrix} \right)$, he is going dizzy $\left(\begin{bmatrix} 0 & -1 \\ 1 & 0 \end{bmatrix} \right)$, he is suffering from 'shear' boredom $\left(\begin{bmatrix} 1 & 1 \\ 0 & 1 \end{bmatrix} \right)$ and is stretched beyond his limit $\left(\begin{bmatrix} 1 & 0 \\ 0 & 2 \end{bmatrix} \right)$. The result of all this would be

$$\begin{bmatrix} 1 & 0 \\ 0 & 2 \end{bmatrix} \begin{bmatrix} 1 & 1 \\ 0 & 1 \end{bmatrix} \begin{bmatrix} 0 & -1 \\ 1 & 0 \end{bmatrix} \begin{bmatrix} 1 & 0 \\ 0 & -1 \end{bmatrix}$$

which simplifies to

$$\begin{bmatrix} 1 & 1 \\ 0 & 2 \end{bmatrix} \begin{bmatrix} 0 & 1 \\ 1 & 0 \end{bmatrix} \quad \text{or} \quad \begin{bmatrix} 1 & 1 \\ 2 & 0 \end{bmatrix}$$

In equation form this is
$$x' = x+y,$$
$$y' = 2x$$
and results in

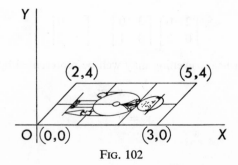

FIG. 102

We expect the reader did not know whether he was on his head or his heels!

Although we have treated this section in a light-hearted manner the ideas behind it are important. In the next section we will deal with even more disastrous transformations and then philosophize on the results. Meanwhile, the reader would do well to practise these ideas via the examples.

Examples 11c

1. We listed both horizontal and vertical types of stretching and shearing. Show that this was unnecessary and that the horizontal types together with the appropriate rotations would have the same effects.

2. Try the effects of a stretching which doubles lengths along the line $y = x$ on
   (a) a square of corners $(0,0)$, $(0,1)$, $(1,0)$ and $(1,1)$,
   (b) a rectangle of corners $(0,0)$, $(0,1)$, $(2,0)$ and $(2,1)$.

3. What is the effect on the square of Question 2 of a shearing of the same type as $\begin{bmatrix} 1 & 1 \\ 0 & 1 \end{bmatrix}$ but in a direction of $30°$ to the x-axis?

4. Prove that the area of a rectangle is unaltered by shearing and hence prove that triangles of the same base and lying between two parallel lines have the same area.

5. Try the effect of the shearings

$$\begin{bmatrix} 1 & -1 \\ 0 & 1 \end{bmatrix}, \quad \begin{bmatrix} 1 & -\frac{1}{2} \\ 0 & 1 \end{bmatrix}, \quad \begin{bmatrix} 1 & \frac{1}{2} \\ 0 & 1 \end{bmatrix} \quad \text{and} \quad \begin{bmatrix} 1 & 1 \\ 0 & 1 \end{bmatrix}$$

on

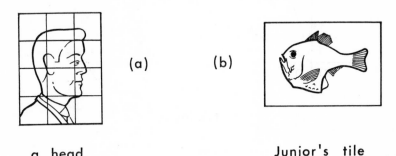

(a)   (b)

a head   Junior's tile

$\begin{bmatrix} 1 & \frac{1}{2} \\ 0 & 1 \end{bmatrix}$ will more or less convert Junior's fish tile, which is *Argyropeleas olfersi*, into *Stermoptyx diaphana*. For this, head shearing and other amusing phenomena see D'Arcy Thompson, *Growth and Form*, vol. 2, Cambridge University Press.

11.7 Transformations which misfire

In view of the relatively untidy form of the matrix $\begin{bmatrix} 1 & 1 \\ 2 & 0 \end{bmatrix}$ the reader may have decided that most if not all 2×2 matrices will produce variations on this particular theme. To a large extent this is true. Let us try, for example, $\begin{bmatrix} 1 & 2 \\ 3 & 1 \end{bmatrix}$ which has no immediate import except to those with a service background. The equations are

$$x' = x + 2y,$$

$$y' = 3x + y$$

which give

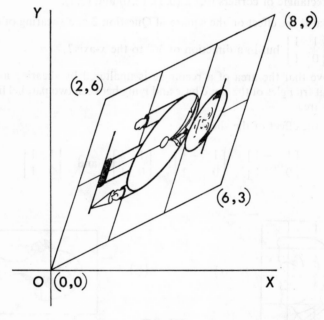

FIG. 103

with a delicate S.W.–N.E. elongation worthy of El Greco. There are however snags. Let us try $\begin{bmatrix} 2 & 1 \\ 4 & 2 \end{bmatrix}$ or

$$x' = 2x + y,$$

$$y' = 4x + 2y.$$

Here y' is always twice x' so that all points of the original plane must now be squashed on to the line $y' = 2x'$. The implications here are that the reader has over-dieted and turned himself into part of a straight line.

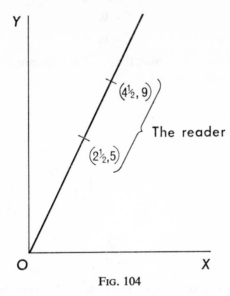

FIG. 104

We must be quite clear as to what has happened here. In previous cases the plane has always been moved, stretched or otherwise distorted, but the result has always been another plane. Here however the situation is drastically altered and the whole plane, not only the little figure, has shrunk into a straight line. Thus the diagram does not represent a line drawn on the plane but the whole plane itself contracted into a line.

Another example which is perhaps easier to visualize is given by $\begin{bmatrix} 1 & 0 \\ 0 & 0 \end{bmatrix}$.

Here
$$x' = x,$$
$$y' = 0,$$

so that whatever point we take on the original plane ends up on the line $y = 0$ directly above or below where it started. Thus

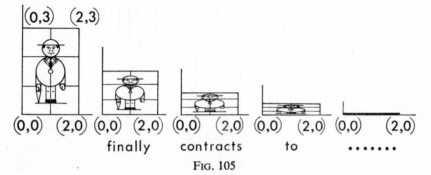

finally   contracts   to $\cdots\cdots$

FIG. 105

The final humiliation occurs with $\begin{bmatrix} 0 & 0 \\ 0 & 0 \end{bmatrix}$ or

$$x' = 0,$$
$$y' = 0.$$

Whatever values x and y are given, the position after transformation is always $(0,0)$ and

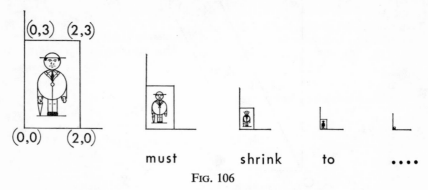

must   shrink   to   ....

FIG. 106

The transformations of the type just examined, where the plane contracts into a line or a point, are certainly different from the earlier ones where a plane merely distorted into another plane. We may locate the basic differences by looking for 1–1 correspondences. The first transformation of this section indicates that to every point (x,y) before transformation there corresponds a point (x',y') after transformation given by the equation

$$x' = x+2y,$$
$$y' = 3x+y.$$

Similarly a little matrix algebra will show that to every point (x',y') after transformation there corresponds a point (x,y) before transformation. Thus

$$\begin{bmatrix} x' \\ y' \end{bmatrix} = \begin{bmatrix} 1 & 2 \\ 3 & 1 \end{bmatrix} \begin{bmatrix} x \\ y \end{bmatrix}$$

$\Downarrow$

$$\begin{bmatrix} 1 & 2 \\ 3 & 1 \end{bmatrix}^{-1} \begin{bmatrix} x' \\ y' \end{bmatrix} = \begin{bmatrix} 1 & 2 \\ 3 & 1 \end{bmatrix}^{-1} \left\{ \begin{bmatrix} 1 & 2 \\ 3 & 1 \end{bmatrix} \begin{bmatrix} x \\ y \end{bmatrix} \right\}$$

$\Downarrow$

$$\begin{bmatrix} -\frac{1}{5} & \frac{2}{5} \\ \frac{3}{5} & -\frac{1}{5} \end{bmatrix} \begin{bmatrix} x' \\ y' \end{bmatrix} = \begin{bmatrix} x \\ y \end{bmatrix},$$

$\Downarrow$

$$x = -\tfrac{1}{5}x' + \tfrac{2}{5}y',$$
$$y = \tfrac{3}{5}x' - \tfrac{1}{5}y'.$$

In other words, there is a 1–1 correspondence between points of the plane before transformation and after transformation.

With the later transformations however this is not the case.

$$x' = x \quad \text{or} \quad \begin{bmatrix} x' \\ y' \end{bmatrix} = \begin{bmatrix} 1 & 0 \\ 0 & 0 \end{bmatrix} \begin{bmatrix} x \\ y \end{bmatrix}$$

is perhaps the easiest to see. From Fig. 105 the points $(2, 3)$ and $(2, 0)$ both end up on $(2, 0)$. Similarly the top of the little man's bowler hat, the middle of his nose, the middle of his coat button and his heels all end up on $(1, 0)$. We can easily locate the destination of points on the plane when we contract it into the line, but, if we expand the line again into a plane, the point $(2, 0)$ could go to $(2, 1)$, $(2, 2)$, $(2, 3)$, $(2, 4)$, or $(2, y)$ where y could be any number, positive or negative. Thus in this case and in others of a similar nature the 1–1 correspondence is upset. Algebraically this appears as follows:

$$\begin{bmatrix} x' \\ y' \end{bmatrix} = \begin{bmatrix} 1 & 0 \\ 0 & 0 \end{bmatrix} \begin{bmatrix} x \\ y \end{bmatrix}$$

$$\Downarrow$$

$$\begin{bmatrix} 1 & 0 \\ 0 & 0 \end{bmatrix}^{-1} \begin{bmatrix} x' \\ y' \end{bmatrix} = \begin{bmatrix} x \\ y \end{bmatrix}$$

but if we try to calculate the inverse of $\begin{bmatrix} 1 & 0 \\ 0 & 0 \end{bmatrix}$ we fail since the associated determinant is $1 \times 0 - 0 \times 0 = 0$ (p. 100). Again we see that we cannot establish a 1–1 correspondence. Thus we may soon test whether a transformation distorts a plane into a plane, or contracts it into a line or point, by putting it in matrix form and calculating the associated determinant. If the result is not zero there is a 1–1 correspondence between points before and after transformation and the plane is transformed into a plane. If the associated determinant is zero then the plane contracts into a line or point.

Examples 11f

1. From your knowledge of transformations predict the effect of the following on a square of sides $(1, 1)$, $(1, 2)$, $(2, 1)$, and $(2, 2)$ and check to make sure you are right.

(a) $\begin{bmatrix} 0 & 0 \\ 1 & 0 \end{bmatrix}$,   (b) $\begin{bmatrix} 1 & 0 \\ 0 & 0 \end{bmatrix}$,   (c) $\begin{bmatrix} 0 & 1 \\ 1 & 0 \end{bmatrix}$,   (d) $\begin{bmatrix} 1 & 0 \\ 0 & 1 \end{bmatrix}$,

(e) $\begin{bmatrix} 0 & -1 \\ 1 & 0 \end{bmatrix}$,   (f) $\begin{bmatrix} 0 & 1 \\ -1 & 0 \end{bmatrix}$,   (g) $\begin{bmatrix} 1 & 1 \\ 0 & 1 \end{bmatrix}$,   (h) $\begin{bmatrix} 1 & 1 \\ 1 & 0 \end{bmatrix}$,

(i) $\begin{bmatrix} 1 & 1 \\ 1 & 1 \end{bmatrix}$,   (j) $\begin{bmatrix} -1 & 1 \\ 1 & -1 \end{bmatrix}$,   (k) $\begin{bmatrix} 3 & 6 \\ 3 & 0 \end{bmatrix}$,   (l) $\begin{bmatrix} 3 & 6 \\ 2 & 4 \end{bmatrix}$.

11.8 Group properties of Transformations in general

We have already demonstrated that the set of all transformations excluding translations do not form a group since, when represented by 2×2 matrices, the awkward specimens of the last section do not have inverses. If we exclude these however we are left with the set of all 2×2 matrices with no zero determinants which we have already proved to form a group under matrix multiplication (p. 101 *et seq.*). Such a group is called the linear group. If we extended the arguments of the last two chapters to include translations so that we were dealing with

$$\begin{bmatrix} a & b & h \\ c & d & k \\ 0 & 0 & 1 \end{bmatrix},$$

the same line of reasoning would still hold good and if we exclude the cases where the determinant for $\begin{bmatrix} a & b \\ c & d \end{bmatrix}$ is zero, we get another group structure, the affine group. This last is a statement of fact rather than a proof, but may be 'philosophized over' after the manner of sections 11.3 and 11.5. We may note that the group of affine transformations includes the group of linear transformations as special cases when no translation is involved. Similarly, it includes the group of Euclidean transformations (p. 210) as special cases where no distortion of shape or size is involved and the group of similitudes (p. 215) where size is altered but shape remains the same.

11.9 Summary of Geometry

Schoolboy geometry of congruent figures is the geometry of Euclidean transformations which leave both shape and size unaltered by their action. After examining this, we extended our ideas to similar figures and worked in the group of similitudes. Now, with more efficient tools at our disposal, we can extend yet again to the motions under the group of affine transformations which allow us to distort both shape and size, but still leaves straight lines as lines and points as points. If this new extended geometry seems unrealistic and impractical as compared with the down-to-earth congruences and similar triangles, consider our bowler-hatted reader once again and for the last time standing in the hot sunshine all day (with his umbrella) meditating on the eccentricities of modern mathematics as his shadow busily maps out a pretty pattern of linear transformations of his various silhouettes.

Fig. 107

12. WHAT WE HAVE LEFT OUT

12.1 Summary

The reader who has valiantly stayed with us during the past eleven chapters may sit back at this stage and feel well pleased with himself. It is a tribute to his stamina and determination that he has been able to do so. He can however legitimately enquire as to the point of his labours. In other words, why 'Modern Mathematics' and how does it differ from the ancient variety?

We started off by adopting the approach of the industrial mathematician to a problem which contained much pattern and form but which was not 'mathematics' in the narrowest sense of the word. We chose Scottish country dancing because it was sufficiently complex to produce some amusing mathematics and because we happened to have a book on the subject. As a result of our tactics we hope that the reader has gained a little insight into the usual way of tackling such situations and has realized that there are many 'arithmetics' apart from the one on which we were brought up, each of which is capable of solving its own special type of problem.

We could well have stopped at this point and left the reader with a new assortment of techniques which would certainly have widened his mathematical experience. These however no more merit the title of 'modern mathematics' than the automatic recitation of multiplication tables merits the title 'arithmetic'. The whole point of modern mathematics is that behind all these various arithmetics, including our own, there is a pattern or structure which we can seek out and analyse, thus increasing our own knowledge and facility with orthodox arithmetic or any other which we may find either useful or amusing.

Most of the situations we have examined have an Abelian group structure and we have seen what this means and how it affects calculation. Also we have, in the group axioms, abstracted the minimum conditions which an arithmetic must fulfil in order to be a group and deduced from these axioms various techniques which are useful in calculation. Thus we can see that modern mathematics is not a thing apart from orthodox mathematics. We have all been doing it for years although the precision and clarity of its ideas have been clouded by over-familiarity and unfortunate teaching techniques during our formative period.

Modern mathematics is not a thing to be grafted on to the end of a syllabus in order to bring it up to date. There is little point in announcing proudly to an eleven- or twelve-year-old that $3+2 = 2+3$. A backward eight-year-old however reduced her task by half by discovering the Commutative Law for herself when learning her simple addition facts. Several not-so-backward thirteen-year-olds were most anxious to know whether to multiply the πr^3 by the 4 and then divide by the 3 or divide the 4 by the 3 and then multiply by the πr^3 when finding the volume of a sphere. A humane but adequate emphasis on the Associative and Commutative Laws at the appropriate stage would have avoided that problem. Either we teach our children by the precepts of modern mathematics or we do not. A compromise situation is at best uneconomical. At worst it is chaotic.

The above is not to be misconstrued as the beginning of a 'Modern Mathematics for Primary Schools' campaign. We believe that even non-specialist mathematics teachers should have at least a very informal knowledge of what groups, fields (see next section) and sets (see next volume) are and their relevance to elementary mathematics. Primary teachers who have received this background have found that it has clarified their ideas enormously and this can have only pleasing repercussions on the children they teach. The same, of course, applies to secondary teachers so that the initial impetus is not wasted and the flow towards more formal work is smooth and uninterrupted.

This is certainly not a book on the theory of mathematics teaching and the preceding few paragraphs are, to some extent, irrelevant. However, a large proportion of our readers will, we hope, be teachers or prospective teachers wanting to know how modern mathematics affects them. Ours is one line. There are others. We naturally prefer ours.

We return to the summary. Once the reader had experienced the delights of group theory we moved on to matrices. The chief point about these is their versatility. They provided a means of notation whereby we could describe situations as diverse as simple arithmetic, Scottish country dancing and congruent triangles. We must however be clear as to their virtue. Matrices are only a means of notation. There is nothing magical in the matrix itself. The underlying ideas in all these diverse situations are basically the same. Matrices are merely the means whereby these similarities are exposed.

The final task of this summary is to fit what we have done into modern mathematics as a whole. We have not gone deeply. That was not our task. Nor have we travelled beyond the bounds of one axiomatic structure although we have covered much ground within those bounds. We have met already a double group structure when we were considering the links between groups and real numbers (p. 74). In the next section we tidy up this idea and have a brief look at the 'field'. This has a more complex structure than the group but its very complexity limits the number of situations where it applies. Finally, we shall consider the 'vector space' which has relevance to both simple arithmetic and geometry.

In Chapter 5 we introduced the reader to sets and simple logic. The attack was intentionally limited as a more formal approach would have been out of place and held up the development of the theme. Sets and logic have their own private set of axioms and are each special cases of what is called a Boolean algebra after the English mathematician George Boole (1815–64). Sets are behind the very foundation of our real number system. The field axioms tell us what numbers do but sets help to explain what they really are. These ideas are no more complex than many we have dealt with, but space prevents us from doing them justice here and we hope therefore to present them in a later volume.

12.2 Commutative Fields

We have already stated that a field is basically a double-group structure. This implies that we need a set of elements and two combining operations which we shall call '+' and '×'. We would be more precise in using '*' and 'o' as '+' and '×' tend to refer us to either real numbers or matrices. However, all our examples will be based on '+' or '×' situations so that we would merely complicate the issue in this very brief survey by using the more general form. As in orthodox algebra we shall miss out '×' when it suits us and just write 'ab' for '$a \times b$'. The reader who prefers a more precise approach may mentally rewrite this section according to the precepts of Chapter 5 or refer to the bibliography for a more advanced text. By the same criteria we shall use 0 and 1 for the identity elements for '+' and '×' respectively and $(-a)$ and a^{-1} for the additive and multiplicative inverses of a.

The axioms for a commutative field are as follows:

Given a set F and two combining operations '+' and '×',

(1) closure and uniqueness are true for both '+' and '×',

(2) the Associative Law is true for both '+' and '×',

(3) there is an identity element for each combining operation; 0 for '+' and 1 for '×',

(4) every element has an inverse for each combining operation except for 0 which has no multiplicative inverse,

(5) the Commutative Law is true for both '+' and '×'.

If the field were not commutative, the Commutative Law would be true for '+' but not for '×'. This may seem curious but is the most convenient arrangement in practice.

There is one more rule which is necessary to complete the axioms and which we have not met before. This provides the connecting link between the two combining operations which so far lead entirely separate existences. We quote it here to complete the axioms but devote the next section to its amplification:

(6) the Distributive Law

$$a(b+c) = ab+ac \quad \forall\ a,b,c \in F.$$

In other words, a multiplying element distributes itself over a '+' bracket.

Apart from the Distributive Law there is nothing that is new in the above axioms. There are merely more of them. We know that the Abelian group axioms list the minimum requirements for a fairly care-free handling of a set with one combining operation. The commutative field axioms do the same thing where two combining operations are involved and with any set which satisfies these axioms we can carry out many of the processes of schoolboy arithmetic and algebra. We have not yet made our axioms stringent enough to guarantee being able to deduce every process of simple arithmetic from them and it is out of the scope of this book to do so. We cannot even deduce, for example, that $a+a = 2a$, but the next few sections will show something of what can be done in this direction.

12.3 The Distributive Law

$$a(b+c) = ab+ac \quad \forall \, a,b,c \in F$$

means that a multiplying element can distribute itself over a '+' bracket as we mentioned in the previous section. We can get a nice counter-example by seeing whether an adding element distributes itself over a '×' bracket. This is such an unfamiliar idea that we must approach it carefully to avoid getting lost. We first of all write in all the '×' signs which are implicit in the definition. Thus

$$a \times (b+c) = a \times b + a \times c$$

and we may well remember as youngsters being told, for reasons unspecified, always to do the multiplications before the additions when working out expressions such as the right-hand side. To emphasize the point we will enclose the multiplications in brackets:

$$a \times (b+c) = (a \times b) + (a \times c).$$

If we wish to test the validity of the Distributive Law for '+' all we have to do is to replace '×' by '+' and '+' by '×' with

$$a + (b \times c) = (a+b) \times (a+c)$$

as the result. This is usually written more neatly as

$$a + bc = (a+b)(a+c)$$

which is not necessarily true. We may test quickly as far as orthodox arithmetic is concerned by trying $a = 1$, $b = 2$, $c = 3$.

$$a + bc = 1 + 2 \times 3 = 1 + 6 = 7.$$

$$(a+b)(a+c) = (1+2)(1+3) = 3 \times 4 = 12$$

which proves our point.

If you were to ask a friend what was the special defining property of 0 as a number you would be more likely to get the equivalent of

$$0 \times x = 0 \quad \forall \, x$$

than

$$0 + x = x \quad \forall \, x$$

but, in fact, the first may be proved from the second by the use of the Distributive Law.

$$ab + ac = a(b+c) \quad \forall \, a,b,c \in F$$
$$\Downarrow$$
$$ab + (a \times 0) = a(b+0) \quad \forall \, a,b \in F$$
$$\Downarrow$$
$$ab + (a \times 0) = ab \quad \text{(since 0 is the neutral element for '+')}$$
$$\Downarrow$$
$$a \times 0 = 0 \quad \text{(by the Cancellation Rule for '+')}$$

Thus, in the particular case of the real number field, the fact that any number multiplied by 0 gives 0 is a theorem deducible from the initial axioms rather than a definition. Of course, it may be possible to redefine the axioms so that

16

the alternative point of view holds good but that, as far as we know, is not the most convenient way of doing things.

To show the versatility of the Distributive Law we now justify a familiar piece of algebraic manipulation in any set which has the properties of a commutative field.

To prove

$$(a-b)(a+b) = a^2 - b^2.$$

$(a-b)(a+b) = c(a+b)$	(where $c = a-b$)
$= ca + cb$	(by the Distributive Law)
$= (a-b)a + (a-b)b$	(since $c = a-b$)
$= a(a-b) + b(a-b)$	(by the Commutative Law for '$\times$')
$= a\{a+(-b)\} + b\{a+(-b)\}$	(rewriting the expression more precisely)
$= aa + a(-b) + ba + b(-b)$	(by the Distributive Law)

Now aa is usually written as a^2.

Also $a(-b) + ba = a(-b) + ab$	(by the Commutative Law for '$\times$')
$= a\{(-b) + b\}$	(by the Distributive Law in reverse)
$= a \times 0$	(by the inverse property of $(-b)$)
$= 0$	(by the earlier part of this section).

We now examine $b(-b)$.

Consider $b\{b + (-b)\} = b \times 0$	(by the inverse properties of $(-b)$),
$= 0$	(by the earlier part of this section).
Also $b\{b + (-b)\} = bb + b(-b)$	(by the Distributive Law),
$= b^2 + b(-b)$.	

Therefore $b^2 + b(-b) = 0$.

This implies that

$-b^2 + \{b^2 + b(-b)\} = -b^2$	(adding the '$+$' inverse of b^2 to each side)
$\{-b^2 + b^2\} + b(-b) = -b^2$	(by the Associative Law for '$+$')
$0 + b(-b) = -b^2$	(by the inverse property of $-b^2$)
$b(-b) = -b^2$	(by the identity property of 0).

Collecting up the bits and pieces we get that

$$(a-b)(a+b) = a^2 - b^2$$

in any commutative field.

The examples give the reader the opportunity to examine further the versatility of the Distributive Law and also give him the chance to look at some commutative fields apart from the real number field.

Examples 12a

1. Justify the statement

$$(x+2)(x+1) = x^2+3x+2$$

in the real number field.

2. Repeat Question 1 for

$$(x-2)(x-1) = x^2-3x+2.$$

3. Show that we are justified in saying that

$$(x+1)^2 = x^2+2x+1$$

in the real number field but not in every commutative field.

4. A favourite way of factorizing a cubic such as

$$3x^3+2x^2-12x-8$$

is by grouping convenient terms together. Justify the complete factorizing process in the real number field.

5. Prove that the Distributive Law for '×' over '+' is true for 2×2 matrices if it is true for the real number field.

6. We may write down both addition and multiplication tables for arithmetic mod 3. (See Question 9, Examples 1d, p. 14.)

+	0	1	2
0	0	1	2
1	1	2	0
2	2	0	1

TABLE 44

×	0	1	2
0	0	0	0
1	0	1	2
2	0	2	1

TABLE 45

Prove the Distributive Law for arithmetic mod 3 by examining all possible cases after the style of Chapter 3.

Why can we not take the three 2×2 matrices which generated a three group and use them to help prove the Distributive Law?

12.4 The Commutative Field Rules in Action

The examples with which we demonstrated the power of the distributive law also, of course, made use of the other field axioms. The solution of a quadratic equation in the real number field, which we examined earlier (p. 159), gives a further illustration of the economy and skill with which the field axioms have been constructed.

Consider once again

$$x^2-3x+2 = 0$$

The reader has already justified the factorization (Question 2, Examples 12a, p. 233) so that

$$(x-2)(x-1) = 0.$$

$(x-2)$ either (a) has a multiplicative inverse $\Big\}$ Field Axiom 4 for '×'.
           or   (b) is 0

   (a) Pre-multiply by $(x-2)^{-1}$

$$(x-2)^{-1}\{(x-2)(x-1)\} = (x-2)^{-1}\times 0$$

⇓

$$\{(x-2)^{-1}(x-2)\}(x-1) = 0 \qquad \text{(Field Axiom 2 for '×' and p. 231)}$$

⇓

$$1\times(x-1) = 0 \qquad \text{(Field Axiom 4 for '×')}$$

⇓

$$x-1 = 0 \qquad \text{(Field Axiom 3 for '×')}$$

⇓

$$(x-1)+1 = 0+1 \qquad \text{(adding the '+' inverse of } -1 \text{ to each side. Field Axiom 4 for '+')}$$

⇓

$$x+(-1+1) = 1 \qquad \text{(Field Axioms 2 and 3 for '+')}$$

⇓

$$x+0 = 1 \qquad \text{(Field Axiom 4 for '+')}$$

⇓

$$x = 1 \qquad \text{(Field Axiom 3 for '+').}$$

   Alternatively,
   (b) $x-2 = 0$

and the argument is parallel to the last five lines of (a) above, giving the answer $x = 2$ which leaves us with the usual two alternatives: $x = 1$ or $x = 2$.

   This the reader has seen before but in rather a different guise. We have used Axioms 2, 3 and 4 for both '+' and '×' in the above. In the proof that $(x-2)^{-1}\times 0 = 0$, following the lines of p. 231, we would have used Axiom 6 in addition. In his justification that

$$x^2 - 3x + 2 = (x-2)(x-1)$$

the reader must have used the Commutative Law for '×'. In order to get any results at all we have to assume that each calculation has just one answer so that Axiom 1 for both operations has been well used. The deduction from all this is that even in the solution of such a common phenomenon as the quadratic equation, every commutative field axiom except the Commutative Law for '+' has been brought into play. This illustrates well the power of the field axioms and also shows what a fantastically complex procedure even the simplest of algebraic processes may be.

Examples 12b

   1. Solve where possible the quadratic equation

$$x^2 - 3x + 2 = 0$$

in
      (a) arithmetic mod 3,
      (b) arithmetic mod 4,
      (c) arithmetic mod 5,
      (d) arithmetic mod 6,
      (e) arithmetic mod 9.

The simplest way to check your results is to write down the '+' and the '×' tables for each arithmetic and check each value in turn. You will need the tables for other questions and you may get some surprises.

2. What really makes the solution of quadratics possible is that if two numbers multiply to 0 then at least one of them must be 0. Show that

$$a \times b = 0 \quad \Rightarrow \quad a = 0 \text{ or } b = 0 \text{ or both}$$

in any commutative field.

3. By carefully examining the tables of Question 1 decide which of the modulus arithmetics are commutative fields and deduce a general rule for this.

4. Which of the following sets of matrices form a commutative field under '+' and '×'? (All the letters represent real numbers.)

(a) $\begin{bmatrix} a & b \\ c & d \end{bmatrix}$, (b) $\begin{bmatrix} a & b \\ c & d \end{bmatrix}$ $(ad \neq bc)$, (c) $\begin{bmatrix} a & -b \\ b & a \end{bmatrix}$,

(d) $\begin{bmatrix} a & 0 \\ 0 & a \end{bmatrix}$, (e) $\begin{bmatrix} a & 0 & 0 \\ 0 & a & 0 \\ 0 & 0 & a \end{bmatrix}$, (f) $\begin{bmatrix} a & 0 \\ 0 & a \\ a & 0 \end{bmatrix}$.

5. Check that the set of all rational numbers, including 0, forms a commutative field under '+' and '×'.

A field isomorphism requires a 1–1 correspondence between the two relevant sets of elements and also that corresponding calculations give corresponding results for both combining operations. Prove that there is a field isomorphism between (d) of Question 4 and the real number system.

12.5 Commutative Field Summary

Of necessity this examination of the commutative field has been sketchy to the point of non-existence. However, we felt that even in a book such as this, which is devoted primarily to the group, we would not be justified in missing it out altogether. Our sole aim was to show the relevance of the commutative field axioms to orthodox arithmetic and algebra and thus to encourage the reader to examine orthodox processes with reference to these axioms. In this way it is hoped that he may clarify his ideas on what can be very complicated basic processes.

Most arithmetic and algebra is a combination of Associative, Commutative and Distributive Laws and is often more easily understood when seen in this light. Field axioms, of course, have their limitations. $5 + 6 = 11$ is true in some commutative fields but not others and similar results based on number facts as opposed to general manipulation are bound to vary from field to field. The formal construction of the number facts is a task for the next volume.

12.6 Vector Spaces

The previous sections of this chapter dealt with the abstract manipulations of number according to the axioms for a commutative field. Unfortunately, the practical applications of some of these ideas follow a rather different line. Consider the issuing of 3 oranges to each of 2 children. This requires 2 lots of 3 oranges or 6 in all. In other words,

$$2 \times 3 = 6$$
lots oranges oranges

The first number on the left-hand side represents 'lots' whereas the other two represent oranges. In other words, although the same number symbols are used and the same abstract number ideas are represented, the 2 in this case represents a different type of thing from the 3 or the 6.

The difference is easier to see when several different types of fruit are used. If each child is to have 3 oranges and 4 apples we can usefully represent the problem in matrix form as

$$\text{lots } 2 \begin{bmatrix} 3 \\ 4 \end{bmatrix} \begin{matrix} \text{oranges} \\ \text{apples} \end{matrix} = \begin{bmatrix} 6 \\ 8 \end{bmatrix} \begin{matrix} \text{oranges} \\ \text{apples} \end{matrix}$$

and we are back to the ideas of Chapter 6.

These ideas spread easily to three or four or any number of different kinds of fruit or any other object for that matter and thus we are now in the process of building a new type of mathematical structure based on real numbers and column matrices.

The above ideas may be shown usefully on a graph. In the first example, where we deal with just oranges, a straight-line graph is sufficient.

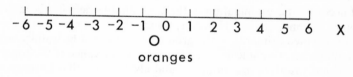

FIG. 108

If each space represents an orange we can mark off 3 spaces anywhere we like to represent 3 oranges. Two lots of 3 oranges are represented by *AB* and *CD* in Fig. 109.

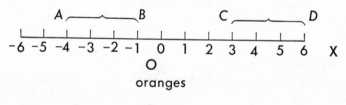

FIG. 109

It is more convenient to mark off the two lengths from 0 so that we may find the total more easily.

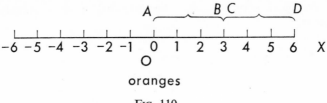

oranges

Fig. 110

Much of the structural apparatus now on the market for primary children uses a similar idea to demonstrate multiplication. 2×3 may be illustrated as 2 lots of 3 rods put end to end to give the equivalent of a 6-rod.

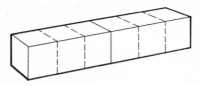

Fig. 111

In this case number × length = length, which is similar to the first oranges example. Thus the demonstration is of the multiplication of this section rather than multiplication in a commutative field. The alternative convention, where the two rods are placed side by side or the idea is abbreviated to putting

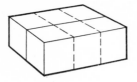

Fig. 112

a 2-rod across a 3-rod, is an example of length × length = area, which is even

Fig. 113

more complicated. These difficulties are inherent in any attempt at a physical representation of the real number system and do not in any way decry the usefulness of this type of apparatus when properly handled.

The graphical approach may be extended more profitably to two dimensions.

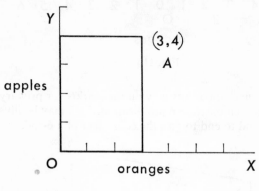

Fɪɢ. 114

The point (3, 4) on the graph adequately represents 3 oranges and 4 apples, and a line of twice the length, or another line *AB* of length *OA* stuck on the end to continue the straight line, would just as adequately represent 6 oranges and 8 apples.

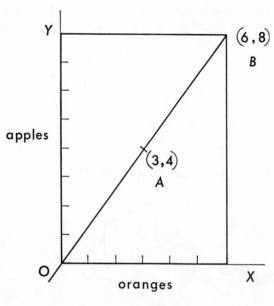

Fɪɢ. 115

A problem based on oranges, apples and pears would lead us into a three-dimensional graph, whereas oranges, apples, pears and peaches would send us into the fourth dimension which would be difficult to illustrate but can be handled easily enough by the processes of the next few sections. We shall restrict ourselves in general to two dimensions. The ideas extend readily enough to any finite number of dimensions, but two will suffice to make our point.

Examples 12c

Write down 10 examples of multiplication from everyday life and catalogue them according to whether they belong to

(a) a commutative field,
(b) this section,
(c) a structure as yet unspecified.

12.7 Addition and Subtraction

Let us approach the following problem from the graphical point of view. We are given 2 oranges and 3 apples and buy another orange and 2 apples. How many have we altogether?

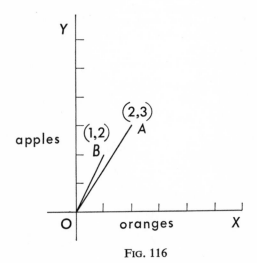

FIG. 116

A line which travels 2 across and 3 up represents what we are given (*OA*). A line 1 across and 2 up represents what we buy (*OB*). In Fig. 116 we have begun both lines at *O* although this is in no way necessary as we demonstrated with the single-line graph. Again following the one-dimensional principle it would seem reasonable to put the line *OB* on the end of the line *OA* to get the final result.

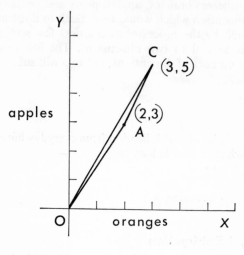

This takes us a further 1 place along and 2 places upward and therefore ends us up at the point C (3, 5) which is what we would expect. The line OC represents the result.

If we now eat 2 oranges and 1 apple we can plot it as

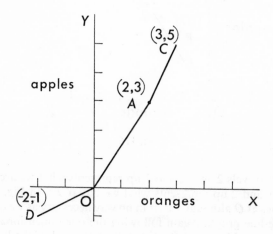

FIG. 118

and we can again find the result by moving the line *OD* up to the position *CE*.

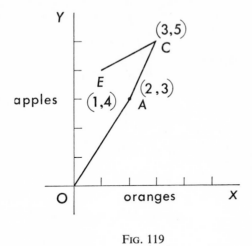

Fig. 119

We may have misfired in Fig. 119 and represented the situation as in Fig. 120, which would obviously misrepresent the problem, and it is therefore

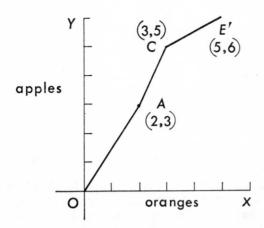

Fig. 120

politic to place arrows along the various lines to show the direction in which they are aiming. Thus the correct representation would initially be Fig. 121.

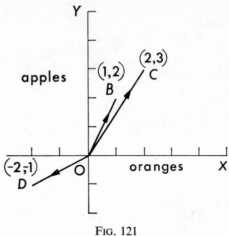

FIG. 121

which would now reorganize as Fig. 122 with the arrows flowing smoothly the

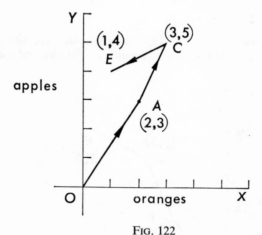

FIG. 122

same way round the system. In the incorrect version we would find two arrows banging their heads together.

By now the reader has almost certainly recognized his old friend the vector which he probably first met in his early days of physics. He almost certainly learnt that vectors have magnitude and direction but no fixed point of application. The above development illustrates the necessity for this. The examples at the end of this section will help recall the versatility of vectors.

We shall in future either represent vectors by their first and last letters with an arrow over the top or by a single letter in bold type. Thus in Fig. 123

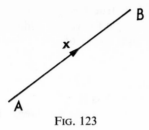

FIG. 123

the vector may be called either *AB* or **x**. When writing the **x** form by hand it is usual to write with normal pressure and just underline the vector if there is any chance of confusion. Ordinary numbers (usually called 'scalars' in these circumstances) will continue to appear in normal type.

Incidentally all matrices of the form

$$\begin{bmatrix} a \\ b \\ c \\ d \\ \cdot \\ \cdot \\ \cdot \end{bmatrix} \quad \text{or} \quad [a \quad b \quad c \quad d \quad \ldots]$$

now appear in the guise of vectors and may be legitimately called column vectors or row vectors respectively.

Examples 12d

$\overrightarrow{OA}$ is a vector of size 3 due east,

$\overrightarrow{OB}$ is a vector of size 2 due north,

$\overrightarrow{OC}$ is a vector of size 4 due north-east,

$\overrightarrow{OD}$ is a vector of size 3 due south-west.

1. Find the result of

  (a) $\overrightarrow{OA} + \overrightarrow{OB}$,

  (b) $\overrightarrow{OC} + \overrightarrow{OD}$,

  (c) $(\overrightarrow{OA} + \overrightarrow{OB}) + \overrightarrow{OC}$,

  (d) $\overrightarrow{OA} + (\overrightarrow{OB} + \overrightarrow{OC})$.

2. Find the result of

  (a) $3\overrightarrow{OA} + 2\overrightarrow{OC}$,

  (b) $-\overrightarrow{OD}$,

(c) $\overrightarrow{OB} - \overrightarrow{OC}$,

(d) $2\overrightarrow{OA} - \overrightarrow{OD}$.

3. Is the Commutative Law true for vector addition?

4. Is the Associative Law true for vector addition?

5. What are the effects on a vector of

    (a) a reflection,

    (b) a rotation,

    (c) a translation,

and what is left invariant in each case?

6. I walk 4 miles east and then 2 miles north-east. How far am I from home as the crow flies?

7. The middle of a piece of rope is tied to a heavy load. Two men each take hold of an end and pull. There is a right-angle between the two ends of the rope. One man pulls twice as hard as the other. In which direction will the load travel?

8. I am running due north at 10 knots across the deck of a ship steering due east at 20 knots in a north-east current of 5 knots. How fast and in what direction am I travelling relative to the sea-bed?

9. I buy 5 oranges and 4 apples and throw away 2 oranges and 1 apple because they are bad. I give a small child 1 orange. I eat 1 apple and 1 orange myself. A friend gives me 1 orange and 2 apples. Plot all this graphically and find out what I have left. What would be the situation if the graph ended up where it started?

12.8   Vectors and Group Theory

We have already discovered that $\begin{bmatrix} a \\ b \end{bmatrix}$ under '+' forms an Abelian group (p. 85), so that vectors in two dimensions (or any other number of dimensions for that matter) also form an Abelian group under '+'. However, it is instructive to prove these laws directly by using the vectors themselves.

By the very nature of the process for carrying out vector addition we know that closure and uniqueness of result must be true.

The Associative Law is a little more tricky (see Fig. 124).

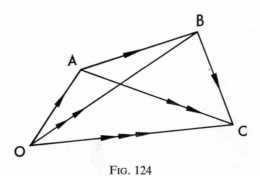

FIG. 124

If we wish to add the three vectors $\overrightarrow{OA}$, $\overrightarrow{AB}$ and $\overrightarrow{BC}$ we may do it as $(\overrightarrow{OA}+\overrightarrow{AB})+\overrightarrow{BC}$.

$$\overrightarrow{OA}+\overrightarrow{AB}=\overrightarrow{OB},$$

$$\overrightarrow{OB}+\overrightarrow{BC}=\overrightarrow{OC}.$$

The alternative approach is $\overrightarrow{OA}+(\overrightarrow{AB}+\overrightarrow{BC})$, now

$$\overrightarrow{AB}+\overrightarrow{BC}=\overrightarrow{AC},$$

and

$$\overrightarrow{OA}+\overrightarrow{AC}=\overrightarrow{OC},$$

so that the two results are the same. The above proof is independent of the properties of the individual vectors so that the Associative Law is true for the addition of vectors.

The neutral vector is the vector of zero size which has, of course, no effect when added to another vector.

The inverse of a vector is very conveniently obtained by reversing the direction of its arrow. Thus the inverse of

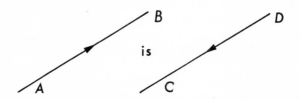

is

since it undoes the work of $\overrightarrow{AB}$ and

$$\overrightarrow{AB}+\overrightarrow{DC}=0.$$

The Commutative Law is easily proved (see Fig. 125).

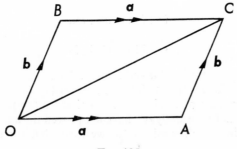

FIG. 125

$$\overrightarrow{OA} = \overrightarrow{BC} = \mathbf{a}, \qquad \text{say,}$$

$$\overrightarrow{OB} = \overrightarrow{AC} = \mathbf{b}, \qquad \text{say,}$$

$$\mathbf{a}+\mathbf{b} = \overrightarrow{OA}+\overrightarrow{AC} = \overrightarrow{OC},$$

$$\mathbf{b}+\mathbf{a} = \overrightarrow{OB}+\overrightarrow{BC} = \overrightarrow{OC}$$

and therefore

$$\mathbf{a}+\mathbf{b} = \mathbf{b}+\mathbf{a}.$$

Again the proof is independent of the individual vectors concerned so that the Commutative Law is true and therefore vectors form an Abelian group under vector addition.

12.9 The Vector Space Axioms

We are now in a position to collect together the ideas in the second half of this chapter. We know the usual properties which we can expect vectors to have and therefore stipulate the following conditions for a vector space.

(a) We must have two sets of elements, one of which we shall call 'vectors' and the other 'scalars'.

(b) We must be able to add and subtract vectors freely. In other words, the vectors must form an Abelian group under '+'.

(c) The scalars are usually, but not necessarily, the real number field. We must be able to manipulate them freely as regards addition and multiplication, so that we will stipulate that scalars must have the properties of a commutative field.

(d) The only ideas which are new in these axioms are the ones concerning the intermingling of the scalars and vectors, i.e. the multiplication of vectors by scalars which started us off on this discourse. For the usual freedom of computation it is deemed necessary that

(i) a composite Associative Law must be true,

$$a(b\mathbf{x}) = (ab)\mathbf{x},$$

(ii) two assorted Composite Distributive Laws must be true,

$$(a+b)\mathbf{x} = a\mathbf{x}+b\mathbf{x},$$

$$a(\mathbf{x}+\mathbf{y}) = a\mathbf{x}+a\mathbf{y},$$

where $\mathbf{x}$ and $\mathbf{y}$ are vectors and a and b are scalars.

Any structure which satisfies all the axioms of (a), (b), (c), and (d) merits the title of vector space and behaves in a similar way to the vectors we have handled in the text. Incidentally, we have not proved the axioms of section (d) for our vectors in two dimensions but we leave that for the reader in the examples.

Examples 12e

1. Prove that the axioms of section 12.9(d) are true for $\left\{ \begin{bmatrix} a \\ b \end{bmatrix} \right\}$ with the real number field as the associated scalar field.

2. Prove by drawing and simple geometry that the axioms of section 12.9(d) are true for vectors in two dimensions.

3. Prove that the following are vector spaces.
(a) $\{0, 1, x, x+1\}$ with arithmetic mod 2 as the associated scalar field.
(b) $a+b\sqrt{2}$ where a and b are rational numbers and the field of rational numbers is the associated scalar field.

4. Which of the following form vector spaces under '+' with the real number system as the associated scalar field?

(a) $\left\{ \begin{bmatrix} a & b \\ c & d \end{bmatrix} \right\}$,

(b) $\left\{ \begin{bmatrix} a & b \\ c & d \end{bmatrix} ; ad \neq bc \right\}$,

(c) $\left\{ \begin{bmatrix} a & 0 \\ 0 & a \\ a & 0 \end{bmatrix} \right\}$,

(d) $\left\{ \begin{bmatrix} a & -b \\ b & a \end{bmatrix} \right\}$, where a, b, c and d are real numbers in each case.

5. We frequently represent the real number system as points on a number line as in the one-dimensional graph of p. 236. Examine the possibility of a vector space with the real number system as both the set of vectors and the associated scalar field.

12.10 Vectors and Geometry

The title of this section is adequate for another book in its own right but we particularly wanted to make a brief mention of geometry from the vector point of view since we considered only transformations in the earlier chapters. On p. 182 we said that it seemed perhaps curious to have a means of adding points. We may now use these points to represent vectors and the addition of vectors has many applications. Vector manipulation is of practical significance in one form or another in most branches of applied mathematics and theoretical physics, but is particularly useful in three-dimensional geometry where it is sometimes frighteningly efficient.

With supreme bathos after this magnificent build-up for vector geometry we finish this volume by proving for the reader two simple theorems. These do not do vectors justice but they do show them in action and the bibliography will aim the interested reader in the right direction.

THEOREM 1. *The diagonals of a parallelogram bisect each other.*

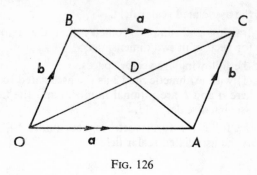

FIG. 126

Proof. We can represent the mid-points of the diagonals by vectors measured from O.

The mid-point of OC is

$$\tfrac{1}{2}\overrightarrow{OC} = \tfrac{1}{2}(\mathbf{a}+\mathbf{b}).$$

The mid-point of AB is

$$\overrightarrow{OA}+\tfrac{1}{2}\overrightarrow{AB} = \mathbf{a}+\tfrac{1}{2}(\mathbf{b}-\mathbf{a}) \quad \text{(see Question 2(c), Examples 12d, p. 243)}$$

$$= \tfrac{1}{2}(\mathbf{a}+\mathbf{b}).$$

Thus both diagonals have the same mid-point and therefore bisect each other.

THEOREM 2.

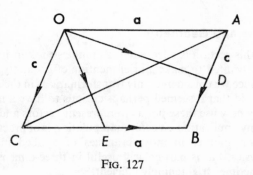

FIG. 127

In the diagram, if D and E are the mid-points of their respective sides, $\overrightarrow{OD}$ and $\overrightarrow{OE}$ trisect AC.

Proof. One trisection point of AC is given by

$$\overrightarrow{OA} + \tfrac{1}{3}\overrightarrow{AC} = \mathbf{a} + \tfrac{1}{3}(\mathbf{c} - \mathbf{a})$$

$$= \frac{2\mathbf{a} + \mathbf{c}}{3}.$$

The vector $\overrightarrow{OD}$ is

$$\overrightarrow{OA} + \tfrac{1}{2}\overrightarrow{AB} = \mathbf{a} + \tfrac{1}{2}\mathbf{c}$$

$$= \frac{2\mathbf{a} + \mathbf{c}}{2}$$

$$= \frac{3}{2}\left(\frac{2\mathbf{a} + \mathbf{c}}{3}\right).$$

Thus $\overrightarrow{OD}$ has the same direction as the vector representing the first trisection point of AC since they differ only by a scalar multiplier. Therefore, since they both start from O, $\overrightarrow{OD}$ must go through the trisection point. A similar argument follows for $\overrightarrow{OE}$.

SOLUTIONS TO EXAMPLES

Chapter 1

Examples 1d

1. (a) e; (b) e; (c) e; (d) a; (e) a; (f) e. The short cuts are developed in Chapters 3 and 4.

2. (a) $A \text{ f } B \text{ f } C = I$; (b) Table 4 again; (c) see Chapter 8, para. 2, page 132 for a similar argument concerning triangles and think of the dancers as standing at the corners of a square.

3. $Q \text{ f } Q \text{ f } Q \text{ f } R \text{ f } R' \text{f} P \text{ f } P \text{ f } P \text{ f } P \text{ f } P = R$.

4. Table 4 again.

5. This is answered gradually in Chapters 3, 4 and 5.

6. Chapter 5, para. 5, page 66, and Examples 5c, Question 1, help here. Examples 2b, Question 4, answers the last part.

7. Table 37, page 135.

8. Table 4 again.

9. Table 4 again.

10. Table 4 again.

Chapter 2

Examples 2b

1. (a) b; (b) b; (c) b; (d) c; (e) a; (f) e. The short cuts are developed in Chapters 3 and 4.

2. (a) $X \text{ f } Y \text{ f } Z = Y$; (b) Table 7 again; (c) see Chapter 8, para. 2, page 132 for a similar argument concerning triangles and think of the dancers as standing at the corners of a square.

3. This is answered gradually in Chapters 3, 4 and 5.

4. Chapter 5, para. 5, page 66 and Examples 5c, Question 1, help here.

Examples 2d

1. (a) 1; (b) 2; (c) 4; (d) 4; (e) 4.

2. (a) 4 version: $1+1 = 2, 1+2 = 3, 1+3 = 4, 2+1 = 3, 2+2 = 4, 3+1 = 4$.
   (b) 0 version: $0+0 = 0, 0+1 = 1, 0+2 = 2, 0+3 = 3, 1+0 = 1, 1+1 = 2,$
   $1+2 = 3, 2+0 = 2, 2+1 = 3, 3+0 = 3$.

3. The most convenient but by no means the only explanation is that $a-x$ is short for $a+(-x)$ where $-x$ is the inverse of x (see Chapter 4). The hour hand is moved back instead of forward.

4. (a) 3; (b) 1; (c) 1; (d) 3; (e) 1, 3.

Examples 2e

2. Read the next three chapters.

3. (a) (i) 3, (ii) 6(0), (iii) 4, (iv) 2, (v) 6.
   (b) (i) 3, (ii) 8(0), (iii) 12(0).
   (c) (i) 3(0), (ii) 1, (iii) 4, (iv) 3, (v) 2, (vi) 1, (vii) 9.

4. (a) (i) 4, (ii) 3, (iii) 2, (iv) 1, (v) 9.
   (b) 4 each.
   (c) (i) 1, (ii) 2, (iii) 3, (iv) 4, (v) 8.
   (d) (i) 2, 4, (ii) 2, (iii) 2, 5, (iv) 2, (v) 2, (vi) 2, 8.
5. $x+y = z$ in ordinary numbers. $x, y <$ mod number, $z \leqslant$ mod number.

Examples 2f
1. (a) Friday; (b) Tuesday; (c) Monday; (d) Friday; (e) Tuesday; (f) Tuesday; (g) Sunday.
2. (a) August; (b) April; (c) October; (d) February; (e) August.
3. Thursday, Monday, Wednesday, Friday, Tuesday, Thursday, Monday, Wednesday, Friday.

Examples 2g
2. (a) 2; (b) 4; (c) 4; (d) 4; (e) 2; (f) 6; (g) 3; (h) 1; (i) ∞.
3. (a) mod 8; (b) mod 4; (c) mod 2.

Chapter 3

Examples 3b
3. See para. 4.4, page 44, and Table 22.

Examples 3c
1. (a) True; (b) true; (c) false.
2. (a) True; (b) true; (c) false; (d) false.

Examples 3d
1. (a) True; (b) true; (c) false.
2. (a) True; (b) true.
3. (a) True; (b) true; (c) false; (d) false.

Chapter 4

Examples 4a
1. 3(0).
2. 5(0).
3. No. ($x \div 1 = x$ yes; $1 \div x = \dfrac{1}{x}$ no.)
4. No. See 3 above for outline of consideration of 0.
5. No. See 4 above.
6. No. See 4 above.

Examples 4b
1. (a) Pairs of inverses (2, 1) and (3, 3).
   (b) Pairs of inverses (6, 6), (5, 1), (4, 2), and (3, 3).
5. (a) I; (b) Y; (c) C; (d) I; (e) 3; (f) 1.

Examples 4c
1. (a) +, ×; (b) +, −, ×; (c) +, ×, ÷; (d) ×, ÷; (e) +, −, ×, ÷.
2. None work.
3. None closed (imaginary roots).
4. Yes, yes.

Examples 4e
   All process B.

Chapter 5

Examples 5a

1. (b) $\{2, 4\}$; (e) $\{2, -2\}$; (f) $\{3, -3\}$; (g) meaningless; (j) there is a number, which, if we double it, gives 4; (k) twice any integer is an integer.

2. (a) $\{1, 2\}$; (b) {colours in traffic lights}; (c) $\{10, 11, 12, ..., 20\}$; (d) $\{\ \}$; (e) $\{0, 6\}$.

3. Mathematicians waste their time. The rest give no valid conclusions.

4. (a) $\{3, 6, 9\}$;

    (b) $x^2 = 9 \Rightarrow x = 3$ or -3.

    (c) $\{x \,|\, x = \dfrac{a}{a+1}, \quad a \in \{\text{integers}\}, a \neq -1\}$

    (d) $x \in \{\text{real numbers}\} \Rightarrow x + 1 \in \{\text{real numbers}\}$.

    (e) $\{1, 4\}$.

Examples 5b

2. (a)

×	0	1	2	, no.
0	0	0	0	
1	0	1	2	
2	0	2	1	

    (b) No.

3. Yes, yes, yes.

4. No, no (check Associative Law).

Examples 5d

(Note: The following are indications rather than proofs.)

1. Pre or post $*$ by x^{-1}.

2. $x^{kn} = (x^n)^k$.

3. n, m orders of x, x^{-1}.

$$\left. \begin{array}{l} x^n * (x^{-1})^n = e \Rightarrow (x^{-1})^n = e \\ x^m * (x^{-1})^m = e \Rightarrow x^m = e \end{array} \right\} \Rightarrow \begin{array}{l} n = k_1 m \\ m = k_2 n \end{array} \quad k_1, k_2 \ \text{positive integers.}$$

$$\Downarrow$$
$$k_1 = k_2 = 1.$$

4. If x of order n, $(x^k)^n = (x^n)^k = e$.

5. E.g. $x^2 = x^3 \Rightarrow x^3 = x^4 = e \Rightarrow x^3 = e$ false. Cyclic 4 group.

6. $\exists x \,|\, a * x = b \Rightarrow \exists x \,|\, a * x = a$.

    $a * x = a \Rightarrow b * x = b$ since $\exists y \,|\, y * a = b$.

Pre $*$ by y to prove this. This proves the existence of the identity. The inverse follows similarly.

7. G finite $\Rightarrow x^n = x^m$ for some $m, n \Rightarrow ax^n = ax^m \Rightarrow ax^{n-m} = a \Rightarrow x^{n-m} = e$. x of order $p \Rightarrow x^q x^{p-q} = e$. Hence inverses.

Chapter 6

Examples 6b

1. (a) $\begin{bmatrix} 9 & 6 \\ 1 & 8 \end{bmatrix}$;   (b) $\begin{bmatrix} 5 \\ -2 \\ 1 \end{bmatrix}$;   (c) Not possible;   (d) $\begin{bmatrix} 7 & 7 & 7 \\ 7 & 7 & 2 \end{bmatrix}$ or $\begin{bmatrix} 0 & 0 & 0 \\ 0 & 0 & 2 \end{bmatrix}$.

2. 11 choc. ices, 8 crunchy bars, 5 lollypops and 3 bags of peppermint creams.

3. Green tie; red, green, pink socks; black shoes.

4. 77–83 in East–West's favour.

Examples 6c

  3. Yes.
  4. No.
  5. Yes.
  6. Yes.

Examples 6d

  1. (a) $\begin{bmatrix} 8 & 12 \\ 2 & 4 \end{bmatrix}$; (b) $\begin{bmatrix} 0 & 4 \\ 0 & 0 \end{bmatrix}$; (c) $\begin{bmatrix} 0 & 0 \\ 0 & 0 \end{bmatrix}$; (d) 16; (e) 17; (f) $\begin{bmatrix} 23 \\ 13 \end{bmatrix}$;

    (g) 27; (h) 27; (i) $\begin{bmatrix} 5 & 9 & 1 \\ 10 & 18 & 2 \\ 20 & 36 & 4 \end{bmatrix}$; (j) $\begin{bmatrix} 5 & 10 & 20 \\ 9 & 18 & 36 \\ 1 & 2 & 4 \end{bmatrix}$; (k) $\begin{bmatrix} 4 & 13 & 5 \\ 10 & 29 & 11 \end{bmatrix}$;

    (l) $\begin{bmatrix} 18 & 11 & 45 \\ 6 & 1 & 18 \\ 7 & 2 & 21 \end{bmatrix}$.

  2. Closure for square matrices of the same size. Uniqueness always true.
  3. True.
  4. $\begin{bmatrix} 1 & 0 \\ 0 & 1 \end{bmatrix}$.
  5. (a) $\begin{bmatrix} 1 & 0 \\ 0 & 1 \end{bmatrix}$; (b) $\begin{bmatrix} 2 & -1 \\ -5 & 3 \end{bmatrix}$; (c) $\begin{bmatrix} 1 & -\frac{1}{2} \\ -\frac{1}{2} & \frac{1}{2} \end{bmatrix}$; (d) $\begin{bmatrix} -\frac{1}{2} & \frac{1}{2} \\ \frac{5}{2} & -\frac{3}{2} \end{bmatrix}$;

    (e) impossible. For general proceedure see page 99.
  6. No, no.
  7. (a) 53; (b) 74; (c) 41; (d) 76; (e) impossible.

Examples 6e

  1. £1,987 14s. 0d.
  2. £3 14s. 0d.
  3. (a) £58 2s. 6d.; (b) £78 5s. 0d.
  4. (a) 15s. 6d.; (b) £4 7s. 4d.

Examples 6f

  1. Cyclic 4-group.
  2. Klein 4-group.
  3. Cyclic 3-group.
  4. Table 22, page 49.
  5. Yes.
  6. No.
  7. (a) $\begin{bmatrix} 1 & 0 \\ 0 & 1 \end{bmatrix}$; (b) none; (c) $\begin{bmatrix} \frac{1}{3} & 0 \\ -\frac{4}{3} & 1 \end{bmatrix}$; (d) none; (e) $[\frac{1}{4}]$; (f) none;

    (g) none.

Chapter 7

Examples 7c

  1. $4x+3y = 50$ $(12\frac{1}{2}, 0)$.
  2. $4x+3y = 6\frac{2}{3}$ $(\frac{2}{3}, \frac{4}{3})$.
  3. $4x+3y = 50$ $(12\frac{1}{2}, 0)$.
  4. $4x+3y = 6\frac{2}{19}$ $(\frac{14}{19}, \frac{20}{19})$.
  5. $4x+3y = 6\frac{2}{11}$ $(\frac{8}{11}, \frac{12}{11})$.

6. £100.
7. No change. Adequate surplus of 'mammoth' tubes already available.
8. £1,300. 1 day Eastleigh, 5 days Westleigh.
9. No. (£1,325).
10. Worse still. (£1,600).
11. 10 apiece.
12. 7 washings up—5 for Junior, 2 for sister.
13.

	x	y	
	J	S	Cost in bread and butter $15x + 15y$.
Aunty Jane	1	1	All ten visits by sister.
Aunty Jean	1	2	
Aunty Joan	1	2	

14. 3 days for true love, 4 days for rival!
15. 607 to A, 242 to B.

Examples 7d

1. $x = 1, y = 2$.
2. $x = 2, y = 2$.
3. $x = 2, y = 3$.
4. $x = 1, y = 1$.
5. $x = 5, y = 6$.
6. $x = 1, y = 1; x = 1, y = 2; x = 2, y = 1; x = 2, y = 2$.
7. $x = 3, y = 1; x = 1, y = 3; x = 2, y = 4; x = 4, y = 2$.

Examples 7e

1. $x = 1, y = 1, z = 1$.
2. $x = 1, y = 2, z = 3$.
3. Impossible.
4. Impossible.
5. $x = 2, y = 0, z = 3$.

Chapter 8

Examples 8a

1. (a) he, eh;
   (b) she, seh, hse, hes, esh, ehs;
   (c) they, thye, tehy, teyh, tyhe, tyeh,
   htey, htye, hety, heyt, hyte, hyet,
   ethy, etyh, ehty, ehyt, eyth, eyht,
   ythe, yteh, yhte, yhet, yeth, yeht.
2. (a) see, ese, ees;
   (b) thee, tehe, teeh, htee, hete, heet,
   ethe, eteh, ehte, ehet, eeth, eeht;
   (c) teee, etee, eete, eeet;
   (d) hehe, hhee, heeh, ehhe, eheh, eehh.

3. $\dfrac{n!}{a!\,b!\,c!\,...}$ where n is the number of letters in the word and $a, b, c, ...$ are

the numbers of times various letters are repeated.

   (a) $5! = 120$;

   (b) $\dfrac{5!}{2!} = 60$;

(c) $\dfrac{5!}{3!} = 20$;

(d) $\dfrac{5!}{3!\,2!} = 10$;

(e) $\dfrac{5!}{4!} = 5$;

(f) $\dfrac{5!}{2!\,2!} = 30$.

4. (a) 24; (b) 24.
5. (a) 120; (b) 60; (c) $n!,\, n(n-1)(n-2)$.
6. (a) $26.25.24.10.9.8$.
    (b) $26^3.10^3$.

Examples 8d

1. Cyclic 4-group.
2. Klein 4-group.
   (b) Table 22 in some form or other.
3. Cyclic 6-group.

Examples 8e

$$\begin{bmatrix} 1 & 0 & 0 \\ 0 & 1 & 0 \\ 0 & 0 & 1 \end{bmatrix},\ \begin{bmatrix} 0 & 1 & 0 \\ 0 & 0 & 1 \\ 1 & 0 & 0 \end{bmatrix},\ \begin{bmatrix} 0 & 0 & 1 \\ 0 & 1 & 0 \\ 1 & 0 & 0 \end{bmatrix},\ \begin{bmatrix} 0 & 1 & 0 \\ 1 & 0 & 0 \\ 0 & 0 & 1 \end{bmatrix}.$$

Examples 8g

Same tables as 8(d) but sometimes in different form.

Examples 8h

1. $\begin{pmatrix} I\,A\,B \\ I\,A\,B \end{pmatrix},\ \begin{pmatrix} I\,A\,B \\ A\,B\,I \end{pmatrix},\ \begin{pmatrix} I\,A\,B \\ B\,I\,A \end{pmatrix}.$

2. $\begin{pmatrix} I\,A\,B\,C \\ I\,A\,B\,C \end{pmatrix},\ \begin{pmatrix} I\,A\,B\,C \\ A\,B\,C\,I \end{pmatrix},\ \begin{pmatrix} I\,A\,B\,C \\ B\,C\,I\,A \end{pmatrix},\ \begin{pmatrix} I\,A\,B\,C \\ C\,I\,A\,B \end{pmatrix}.$

3. $\begin{pmatrix} I\,X\,Y\,P\,Q\,R \\ I\,X\,Y\,P\,Q\,R \end{pmatrix},\ \begin{pmatrix} I\,X\,Y\,P\,Q\,R \\ X\,Y\,I\,R\,P\,Q \end{pmatrix},\ \begin{pmatrix} I\,X\,Y\,P\,Q\,R \\ Y\,I\,X\,Q\,R\,P \end{pmatrix},$

$\begin{pmatrix} I\,X\,Y\,P\,Q\,R \\ P\,Q\,R\,I\,X\,Y \end{pmatrix},\ \begin{pmatrix} I\,X\,Y\,P\,Q\,R \\ Q\,R\,P\,Y\,I\,X \end{pmatrix},\ \begin{pmatrix} I\,X\,Y\,P\,Q\,R \\ R\,P\,Q\,X\,Y\,I \end{pmatrix}.$

Rotation through multiples of 120° and twisting of 'Star of David' labelled $IQ\,XP\,YR$. (Note order carefully!)

Chapter 9

Examples 9a

2. Consider Junior's tile as a square and leave the dancers hanging on grimly to each corner.
3. The dancers must now be perched on the ends of two of the rods.

Examples 9b

(a) 1. No. Yes if $a \in$ {real numbers}.
    2. No.
    3. Yes.
    4. No.
    5. No. Yes if $a = b$ or $a = 0$ or $b = 0$.
    6. No.

(b) 1. No. Yes if $a \in$ {integers}.
    2. No.
    3. No. Yes if $a \in$ {integers}.
    4. No.
    5. No. Yes if $a = b$, $a = 0$ or $b = 0$ and $a, b \in$ {integers}.
    6. No.

(c) All No. 2 yes if $a \in$ {reals without 0}.

(d) All No. 2 yes if $a \in$ {positive rationals}.

Examples 9c

(a) 1. No. Yes if $a \in$ {real numbers}.
    2. No.
    3. Yes.
    4. No.

(b) 1. No. Yes if $a \in$ {all integers}.
    2. No.
    3. No. Yes if $a \in$ {all integers}.
    4. No.

(c) 1. No.
    2. No.
    3. No.
    4. No. Yes if $a \in$ {real numbers excluding 0}.

(d) 1. No.
    2. No.
    3. No.
    4. No. Yes if $a \in$ {positive rationals}.

Examples 9d

All answers based on $\begin{bmatrix} a & b \\ c & d \end{bmatrix}$. All a, b, c and d such that

1. $a = -d$, $bc = -d^2$.
2. $a = -d$, $bc = 1 - d^2$.
3. $a = -d$, $bc = -1 - d^2$.
4. $a = 2 - d$, $bc = 2a - 1 - a^2$.
5. $a = 5 - d$, $bc = 5a - 4 - a^2$.
6. $a = 1 - d$, $bc = a - 3 - a^2$.

Examples 9e

1. $x = 0$ (twice!).
2. $x = \pm 1$.
3. $x = \pm i$.
4. $x = 1$ (twice!).
5. $x = 1$ or 4.
6. $x = \frac{1}{2}(1 \pm i\sqrt{11})$.

Chapter 10

Examples 10a

1. (a) 45° clockwise, 1 to the right and $\sqrt{2}$ down.

(b) 45° anti-clockwise, 4 to the left and $3\sqrt{2}+1$ down; or 135° anti-clockwise, $4-2\sqrt{2}$ to the left and $1+\sqrt{2}$ down; or 225° anti-clockwise, 4 to the left and $\sqrt{2}-1$ up; or 315° anti-clockwise, $2\sqrt{2}+4$ to the left and $\sqrt{2}+1$ down.

(c) The simplest is 8 down. Any rotation with appropriate translation will do.

(d) 90° clockwise, 2 to the right and 2 down.

The several possibilities are due to the symmetry of the figures concerned (see page 210).

2. No.

3. Join the corresponding points and draw the perpendicular bisectors of the lines. These intersect at the centre of rotation.

4. Yes.

5. Yes.

Examples 10b

1. (a) reflection, rotation 90° clockwise, translation 6 to the right and 1 up.

(b) reflection, rotation 90° clockwise, translation 1 to the left and 1 down.

2. None.

3. Translation 2″.

4. Rotation about point of intersection through 60°, 180°.

Examples 10c

1. (a) $\begin{bmatrix} 1 & 0 \\ 0 & 1 \end{bmatrix}$ (d) $\begin{bmatrix} \dfrac{1}{2} & -\dfrac{\sqrt{3}}{2} \\ \dfrac{\sqrt{3}}{2} & \dfrac{1}{2} \end{bmatrix}$ (g) $\begin{bmatrix} -\dfrac{1}{\sqrt{2}} & -\dfrac{1}{\sqrt{2}} \\ \dfrac{1}{\sqrt{2}} & -\dfrac{1}{\sqrt{2}} \end{bmatrix}$

(b) $\begin{bmatrix} \dfrac{\sqrt{3}}{2} & -\dfrac{1}{2} \\ \dfrac{1}{2} & \dfrac{\sqrt{3}}{2} \end{bmatrix}$ (e) $\begin{bmatrix} 0 & -1 \\ 1 & 0 \end{bmatrix}$ (h) $\begin{bmatrix} -\dfrac{\sqrt{3}}{2} & -\dfrac{1}{2} \\ \dfrac{1}{2} & -\dfrac{\sqrt{3}}{2} \end{bmatrix}$

(c) $\begin{bmatrix} \dfrac{1}{\sqrt{2}} & -\dfrac{1}{\sqrt{2}} \\ \dfrac{1}{\sqrt{2}} & \dfrac{1}{\sqrt{2}} \end{bmatrix}$ (f) $\begin{bmatrix} -\dfrac{1}{2} & -\dfrac{\sqrt{3}}{2} \\ \dfrac{\sqrt{3}}{2} & -\dfrac{1}{2} \end{bmatrix}$ (i) $\begin{bmatrix} -1 & 0 \\ 0 & -1 \end{bmatrix}$

Examples 10g

1. Reflections as well as translations occur.

3–8. No group structures.

Examples 10h

1 and 2. The various ways are too many to list. The two situations differ because of the greater symmetry of the first figure.

Chapter 11

Examples 11a

3. $\begin{bmatrix} 1 & 0 \\ 0 & 1 \end{bmatrix}$, $\begin{bmatrix} -\frac{1}{2} & -\frac{\sqrt{3}}{2} \\ \frac{\sqrt{3}}{2} & -\frac{1}{2} \end{bmatrix}$, $\begin{bmatrix} -\frac{1}{2} & \frac{\sqrt{3}}{2} \\ -\frac{\sqrt{3}}{2} & -\frac{1}{2} \end{bmatrix}$,

       I   *X*   *Y*

$\begin{bmatrix} -1 & 0 \\ 0 & 1 \end{bmatrix}$, $\begin{bmatrix} \frac{1}{2} & -\frac{\sqrt{3}}{2} \\ -\frac{\sqrt{3}}{2} & -\frac{1}{2} \end{bmatrix}$, $\begin{bmatrix} \frac{1}{2} & \frac{\sqrt{3}}{2} \\ \frac{\sqrt{3}}{2} & -\frac{1}{2} \end{bmatrix}$

       P   *Q*   *R*

for example. There are others.

Examples 11b

1. (a) Rotation anti-clockwise through 90° and translation (1, 1).
   (b) Reflection $y = 0$, rotation anti-clockwise through 90° and translation (1, 1).
   (c) Magnification 2, reflection in $y = 0$, rotation anti-clockwise through 90° and translation (2, 2).

2. (a) $\begin{bmatrix} \frac{1}{\sqrt{2}} & \frac{1}{\sqrt{2}} & 1 \\ -\frac{1}{\sqrt{2}} & \frac{1}{\sqrt{2}} & -\sqrt{2} \\ 0 & 0 & 1 \end{bmatrix}$

(b) (i) $\begin{bmatrix} \frac{1}{\sqrt{2}} & -\frac{1}{\sqrt{2}} & -4 \\ \frac{1}{\sqrt{2}} & \frac{1}{\sqrt{2}} & -3\sqrt{2}-1 \\ 0 & 0 & 1 \end{bmatrix}$ (ii) $\begin{bmatrix} -\frac{1}{\sqrt{2}} & -\frac{1}{\sqrt{2}} & 2\sqrt{2}-4 \\ \frac{1}{\sqrt{2}} & -\frac{1}{\sqrt{2}} & -\sqrt{2}-1 \\ 0 & 0 & 1 \end{bmatrix}$

(iii) $\begin{bmatrix} -\frac{1}{\sqrt{2}} & \frac{1}{\sqrt{2}} & -4 \\ -\frac{1}{\sqrt{2}} & -\frac{1}{\sqrt{2}} & \sqrt{2}-1 \\ 0 & 0 & 1 \end{bmatrix}$ (iv) $\begin{bmatrix} \frac{1}{\sqrt{2}} & \frac{1}{\sqrt{2}} & -2\sqrt{2}-4 \\ -\frac{1}{\sqrt{2}} & \frac{1}{\sqrt{2}} & -\sqrt{2}-1 \\ 0 & 0 & 1 \end{bmatrix}$

4. (a) Translation 2 up;
   (b) Translation 2 down;
   (c) Translation $2b-2a$ up.

5. $\begin{bmatrix} \frac{1}{\sqrt{2}} & \frac{1}{\sqrt{2}} & -2 \\ \frac{1}{\sqrt{2}} & -\frac{1}{\sqrt{2}} & -3 \\ 0 & 0 & 1 \end{bmatrix}$; $\left(\frac{3}{\sqrt{2}}-2, -\frac{1}{\sqrt{2}}-3\right)$, $(2\sqrt{2}-2, \sqrt{2}-3)$, $(\sqrt{2}-3, -3)$.

Examples 11c.

1. (a) 8; (b) 2; (c) 4; (d) 10.
2. (a) 2; (b) 8; (c) 8; (d) 8; (e) 2; (f) 12; (g) 6; (h) 2; (i) ∞.
3. (a) 12; (b) 24; (c) 4.

Examples 11d

1. The magnification may be done at any stage but the reflection and rotation must be done in the same order.

Examples 11e

2. (a) $(0, 0)$, $(\frac{1}{2}, \frac{3}{2})$, $(\frac{3}{2}, \frac{1}{2})$, $(2, 2)$;
   (b) $(0, 0)$, $(\frac{1}{2}, \frac{3}{2})$, $(3, 1)$, $(\frac{7}{2}, \frac{5}{2})$.

3. $(0, 0)$, $\left(\frac{3}{4}, 1+\frac{\sqrt{3}}{4}\right)$, $\left(1-\frac{\sqrt{3}}{4}, -\frac{1}{4}\right)$, $\left(\frac{7}{4}-\frac{\sqrt{3}}{4}, \frac{3}{4}+\frac{\sqrt{3}}{4}\right)$.

Chapter 12

Examples 12a

6. Matrices which generate Table 44 under '×' will not generate Table 45.

Examples 12b

1. (a) Not possible. 3 and 0 not both available in arithmetic mod 3;
   (b) $x = 1$ or 2;
   (c) $x = 1$ or 2;
   (d) $x = 1, 2, 4$, or 5;
   (e) $x = 1$ or 2.
2. *Outline* $\quad a \in F \Rightarrow a = 0 \quad \text{or} \quad \exists\, a^{-1}$
   $$a^{-1} \times (a \times b) = 0 \Rightarrow b = 0.$$
3. Modulus number to be prime number.
4. (a) No; (b) no; (c) yes; (d) yes; (e) yes; (f) no.

Examples 12d

3. Yes.
4. Yes.
5. (a) Length; (b) length; (c) length and direction.
6. $\sqrt{(20+8\sqrt{2})} \simeq 5{\cdot}6$.
7. $\theta°$ with direction pulled by stronger man where $\tan \theta = \frac{1}{2}$.
8. $10\sqrt{(6+3\sqrt{2})} \simeq 32$ knots.
9. (a) 2 oranges, 4 apples; (b) nothing left.

Examples 12e

4. All except (b).
5. Yes.

BIBLIOGRAPHY

MILLIGAN, J. 101 *Scottish Country Dances*. Collins. The source of the Scottish country dancing material in this book.

The following provide interesting background reading:
D'ARCY THOMPSON, J. *Growth and Form*. Cambridge.
CRANK, J. *Mathematics in Industry*. Oxford.
DANTZIG, T. *Number, The Language of Science*. Allen and Unwin.
SMELTZER, D. *Man and Number*. A. & C. Black.

The following are simple general texts in modern mathematics which have topics in common with this book:
ADLER, I. *The New Mathematics*. Dobson.
ANDREE, R. V. *Selections from Modern Abstract Algebra*. Constable.
FLETCHER, T. J. (Ed.) *Some Lessons in Mathematics*. Cambridge.
KEMENY, J. G. et al. *Introduction to Finite Mathematics*. Prentice Hall.
RICHARDSON, M. *Fundamentals of Mathematics*. Macmillan.
SAWYER, W. W. *Prelude to Mathematics*. Penguin.
SAWYER, W. W. *A Concrete Approach to Abstract Algebra*. Freeman.

The following deal specifically with groups:
ALEXANDROFF, P. S. *Introduction to the Theory of Groups*. Blackie.
PAPY, G. *Groups*. Macmillan..
LEDERMANN, W. *Introduction to the Theory of Finite Groups*. Oliver and Boyd.

The following deal specifically with other topics touched on in this book:
ADLER, I. *Probability and Statistics for Everyman* (*Permutations and Elementary Set Theory*). Dobson.
HOHN, F. E. *Elementary Matrix Algebra* (*Determinants and Matrices*). Macmillan.
MACBEATH, A. M. *Elementary Vector Algebra*. Oxford.
VAJDA, S. *Introduction to Linear Programming and the Theory of Games*. Metheun–Wiley.
YAGLOM, I. M. *Geometric Transformations*. Random House.

INDEX

Abel, 58.
abstraction, 11, 29, 32, 43, 64.
algebra, 35, 60, 123, 168, 235.
—, Boolean, 229.
alternating current theory, 161.
apparatus, structural, 237.
arch, 212.
area of interest, 109, 110, 112.
Argand, 182
Argand diagram, 181–5, 186, 189, 215.
arithmetic, 5, 8, 20, 21, 23, 30, 32, 39, 41, 66, 74–76, 153, 159, 168, 228, 229, 230, 231, 235.
—, extended, 159, 159–63.
—, modulus, 20, 21–23, 24, 26, 27, 28, 29, 32, 35, 38, 39, 40, 42, 43, 64, 65, 86, 147, 148, 233, 234, 235, 247.
associative law, composite, 246.
associativity, 32–34, 35, 36–38, 41, 44, 50, 52, 58, 63, 64, 66, 73, 74, 76, 83, 84, 93, 96, 98, 99, 101, 118, 135, 136, 142, 145, 146, 167, 176, 204, 209, 229, 230, 232, 235, 244, 245.

belongs to, 59, 62.
Boole, George, 229.

calculation, 30–32, 34, 36, 38, 42.
—, flexibility in, 32, 33.
cancellation rule, 65–66, 67, 68, 71, 74, 231.
Carroll, Lewis, 168.
Cayley, 146.
Cayley's Theorem, 146–7, 166–7.
chemistry, 196.
chess, 19, 190.
Choleski method, 122–8.
circling system—*see* system, circling.
clock, four-hour, 19–21, 150, 152, 179, 180.
closure, 43–44, 48, 49, 58, 63, 68, 73, 74, 83, 93, 98, 101, 135, 176, 203, 209, 230, 244.

Clydeside Lassies, 55.
combining operation, 10.
commutativity, 32–35, 36, 37, 38, 39, 41, 44, 47, 50, 52, 63, 64, 65, 66, 72, 76, 85, 93, 98, 101, 102, 142, 176, 203, 210, 228, 229, 230, 232, 234, 235, 244, 245, 246.
computer, 103, 114, 119, 121.
congruence, 168–72, 172–5, 197, 205, 207, 209, 226, 229.
consistency, 65.
constraints, 104, 107, 108, 114, 115.
correspondence, 144.
—, one-to-one, 152, 153, 154, 155, 167, 181, 224, 225, 235.
Crank, J., 5.
crows, white, 23, 43.
cube, 212.
cuboid, 212.

D'Arcy Thompson, 221.
dancing, Scottish country, 1–5, 10, 11, 15–18, 30–32, 40, 44–57, 145–7, 150, 151, 152, 159, 198, 200, 201, 228, 229.
Dantzig, 11.
days of the week, 23–25.
determinant, 100, 101, 162.
—, associated, 100, 101, 121, 179, 215, 216, 225.
— of coefficients, 127.
dextrose, 196.
diagonal, leading, 17, 35, 123, 125.
direction, 242.
distributive law, 230, 231–3, 235.
— —, composite, 246.

El Greco, 222.
elements, 10.
—, identity (neutral), 39–40, 41, 42, 44, 50, 58, 63, 64, 66, 67, 68, 71, 72, 74, 76, 84, 93, 99, 101, 137, 176, 209, 211, 230, 231, 232, 245.
—, inverse, 40–43, 44, 50, 58, 64, 66, 71, 72, 73, 74, 76, 84, 99, 101, 102, 121, 158, 162, 163, 209, 226, 230, 232, 245,